THE GLIDER PILOT'S MANUAL

by

KEN STEWART

Illustrated by
MARK TAYLOR

Airlife
England

ACKNOWLEDGEMENTS

I would like to thank all those who have helped in the production of this book, and in particular, Peter and Harriette Disdale who put in many hours checking and correcting the text, and my wife Lynn for her support and the hours spent typing. Also I would like to thank Derek Piggott, Frank Irving and Tom Bradbury for their suggestions, which I am sure have increased the accuracy of the contents. I am indebted to Lasham Gliding Society for allowing me to reproduce their Training Progress Sheet and the British Gliding Association for allowing the reproduction of their Limitations Placard. Lastly, I would like to thank all of the students who have taught me so much.

Ken Stewart

First published in the UK in 1994
by Airlife Publishing Ltd.

British Library Cataloguing in Publication Data
A catalogue record for this book
is available from the British Library

ISBN 1 85310 504 X

Printed in England by Livesey Ltd., Shrewsbury.

Airlife Publishing Ltd.

101 Longden Road, Shrewsbury SY3 9EB, England

CONTENTS

Acknowledgements iv

Illustrations vii

Introduction xiii

SECTION 1 BASIC FLYING TRAINING

1 The Glider 2

2 The Gliding Site 10

3 Your First Flight 16

4 How Aeroplanes and Gliders Fly 19

5 Preparation for Flight 30

6 The Primary Controls 37

7 Turning the Glider 43

8 The Stall 50

9 The Spin 64

10 The Trimmer 73

11 The Airbrakes 78

12 Landing the Glider 84

13 The Approach 91

14 The Effect of the Wind 96

15 Wire Launching 114

16 Aerotow Launching 126

17 Circuit Planning 139

18 Launch Failures During Wire Launches 159

19 Aerotow Launch Failures and Emergencies 168

20 Sideslipping 175

21 Use of Flaps 182

SECTION 2 TECHNICAL SECTION

22 Glider Design 194

23 Design Features Which Provide Good Handling 196

24 Design Features Aimed at Giving Better Performance 213

SECTION 3 BASIC SOARING

25 Soaring 232

26 Hill Lift 234

27 Hill Soaring 238

28	Thermals	244
29	Thermal Soaring	251
30	Mountain Lee Waves	263
31	Wave Soaring	266
SECTION 4	**RULES OF THE AIR**	
32	Rules of the Air	274
APPENDIX 1	How the Instruments Work	276
APPENDIX 2	The Use of Radio	282
APPENDIX 3	The Use of Tailchutes	285
APPENDIX 4	Tow-plane Upsets	287
APPENDIX 5	Gliding Awards and Records	290
APPENDIX 6	Log Books and Progress Cards	293
APPENDIX 7	Converting from Power Flying to Gliding	295
APPENDIX 8	Converting to New Types of Glider	297
APPENDIX 9	Useful Conversion Factors	300
APPENDIX 10	Useful Addresses	301
INDEX		302

ILLUSTRATIONS

1.1	The glider.	2
1.2	The main controls.	3
1.3	The airbrakes.	4
1.4	The spoilers.	4
1.5	The trim tab.	5
1.6	The cockpit layout.	6
1.7	The airspeed indicator.	7
1.8	Airspeed versus groundspeed.	8
1.9	The variometer.	9
1.10	The altimeter.	9
2.1	Car launching.	11
2.2	Reverse pulley launching.	11
2.3	Winch launching.	11
2.4	Aerotow launching.	12
2.5	Ground handling points.	14
2.6	Ground handling.	15
2.7	Parking the glider.	15
3.1	Who has control?	17
3.2	Flying by attitude.	18
4.1	Lift versus weight.	19
4.2	Bernoulli's theorem.	20
4.3	Venturi experiment.	20
4.4	Experiment showing lift.	21
4.5	The wing section.	21
4.6	Angle of attack.	22
4.7	Increasing the angle of attack.	22
4.8	Lift distribution.	23
4.9	How the controls work.	23
4.10	Drag.	24
4.11	Induced drag.	25
4.12	Forces in balance.	26
4.13	Resolution of forces.	26
4.14	Propelling the glider forwards.	27
4.15	Weight, lift and drag.	28
4.16	Lift and drag versus weight.	28
4.17	Lift and weight versus drag.	29
5.1	The daily inspection.	32
5.2	The limitations placard.	34
6.1	The axes of control.	37
6.2	Pitching the glider.	37
6.3	Rolling the glider.	38
6.4	Yawing the glider.	38
6.5	The elevator controls pitch.	39
6.6	The ailerons control roll.	39
6.7	The rudder controls yaw.	39
6.8	Air Exercise – the effect of elevator.	40

6.9	Air Exercise – the effect of aileron.	41
6.10	Air Exercise – the effect of rudder.	42
7.1	Forces in a turn.	44
7.2	Aileron drag.	45
8.1	The stall.	50
8.2	Increased stalling speed in turns.	51
8.3	Lift and drag at the stall.	51
8.4	Attitude doesn't always indicate angle of attack.	53
8.5	Buffeting at the stall.	54
8.6	Nose-drop at the stall.	55
8.7	The need for stall recovery action.	56
8.8	Air Exercise – Stalling.	57
8.9	The incipient spin.	58
8.10	Use of aileron at the stall.	59
8.11	Positive 'g'.	61
8.12	Reduced 'g'.	61
8.13	Forward control column movements and reduced g.	62
9.1	Roll dampening.	64
9.2	Autorotation.	65
9.3	The spin.	66
9.4	The danger of yawing at slow speed.	67
9.5	Spinning from a shallow turn.	68
9.6	Steeper turns are safer.	69
9.7	The spiral dive.	71
10.1	How a trim tab works.	74
10.2	The spring trimmer.	75
11.1	40:1 glide angle.	78
11.2	How airbrakes work.	79
11.3	5:1 glide angle.	79
11.4	Why airbrakes "suck" open.	80
11.5	How spoilers work.	81
11.6	The tailchute.	82
12.1	Stages of the landing.	84
12.2	The round out.	86
12.3	"Ballooning" whilst landing.	87
12.4	Round out technique.	87
12.5	Judging the point of round out.	88
13.1	The reference point.	92
13.2	Correct approach.	92
13.3	Overshooting on the approach.	93
13.4	Undershooting on the approach.	93
14.1	The wind and the glider.	96
14.2	Drift.	97
14.3	Track and heading.	98
14.4	Wind causes the glider to drift.	99
14.5	Correcting for drift.	100
14.6	Wind effect on a circling glider.	101
14.7	The wind's effect on ground distance covered.	102
14.8	The wind's effect on the take-off distance.	102
14.9	The wind's effect on wire launch heights.	103
14.10	The wind's effect on an aerotow launch.	104
14.11	Crosswind landing – crabbing method.	106
14.12	Wing-down crosswind landing technique.	106

14.13	Weathercocking.	107
14.14	Obstructions causing turbulence.	108
14.15	Curl-over at a hilltop airfield.	109
14.16	The wind gradient.	110
14.17	The wind gradient's effect on the glider's airspeed.	111
14.18	Increased angle of attack due to the wind gradient.	111
14.19	The wind gradient causing an undershoot.	112
14.20	Turning in a wind gradient.	113
15.1	The glider end of a winch launch cable.	114
15.2	Stages of a winch launch.	117
15.3	The angle of attack during a winch launch.	119
15.4	Increased stalling speed during a winch launch.	120
15.5	"Hunting" on a winch launch.	122
15.6	Correcting for drift on a winch launch.	123
16.1	The versatile aerotow launch.	126
16.2	The aerotow launch point.	128
16.3	The take-off on aerotow.	130
16.4	Aerotowing – combination just airborne.	130
16.5	The normal tow position.	131
16.6	Margins for vertical movement behind tow-plane.	132
16.7	Turning on aerotow.	133
16.8	Encountering rising air on aerotow.	133
16.9	Correcting lateral displacement on aerotow.	134
16.10	The effect of tow-rope length when aerotowing.	136
16.11	The low tow position.	137
16.12	"Boxing the tow".	137
17.1	Typical circuit pattern.	140
17.2	The high key point.	141
17.3	High key point too far away.	141
17.4	High key point too close.	142
17.5	Downwind leg too close.	142
17.6	Downwind leg too far out.	143
17.7	The low key point.	144
17.8	Lower end of the circuit.	145
17.9	Base leg.	146
17.10	Effect of a wind blowing towards the airfield.	148
17.11	Correcting for drift on the downwind leg.	148
17.12	Correcting for a strong crosswind blowing towards the airfield on the downwind leg.	149
17.13	Strong crosswind blowing away from the airfield on the downwind leg.	150
17.14	Correcting for a wind blowing the glider away from the airfield.	150
17.15	Effect of a strong wind blowing diagonally across the airfield.	151
17.16	Effect of a strong tail wind on the downwind leg.	151
17.17	Rising air on the downwind leg.	153
17.18	Rising air on the base leg.	154
17.19	Sinking air on the downwind leg.	154
17.20	Sinking air on the base leg.	155
17.21	Circuits at hilltop sites.	156
17.22	Sinking air in the lee of a hill affecting the circuit.	157
17.23	Hill lift affecting the circuit.	157
18.1	Angle of attack change after a cable break.	160

18.2	Landing ahead after a cable break.	162
18.3	"Dog leg" manoeuvre after a cable break.	163
18.4	360° turn versus "S" turn after a cable break.	164
18.5	Downwind landing after a cable break.	164
18.6	Impulsive use of airbrakes after a cable break.	165
18.7	Options after a cable break at a large airfield.	166
19.1	Aerotow launch failure shortly after take-off.	168
19.2	Field landing after a low aerotow launch failure.	169
19.3	Return to airfield after aerotow launch failure.	170
19.4	Aerotow launch failure in strong winds.	170
19.5	"Release immediately" signal.	171
19.6	"Check airbrakes" signal.	172
19.7	Glider unable to release tow-rope.	173
20.1	Sideslipping.	176
20.2	Forces in a sideslip.	176
20.3	The sideslip.	177
20.4	Increased lift required in a sideslip.	177
21.1	Early wing section.	182
21.2	Modern wing section.	182
21.3	Flaps.	183
21.4	Fuselage alignment with flaps.	183
21.5	Area-changing flaps.	183
21.6	Positive flap.	184
21.7	Negative flap.	184
21.8	Flap control.	185
21.9	Trailing edge airbrakes.	189
21.10	Flap brakes – stage 1 movement.	190
21.11	Flap brakes – stage 2 movement.	190
21.12	Air speed indicator calibrated with flap speeds.	192
23.1	Stability.	196
23.2	Instability.	196
23.3	Directional stability.	197
23.4	Dorsal strake.	198
23.5	Lateral stability – dihedral.	199
23.6	How dihedral works	199
23.7	Sweepback.	200
23.8	How sweepback works.	200
23.9	Longitudinal instability of the wing.	201
23.10	The tailplane gives the glider longitudinal stability.	202
23.11	Longitudinal instability due to an underweight pilot.	203
23.12	Angled lift from dihedral.	204
23.13	Horn balance.	205
23.14	Geared tab.	205
23.15	Frise ailerons.	206
23.16	Differential ailerons.	206
23.17	Nimbus 3 aileron/spoiler system.	207
23.18	Anti-balance tab.	209
23.19	Control flutter.	210
23.20	Mass balancing.	211
23.21	Washout.	211
24.1	The polar curve.	213
24.2	The polar curve of an older glider.	214
24.3	The modern glider.	215

24.4	Aspect ratio.	216
24.5	Ideal lift distribution.	217
24.6	Actual lift distribution.	217
24.7	Wing fence.	218
24.8	Winglet.	218
24.9	Sweeping the wing tips backwards.	219
24.10	Laminar boundary layer.	220
24.11	Contaminated wings.	220
24.12	Turbulators.	221
24.13	Interference drag.	222
24.14	Sealing of joints.	223
24.15	Cruciform tail.	224
24.16	"T" tail.	224
24.17	"V" tail.	225
24.18	Control surface movement on a "V" tail.	226
24.19	All moving tailplane.	227
24.20	Streamlining.	228
24.21	Water ballast.	230
25.1	Rising air arresting the glider's descent.	233
25.2	Rising air causing the glider to gain height.	233
26.1	Hill lift.	234
26.2	A wind at an angle to the hill.	235
26.3	Outcrops producing hill lift.	235
26.4	Sink near a steep hill face.	236
27.1	Area of best hill lift.	239
27.2	Tracking in the hill lift.	239
27.3	Turning at the end of each beat in the hill lift.	240
27.4	Field landing near a hill.	241
27.5	Approaching another glider head-on while hill soaring.	242
27.6	Overtaking while hill soaring.	242
28.1	Solar heating and the environmental lapse rate.	244
28.2	Dry adiabatic lapse rate.	245
28.3	Relative humidity.	246
28.4	Formation of cumulus cloud.	246
28.5	Cumulonimbus cloud	247
28.6	Thermal sources.	248
28.7	Birth of a thermal.	248
28.8	Thermal bubble.	249
28.9	Thermal column.	250
28.10	Cloud streets.	250
29.1	Life of a cumulus cloud.	251
29.2	Sloping thermal ascent.	252
29.3	The angle of the sun's rays and wind shadow thermals.	253
29.4	Thermals indicated by smoke.	255
29.5	Heading deviations due to thermals.	256
29.6	Thermal centring.	258
29.7	The need for accurate flying when thermalling.	261
30.1	Mountain lee waves.	263
31.1	Position of wave lift.	266
31.2	Wave affecting hill lift.	267
31.3	Wave interfering with thermals.	268
31.4	Wave lift position sloping with altitude.	269
32.1	Approaching another aircraft head-on.	274

32.2	Converging with another aircraft.	275
A1.1	Simplified workings of the airspeed indicator.	277
A1.2	Simplified workings of the altimeter.	278
A1.3	Simplified variometer system.	279
A1.4	Total energy system.	281
A4.1	Tow-plane upsets.	287
A4.2	One theory of how a tow-plane upset occurs.	288
A4.3	Normal load on an aerotow rope.	288
A4.4	Load increase on aerotow rope if glider diverges.	289
A6.1	Student's progress card.	293

INTRODUCTION

Gliding is one of the most challenging of aerial sports. It requires skill in handling the glider and judgement both associated with flying the glider safely and utilising the energy present in the atmosphere to keep the glider airborne.

Gone are the days when gliders were frail machines, which were launched to a height, only to float unceremoniously to earth again. The modern glider is a strong aircraft made of the latest composite materials, capable of speeds in excess of 150 miles per hour. Such aircraft are capable of flights lasting ten hours or more and covering distances of over 1000 miles without landing.

Learning to fly is a process which takes time. With each new aspect learned comes a sense of achievement. The learning process is aided by good instruction, both in the air and on the ground. As gliding is a recreational activity, most glider pilots are trained by part-time instructors who although competent, do not always have the time to impart all the necessary backup theory which should be available to their students. This manual is intended not only to supply some of this information but also to give you a broader picture of where your training is leading. It also includes the exercise plans of all of the main training exercises which you can expect to complete before flying solo.

After your first solo flights you will want to progress towards the principal objective of the sport; soaring. The soaring section in this manual is designed to carry on from your basic training. Therefore this manual will give you all the information required to safely progress, from the day when you first arrive at the gliding club, to a reasonable stage of soaring proficiency. It will give you a sound base from which to develop within the sport, without delving deeply into aerodynamics and meteorology, thus remaining readable to those readers who consider themselves "non-technically minded".

The air exercises given throughout this book are included to give you an idea of what you will practise as your training progresses. Some exercises may be varied slightly, at your instructor's discretion, to allow for such variables as the weather conditions on the day, and your individual requirements. The entry speeds quoted for some of the exercises will be suitable for most training gliders, but these speeds may have to be altered for some older types of glider. Some exercises may only be demonstrated, if your instructor deems your attempting the exercise unnecessary. The order of the subjects and exercises covered is set out in a way which is designed to lead you through the knowledge required to fly a glider. From necessity, this will vary from the order in which a few of the exercises are introduced in practice. This is due to the need to make the best of conditions and the limited time in the air often available in gliding.

Where it is not practical to outline the whole of an exercise, a brief description of what is involved is given instead of the exercise layout. All exercises should be practised under the guidance of an instructor.

In addition to the exercises included in this manual, some national gliding authorities may also incorporate other exercises designed to improve your understanding of various control aspects of the glider.

Lastly, no book can replace the demonstrations and advice of a good gliding instructor. Therefore this manual is not intended as a substitute for qualified instruction and practice time in the air, but simply as an aid to your training and subsequent gliding.

SECTION 1

BASIC FLYING TRAINING

CHAPTER 1

THE GLIDER

Gliders come in a variety of colours, shapes and sizes, and are made of several different materials. The modern glider is an aircraft made of the latest composite materials, usually glass fibre or carbon fibre, whereas older types tend to be made of wood and fabric or metal. Almost without exception, gliders have conventional controls, similar to those on powered aircraft. Despite designers' attempts over the years to extract every small performance advantage from their designs, gliders have kept one general planform or shape. Often the only obvious variation noticeable to the casual observer is in the design of the tail area, where sometimes the tailplane is set at the top of the fin and on others it is set much lower. On some gliders the tailplanes are designed to form a "V" shape, but this is less common.

MAIN EXTERNAL FEATURES

Fig 1.1 shows a single-seat glider with the main features illustrated.

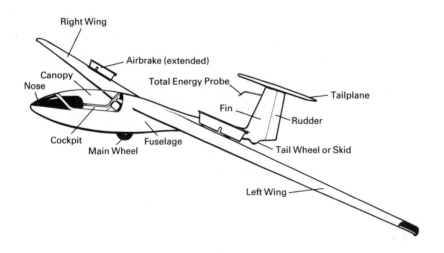

Fig 1.1   The glider. A typical single-seat glider.

The WINGS are often referred to as just the WING. On older types of glider the wing was of large area when looked at from above, and of thick profile when viewed from the front. However, in modern sailplanes the wing tends to be long in relation to its width in planform and much thinner than that of older gliders. The length of the wing from wing tip to wing tip is called the WINGSPAN, or simply the SPAN.

2

The FUSELAGE is the body of the glider. It provides accommodation for the pilot, houses the controls and instruments, and the necessary control rods and cables which activate the control surfaces on the glider's wings and at the tail.

The FIN is that part of the rear fuselage which is vertical.

The TAILPLANE is the horizontal surface at the rear of the glider. It is either fitted directly onto the fuselage or on the fin, sometimes just above the fuselage but more often at the top of the fin, as in the case of the glider shown in Fig 1.1. (For obvious reasons this is known as a "T" tail.)

In addition to the main structural parts of the glider mentioned above, there are several control surfaces.

The ELEVATOR is the horizontal control surface which is attached to the rear of the tailplane by hinges which allow it to move up and down.

The AILERONS are the control surfaces situated one at the rear of each wing. Like the elevator, they are attached by hinges to enable them to move up and down. However, they are linked so that when one goes up, the other goes down.

The RUDDER is a vertical control surface which is attached to the rear of the fin by hinges, which allow it movement to the left and to the right.

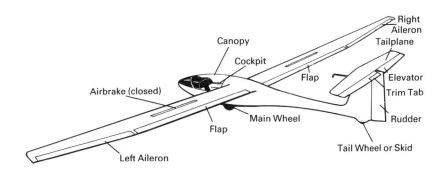

Fig 1.2   The main controls. The situation of the glider's control surfaces.

The AIRBRAKES are flat, oblong surfaces which can be made to project vertically from either the top, or both the top and bottom, of both wings. They are linked so that, when opened, the airbrake surface on both the left-hand and right-hand wings project from the surface at the same time and to the same extent. (Fig 1.3)

On some older gliders SPOILERS are fitted instead of airbrakes. Unlike airbrakes which extend vertically, spoilers are hinged surfaces which, when closed, lie flush with the upper surface of the wing. When operated they hinge upwards into the airflow. (Fig 1.4)

3

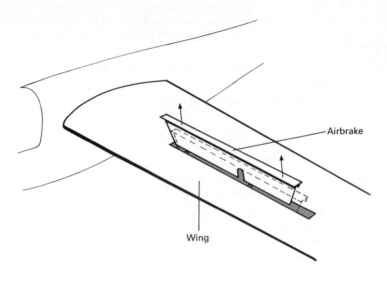

Fig 1.3   The airbrakes. Most airbrakes extend vertically from the wing.

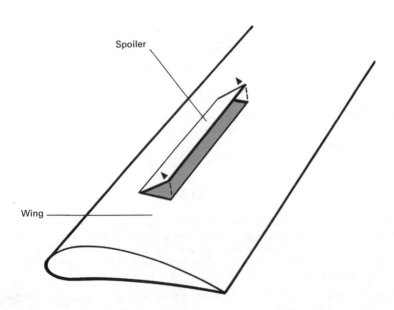

Fig 1.4   The spoilers. Spoilers hinge upwards from the top surface of the wing.

The TRIM TAB is a small surface fitted by hinges to the elevator, in much the same way as the elevator is to the tailplane. Occasionally there is a trim tab on both sides of the tailplane. It can be moved up or down. Trim tabs are not present on all gliders, as some manufacturers use other devices to do the same job.

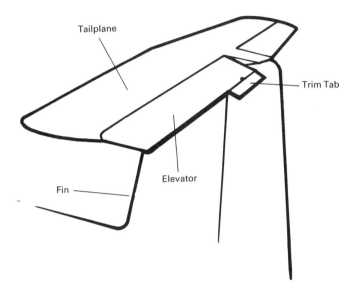

Tailplane

Trim Tab

Elevator

Fin

Fig 1.5   The trim tab. A trim tab is often fitted on the trailing edge of the elevator.

The COCKPIT is the pilot's accommodation. The cockpit determines whether the glider is a single or a two-seater. It is in the latter that all training will be done as it is equipped with, not only a second seat, but also a duplicate set of controls. These days it is covered by a perspex bubble called the CANOPY, although there are still many older types of glider to be seen which do not have this luxury.

Most gliders are fitted with only one MAIN WHEEL (referred to as the UNDERCARRIAGE). This is situated in the fuselage just aft of the cockpit. It may or may not be designed to be retracted into the fuselage in flight. Having only one main wheei means that gliders at rest will have one wing on the ground and will require an assistant to support the wing during the initial part of the take-off run. Other smaller wheels may be used on the front and rear fuselage to prevent damaging the fuselage structure. Skids may be used for this purpose on some types.

FLAPS are surfaces attached to the rear of each wing, between the ailerons and the fuselage. They are hinged so as to move up and down to the same amount and in the same direction on both wings. There are various types and they are mainly used on high performance sailplanes.

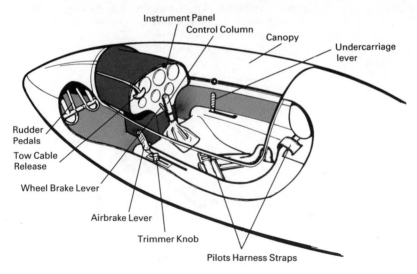

Fig 1.6   The cockpit layout. The cockpit of a modern glider showing the various controls.

THE COCKPIT

THE MAIN CONTROLS

The CONTROL COLUMN (often referred to as the STICK) is linked to the elevator and the ailerons. Forward or aft movement of the control column will move the elevator down or up respectively. Moving the control column to the left simultaneously causes the aileron on the left wing to move up and the aileron on the right wing to move down. Movement of the column to the right makes the right aileron move up and the left aileron move down. The control column controls the glider's speed and direction. Simply put, the glider will move in the same direction as the pilot moves the control column.

The RUDDER PEDALS are linked to the rudder. If the pilot moves the right rudder pedal forward the rudder moves to the right. At this stage it is important not to believe that the rudder changes the glider's direction. Unfortunately the "rudder" is badly named as it doesn't turn the glider on its own (unlike its counterpart on a boat), but only helps to make the turns smoother and more accurate. As mentioned above, it is the control column which controls the turning forces.

ANCILLARY CONTROLS

The TRIMMER KNOB or LEVER controls the position of the trim tab (or other trimming device).

The AIRBRAKE LEVER controls the airbrake surfaces allowing them to be extended or retracted as necessary.

The TOW CABLE RELEASE is a yellow knob or handle which is used to attach the TOW-ROPE or LAUNCH CABLE before flight and to release it in flight when desired. Sometimes a glider may have two separate release mechanisms; one near the nose for when the glider is being launched behind a light aeroplane, and another further back, for use if the glider is being launched by winch or tow car. If this is the case then this one control will operate both mechanisms.

If the glider is fitted with flaps there will be a FLAP LEVER (not shown) which allows the pilot to select the desired angle of flap for the phase of flight.

The UNDERCARRIAGE LEVER allows the pilot to raise or lower the undercarriage.

The WHEEL BRAKE LEVER is used to apply a brake on the main wheel as required. Some gliders incorporate this control in the airbrake system, either as a separate trigger type of lever or as an integral part of the airbrake system, whereby the wheel brake is applied if the airbrake lever is pulled to the limit of its range. On some other gliders a heel or toe pedal is used to apply the wheel brake.

THE INSTRUMENTS

There are only three instruments that need to be considered by an early student.

The AIRSPEED INDICATOR (ASI) tells the pilot how fast the glider is flying *through the air*.

Fig 1.7   The airspeed indicator. The airspeed indicator indicates the glider's speed through the air.

It receives the information necessary to measure the glider's speed through the air from a sensing point called a PITOT TUBE which is usually situated in the nose of the glider. This information is compared to the readings of local atmospheric pressure taken at other points on the fuselage known as STATIC VENTS to give the reading shown on the airspeed indicator. These sensing points are also used by other instruments.

If there was no wind then the speed indicated on the instrument would be the same as the glider's speed over the ground (its GROUNDSPEED). However, as there is almost always some wind (that is, the air mass is moving) the airspeed indicator only indicates the speed of the glider through the air mass in which it is flying (that is, the glider's AIRSPEED) and not its speed over the ground. For instance in Fig 1.8(a) the glider is flying at an airspeed of 40 knots (40 nautical miles/hour) through a parcel of air which is stationary; that is, no wind. The glider is crossing the ground at 40 knots.

7

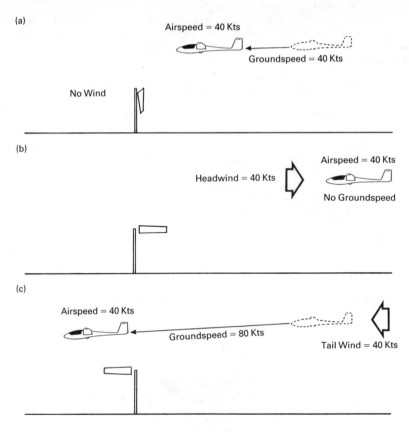

(a) Airspeed = 40 Kts
Groundspeed = 40 Kts
No Wind

(b) Airspeed = 40 Kts
Headwind = 40 Kts
No Groundspeed

(c) Airspeed = 40 Kts
Groundspeed = 80 Kts
Tail Wind = 40 Kts

Fig 1.8   Airspeed versus groundspeed. The groundspeed will differ from the airspeed if there is any wind.

In Fig 1.8(b) the glider is flying at the same airspeed (40 knots) but now the parcel of air is moving in the opposite direction at 40 knots (that is, 40 knots of wind) and the glider is now stationary over the ground. If the glider were to turn and fly in the same direction as the wind, whilst maintaining an indicated airspeed of 40 knots, it would be crossing the ground below at 80 knots. (Fig 1.8(c))

The example given of a 40-knot wind is somewhat extreme and normally the wind strength will be much less. There will be occasions however, especially at higher altitudes, when the wind speed will reach or even be in excess of this sort of figure. The presence of such strong winds can be advantageous as you will discover later when different types of soaring are discussed.

At first this lack of ground reference may appear to make the airspeed indicator a fairly useless instrument , but the glider's control and handling depend upon the glider's speed relative to the air through which it is flying, making the airspeed indicator an essential instrument.

The VARIOMETER is a "rate of climb (or descent) indicator". It tells the pilot how fast the glider is rising or descending. The basic instrument will be affected by changes in airspeed and the airspeed at which the glider is flying. These effects can give misleading indications. It is possible and common to modify the instrument's output to eliminate some of these, thus giving the pilot a better idea of the vertical characteristics of the air through which the glider is flying.

Fig 1.9   The variometer. The variometer indicates the glider's rate of climb or descent.

The ALTIMETER shows the pilot how high the glider is flying relative to a preset datum, which, on local training flights, is usually the airfield height. The type normally used in gliders gives a three-needle presentation which is read like the hands of a clock. (Fig 1.10) Needle A indicates 100s of feet, while needle B indicates 1,000s of feet (that is, when the needle A passes 999 feet, needle B would be at the 1 on the dial, indicating 1,000 feet. Needle A would then continue to show 100s of feet between 1,000 and 2,000 feet). Needle C behaves the same for 10,000s of feet. There is also a small sub-scale within the main dial. This is used for setting the datum air pressure but can be ignored at this stage.

Fig 1.10   The altimeter. The altimeter indicates the glider's height.

Other instruments usually included are:

The TURN AND SLIP INDICATOR is an instrument used for cloud flying. It combines an electrically-driven RATE OF TURN INDICATOR, with a SLIP INDICATOR which is essentially a pendulum. The Slip Indicator is useful in that it helps the pilot judge if the glider's turns are balanced.

A COMPASS will normally be mounted on the instrument panel or canopy. Again this is used later on and as an early student you should not concern yourself with it until it is formally introduced.

The main points in this chapter will be mentioned as you are briefed for your first flight. At this stage however, a general idea of the glider's layout will help you appreciate the machine in which you are about to fly.

CHAPTER 2

THE GLIDING SITE

For someone beginning gliding, or even for power pilots visiting a gliding club, the gliding site can be a strange place.

For one thing, it can be unpredictable, both in terms of operation and size. For another, more often than not, there will be an absence of air traffic control and the strict control of aircraft and vehicle movements which exist at larger airfields. Despite this, gliding clubs operate successfully and safely, with the minimum of rules, thanks mainly to the self-discipline and airmanship of their pilots.

To attempt to discuss the average gliding site would be impossible, as gliding sites vary immensely in both size and operation. What we can do here is look at the general layout and situation of gliding sites, the launch methods used and give some safety guidance when on or flying near a gliding field.

The size and layout of a gliding site will depend, to a large extent, on the land available. Often the gliding field may be an active or disused airfield. The gliding operation may have the use of all of this area or only part of it, either because the remainder is unusable or is used by another operator such as a power-flying school. On such an airfield the gliders may take-off and land on concrete runways, operate from grass areas, or utilise both surfaces depending on availability and surface condition. Many clubs operate from "green field" sites which may be farmers' fields or areas of level heath land. (Obviously such sites will lack a runway in the usual sense of a long strip of concrete, but for convenience, the term RUNWAY will be generally used throughout the text to mean the line of the intended landing or take-off run. Similarly, mention of the AIRFIELD should be taken to mean the area of take-off or intended landing and not limited to a purpose-built aerodrome.)

The situation of gliding clubs will vary from sites in flat countryside to some on top of hills. Many of the older established gliding clubs were established on the top of a hill where gliders could be launched easily into the rising air currents which exist when the wind is deflected upwards as it encounters the hillside. As launch methods developed, being situated on top of a hill became less important and many gliding sites were formed near the bottom of ridges and hills. Once other forms of rising air other than "hill lift" were discovered, the requirement to have a hill as a neighbour diminished and gliding sites appeared in almost all landscapes.

LAUNCHING METHODS

The type of launching employed at a particular gliding site is determined to a great extent by the size of the airfield and its surface.

Long, hard-surfaced runways will make it possible to launch gliders by CAR LAUNCH. This technique uses a powerful car or pick-up truck to drag the glider down the runway on the end of a 1,500 feet long launch cable, until the glider reaches take-off and climb speed. The vehicle continues down the runway supplying the necessary power for the glider's climb until the glider reaches the top of the launch and releases its end of the cable.

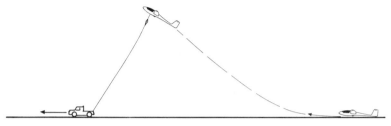

Fig 2.1   Car launching.

A variation on this technique, used when less runway length is available, or a greater height is required, involves looping the launch cable around a fixed pulley system. Using this system, known as a REVERSE PULLEY LAUNCH, the car drives back down the runway towards the glider during the launch.

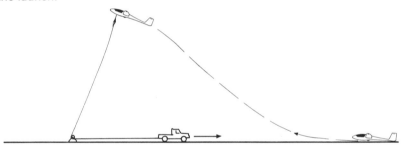

Fig 2.2   Reverse pulley launching.

By far the most common method of WIRE LAUNCH techniques is the WINCH LAUNCH. The winch launch does not require a smooth, hard surface capable of supporting a fast-moving launch vehicle. It employs a stationary winch positioned at the opposite end of the airfield to the glider. The winch is connected to the glider by a 3,000 feet long cable and provides the acceleration required for the launch, by winding in the cable as the launch commences.

Fig 2.3   Winch launching.

Where the glider is towed into the air behind a light aircraft, this is known as AEROTOW LAUNCHING or AEROTOWING. This type of launching can be carried out from both hard and soft runway surfaces and is mostly limited by obstructions and runway length. It is a relatively more expensive method of launch, requiring considerable cost in obtaining and maintaining the towing aircraft. However, with the correct aircraft it is probably the most versatile of all launch methods.

Fig 2.4   Aerotow launching.

At least one hilltop site still practises one of the oldest and most enjoyable methods of launch; that of BUNGEE (or CATAPULT) LAUNCHING. With this method a large elastic rope called a BUNGEE is used to catapult the glider into the strong wind which is being deflected upwards by the face of the hill. Bungee launching requires no fuel, only the assistance of six or more fit helpers. It may sound primitive, but no glider pilot can claim to have lived until this now rare, but delightful method of launch has been experienced.

Often, aerotowing and one of the wire launch methods will be used alongside each other on a particular airfield. It is not uncommon to find airfields which accommodate both gliding and power-flying activities. With a little organisation and co-operation the two disciplines can co-exist perfectly amicably and safely. At one airfield in the U.K., gliders share the airfield with both fixed-wing powered aircraft and helicopters, while at another the gliding club operation has to stop launching occasionally to allow an airliner to land or take-off!

SAFETY ON THE AIRFIELD

With gliders and tow-planes taking-off or landing, launch cables moving rapidly, spinning propellers, and numerous vehicles and machines operating on it, it is important that everyone on the airfield has a high regard for safety.

The following advice, together with any local rules and the application of some common sense should help you to enjoy your gliding safely.

- When on the airfield, keep a good lookout. Landing gliders may appear from any direction and a glider can not overshoot to avoid you. You will not hear them as they approach.

- Cross landing areas only when necessary, and do not loiter on them.

- Landing tow-planes usually trail a rope, which has metal fittings on its end. Never stand close to or under their approach path.

- Never cross the take-off run of a glider, even if it does not appear ready for launch. It is safer to go around the rear of the launch point.

- Never walk near or across wire launch cables, or an area where they may be. Cables are difficult to see and move very quickly once a launch begins or if they are being retrieved after a launch.

- Do not touch cables or their attachments unnecessarily.

- Never walk in front of, or stand near a glider which has a launch cable attached.

- Never approach an aircraft which has its propeller turning, unless the pilot has acknowledged your intention. In that case keep the wing between you and the propeller as you approach. Never touch a stationary propeller; moving it even slightly may cause the engine to start.

- Winch operators are protected by a cage against a flailing cable, should the launch cable break. Stay well away from winches during a launch unless you are inside this cage.

- Tow cars travel fast and the driver's concentration will be focused on the glider being launched. Stay well clear of their path at all times.

- If flying in the vicinity of the gliding site, avoid overflying the airfield as wire launching can occur up to 3,000 feet and launch cables are difficult to see.

Once you are familiar with gliding site operation, you will discover that these safety points come naturally. You will also find yourself assisting in the launching of gliders, driving winches, tow cars and tractors, and generally joining in the teamwork which helps make gliding such an enjoyable sport. Like all situations where powerful machinery is involved, safety consciousness is essential. If you are unsure about anything do not hesitate to ask. If you see someone doing something which you think is unsafe, challenge them. What they are doing may be perfectly safe, but if they were mistaken, they will be grateful.

GROUND HANDLING

The success of a gliding club depends greatly on the equipment being maintained in good condition. Apart from the need of the individuals on the airfield to look after their own safety, they in turn must take care of the equipment, especially the gliders.

Gliders may appear elegant and graceful when in the air, but on the ground they are heavy, bulky objects which require much ground handling in order to prepare them for launch. While the glider's structure is well-designed to withstand the aerodynamic loads imposed upon it in flight, and the potentially large loads during a landing, it is not so well-designed for any mishandling it may get on the ground. In order to safeguard it against ground handling damage, some understanding of how to handle the glider on the ground is essential.

While manoeuvring the glider around the airfield, whether it is being towed behind a vehicle or pushed by individuals, it is important to know on which parts of the structure force can be applied. This is especially the case with older gliders which are often constructed of wood and fabric.

Fig 2.5 shows the areas which are strong enough to support a push or lift force and those which are not.

In general the leading edge of the wing close to where the wing meets the fuselage is the best place to push. As many gliders have tailskids, the tail

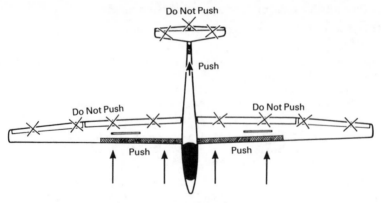

Fig 2.5   Ground handling points. Parts of the glider where it is safe to lift or push and those where it is not.

will have to be lifted if the glider is to be pushed backwards. To facilitate this, many gliders have special handles fitted to the rear fuselage. These strengthened points will also withstand pull or push forces. On gliders constructed of glass fibre, the fuselage immediately behind the wing will provide a suitable structure on which to push, if the glider is to be moved forwards.

The trailing edges of the wings, the control surfaces and the tailplane areas all tend to be of lighter construction and these areas are unsuitable for manhandling. Never lift the tail or push the glider by applying a force to the tailplane. Do not push or pull the glider by the wing tips as the large leverage created by the wings will result in considerable force being applied to the wing fittings at the point where the wing is attached to the fuselage. The strain placed on these fittings will be especially high if the ground is soft or rutted.

Whichever way the glider is moved, whether it be towed behind a vehicle or by manpower alone, the wing must be supported off the ground. This will require someone to lift and walk with the wing tip. This person is best placed to steer the glider, but should not exert forces which counter those of other helpers on the tail. Only one wing tip should be held to avoid strain being placed on the wing fittings should any confusion arise as to who is steering. In windy conditions this wing tip holder should be positioned on the windward wing tip to prevent the wind lifting the wing and potentially blowing the glider over.

When the glider is being towed behind a vehicle the tow-rope should be long enough to prevent any danger of the glider running into the back of the vehicle should an over-run occur. When towing the glider in this way there should be someone walking beside the nose of the glider to release the tow-rope in case of an over-run.

In windy conditions, more ground crew are necessary and great care must be exercised when towing the glider into wind. In such circumstances, it is advisable to have someone sit in the cockpit to reduce the chance of the glider accidentally becoming airborne and also to prevent the control surfaces banging against their stops when turning across the wind.

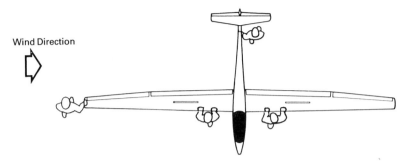

Fig 2.6   Ground handling. When moving a glider on the ground the wind must be taken into account.

The use of fixed bar towing attachments and wing tip fittings can reduce much of the effort and risks of ground manoeuvring. Such fittings must be well-designed and of good quality otherwise they themselves can cause damage to the glider.

PARKING THE GLIDER

When the glider is left unattended it should be secured so as not to be affected by the wind or the propeller wash from tow-planes or other aircraft. The canopy should be closed and locked. The glider's nose should be left pointing in such a way that the wind is not blowing from in front of the wing and such that the controls will not be caused to bang against their stops by the wind. The wing should be secured to prevent the wind lifting the wing and causing it or the other wing to hit the ground. It is common to prevent the lowered wing from rising by using old car tyres to weigh it down. However, with glass fibre gliders the wings are often supported level on trestles or tied to anchor points.

In very windy conditions, when the wind is striking the glider's tail, the glider will want to swing nose into wind. To prevent this, it will be necessary to place a tyre on the downwind side of the tail. A tyre may also be required to be jammed under the nose skid to stop the tail from rising.

One golden rule for safety is to "look after your glider and it will look after you".

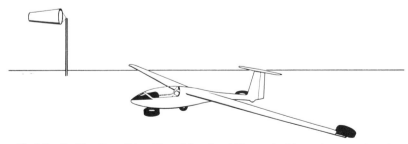

Fig 2.7   Parking the glider. The glider should be parked in such a way that the wind will not move it.

CHAPTER 3

YOUR FIRST FLIGHT

The main aim of your instructor on your first flight is to introduce you to the sport of gliding. In so doing, your instructor will show you around the glider, its cockpit and controls, and instruct you on the relevant safety aspects such as securing your harness. You will also be shown how to adjust your seating position with respect to your comfort, your access to the various controls and to your view from the cockpit.

If the glider has the seats arranged in tandem, you will be given the front seat. Not only will this give you a better view, it is also the seat which you will have throughout your training on this type of glider. The reason for this is that when the day comes when your instructor decides you should fly solo, it is from the front seat that you will fly the glider. Your first solo flights will therefore be from the seating position you are used to.

Once in the air, your instructor will allow you to settle down in this new environment, and point out local features and landmarks. The primary controls will be demonstrated and you will be allowed to try some gentle manoeuvres. This will enable you to see how easy and logical flying a glider really is.

If you are launched by aerotow your instructor will probably have adequate time to give you several demonstrations, and to allow you to attempt some basic manoeuvres for yourself. These will include trying out the effects of the controls and turning the glider. If on the other hand you are launched on your first flight by car launch or winch launch, you will probably not have as much time for demonstrations and attempts as on aerotow. In this case, your instructor will structure the exercises so that they can progress easily on subsequent flights.

At all times in flight, it is important that there is no confusion as to whether you or your instructor is actually controlling the glider. After your instructor has demonstrated a manoeuvre, he will give you control by saying, "You have control". Once you have placed your hands and feet on the controls, you should reply by saying, "I have control". Your instructor can then release the controls to allow you to attempt the manoeuvre. When your instructor wants to retake control, he will say, "I have control". You can now release the controls and confirm that you have done so by saying, "You have control".

During the flight (assuming that you are new to the world of flying light aircraft) your body will be subjected to some new sensations. Don't worry, these are not the sensations experienced by the jet fighter pilot. Indeed, they are not even of the magnitude of those experienced at the fair ground. (This is one author you won't get on a big dipper!) They are worth mentioning only because they may be unexpected. If the glider is launched by winch (or to a lesser extent, by car) the initial acceleration will be quite rapid. This will have the effect of pushing you more firmly into your seat, similar to accelerating from a stationary position in a powerful car.

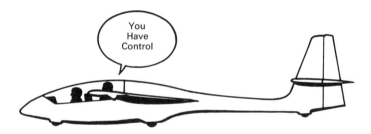

Fig 3.1   Who has control? Knowing who has control is essential.

Once in the air the sensations experienced are mainly due to the buoyancy of the air. If the day is windy or there are rising air currents then you will feel the glider being pushed up and down, or even feel as if a wing is occasionally being lifted. On a still, calm evening, the air will probably feel smooth and less of these sensations will be felt. Similar sensations can also be induced by control movements which are too rapid, especially if the control column is moved forwards too quickly.

Your instructor will explain such sensations at first, but as your time in the air increases, you will quickly get used to them and eventually be able to use them to assess the glider's position relative to rising air. Other sensations will become apparent which will help you decide whether or not you are controlling the glider accurately in turns.

All of these sensations will be covered further in later sections as they become more relevant. For now, it is sufficient to say that on most occasions, when the glider is being flown correctly, even a pilot with a few launches in his log book will not experience any unpleasant sensations.

Apart from getting comfortable in this new environment, one of the most important aspects to prepare you for your basic instruction, is to become accustomed to the view from the cockpit, and in particular, the position of the nose of the glider relative to the horizon. This view, known as the glider's ATTITUDE, is of primary importance when it comes to controlling the glider. It is used to tell you if the glider is likely to be maintaining a steady and reasonable airspeed, and whether or not the wings are level.

LOOKOUT

It is also of utmost importance, at this early stage, that you learn a lookout technique; your glider will not be the only aircraft in the air. The airspace in which you will be flying will also be used by private and commercial aeroplanes and helicopters, military traffic and other sporting activists such as microlight aircraft, hang-gliders, parachutists and of course, other gliders. It is essential that most of your attention is "outside" of the cockpit and to this aim, you will be taught to regularly scan around your field of vision, with particular emphasis when carrying out any manoeuvres such as turns.

Your first flight will probably last for fifteen to twenty minutes if you have an aerotow launch to 2000 feet. This is ample time for you to experience what gliding is like. If launched by winch or car launch, the time spent in

Fig 3.2   Flying by attitude. The glider's attitude (the view which the pilot has over the nose of the glider) is the main reference when gliding.

the air will be more like five minutes but there will probably be the opportunity to have a second or even a third flight on the same day.

There are very few formalities involved in preparing for your first glider flight, but in order that you know what will be required, they are outlined below.

Before flying at a gliding club, it is necessary for you to become a member. To help you avoid paying a year's subscription before knowing whether or not you will enjoy the sport, clubs normally have a temporary membership fee included in the cost of your trial flight.

You will also be asked to sign a declaration that you do not suffer from ailments such as epilepsy, heart problems or dizziness. If you have any doubts, then it does not mean you will not be able to take up gliding, but you should consult your doctor beforehand. His approval may be required. (By the way, your instructor will have been cleared by a doctor before he was allowed to become an instructor).

CHAPTER 4

HOW AEROPLANES AND GLIDERS FLY

The planet Earth attracts all objects on it or near it, pulling them down towards its centre. We call this pull the effect of gravity. When you stand on your bathroom scales your body is being pulled down onto the scales by gravity and the resulting force, the magnitude of which is indicated on the dial of the scales, is known as your weight. The total weight of a object can be assumed to act through one point, known as the CENTRE OF GRAVITY.

If you stood on a layer of thin ice, your weight would cause you to break through the ice and sink into the water below. On the other hand, when you stand on a solid surface, such as a floor, the floor supports your weight. The difference is that the floor is capable of providing a force which is of equal magnitude, acting in the opposite direction to your weight. This force is called the REACTION FORCE or simply the REACTION. The ice was not capable of supplying a reaction force of the same magnitude as your weight force.

Sir Isaac Newton stated that if an unbalanced force (that is, one without an equal and opposite reaction) is applied to an object, the object will accelerate in the direction of the applied force. (Just as you would accelerate down through the ice.) He identified this as a scientific law and we have been stuck with it ever since.

Aeroplanes and gliders are affected by the same law. When on the ground, the aircraft's weight is supported by the ground, that is the ground provides the reaction force to its weight. When in the air, the aircraft itself must produce a reaction force to counter its weight. This force is provided by the wing and is called LIFT.

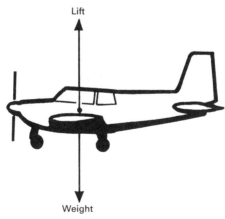

Fig 4.1   Lift versus weight. Lift produced by the wing normally balances the aircraft's weight.

HOW THE WING PRODUCES LIFT

If air is blown through a passage with a restriction (called a venturi), the speed of the air increases as it approaches the narrowest point, reaching its maximum speed at the point of maximum restriction and then decelerating as the passage widens again. Mr Bernoulli (another scientific lawman) stated that if you increase the speed of the airflow, you reduce the pressure it exerts.

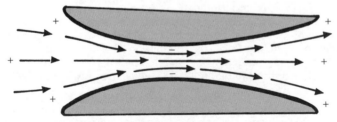

Fig 4.2   Bernoulli's theorem. As air accelerates through a venturi it causes a reduction in pressure.

If this sounds complex, try this simple experiment:

Take two sheets of paper and fold them slightly to approximately the angle shown below in Fig 4.3

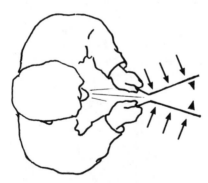

Fig 4.3   Venturi experiment. Blowing between two sheets of paper causes them to "suck" together.

Hold them vertically on edge on a flat surface and blow through the gap at one end. Blowing increases the speed of the airflow and causes a pressure reduction between the sheets of paper causing them to be sucked closer together.

The same reduction of pressure occurs if the airflow is increased over just one cambered surface.

Another experiment:

Hold a sheet of paper at one end, allowing the other end to droop under its own weight.

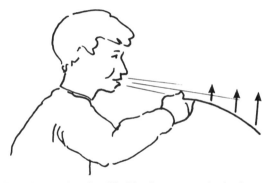

Fig 4.4   Experiment showing lift. Blowing over a single sheet of paper creates lift.

Blow along the upper surface as shown and the paper lifts due to the reduced pressure created above the upper surface. What is happening is that the air below the paper, which is at normal atmospheric pressure, is trying to flow upwards to equalise the lower pressure created above the paper. In so doing, it lifts the paper. This is the principle by which the wing develops lift. The faster you blow, the more the paper lifts.

The cross-section through a conventional wing (known simply as the WING SECTION) will show a structure which has two surfaces. An upper surface which is cambered and a lower surface, which, in its simplest form, is essentially flat. As the wing travels through the air (or as the air passes the wing; it is the relative movement of the wing and air that matters) the same pressure reduction effect occurs as with our piece of paper. The faster the air flows past the wing, the greater the amount of lift which is produced.

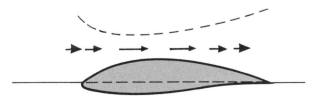

Fig 4.5   The wing section. The upper surface of the wing accelerates the airflow over it, creating reduced pressure and lift.

In Fig 4.5 the dotted line completes the comparison with the venturi principle, with the wing being the lower surface of the venturi.

As the wing's shape is a somewhat complex curve, measuring the angle at which the airflow meets it would be difficult. Therefore the aerodynamicist uses a reference line, called the CHORD LINE. This line is simply a line drawn from the leading edge of the wing section to the trailing edge. The angle at which the RELATIVE AIRFLOW meets the CHORD LINE is called the ANGLE OF ATTACK. In normal flight the angle of attack will be between 0 and 12 degrees. Note at this point that the relative airflow is not necessarily horizontal and may in theory come from any direction.

21

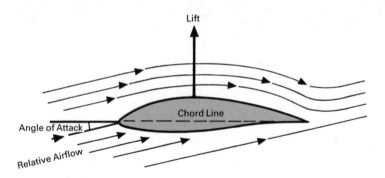

Fig 4.6   Angle of attack. The angle at which the relative airflow meets the chord line is called the angle of attack.

So far we have seen that increased lift can be gained by increasing the speed of the airflow past the wing (or the speed of the wing through the air). There is another way in which the amount of lift that the wing produces can be increased. If we incline the wing so that the airflow meets it at an increased angle of attack, this has an effect similar to decreasing the passage through the venturi (see Fig 4.7).

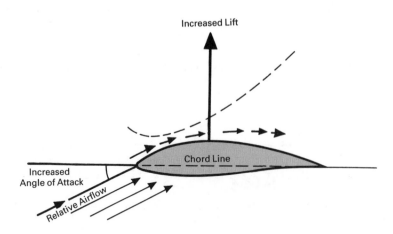

Fig 4.7   Increasing the angle of attack. Increasing the angle of attack generally produces more lift.

The pressure reduction increases and again more lift results. The lift produced will continue to increase as the angle of attack is increased, providing the angle does not become so great that the airflow can no longer flow smoothly over the upper surface of the wing. If the angle of attack exceeds this critical angle then the amount of lift produced will reduce sharply and the wing is said to be STALLED. The angle of attack is said to have reached or exceeded the STALLING ANGLE.

To summarise.

In balanced flight the weight of a powered aeroplane is balanced by an equal and opposite reaction force called lift.

The wing is designed to produce lift by having an upper surface that is more cambered than its lower surface, and by inclining it at an angle to the airflow.

More lift is produced if the speed of the relative airflow past the wing is increased.

More lift is produced if the angle between the relative airflow and the wing is increased, provided that the stalling angle is not exceeded.

The distribution of lift created by the wing varies with the angle of attack. However, as a rough guide, 2/3 of the total lift produced by the wing is created by the airflow over the upper surface.

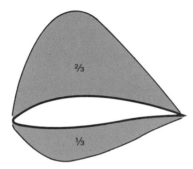

Fig 4.8   Lift distribution. The airflow over the upper surface of the wing creates about 2/3 of the total lift.

For simplicity, the lift force can be assumed to act through one point, the CENTRE OF PRESSURE, which unlike the centre of gravity can move forward and aft across the wing as the angle of attack is varied.

Control of the glider is done by deflecting the control surfaces described in CHAPTER 1. These deflections of the control surfaces create forces similar to small lift forces by cambering the surface, just as the camber of the wing generates the lift force.

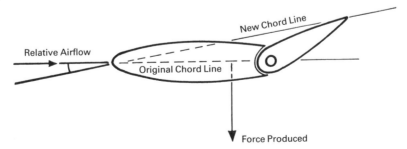

Fig 4.9   How the controls work. Deflection of a control surface creates a cambered surface and produces a force in the desired direction.

23

DRAG

When an aeroplane or glider moves through the air it creates another force called DRAG. Drag is that force which resists the aircraft's movement through the air. It is an unwanted force as far as the aircraft's performance is concerned.

The TOTAL DRAG is made up of two types of drag, PROFILE DRAG and INDUCED DRAG.

PROFILE DRAG is itself comprised of various elements, the main ones of which are FORM DRAG and SKIN FRICTION.

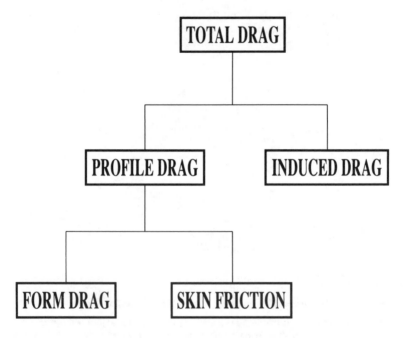

Fig 4.10   Drag. The main types of drag.

FORM DRAG is drag which is caused as the aircraft's form (or shape) moves through the air. If you imagine standing in a swimming pool and sweeping your hand through the water, imagine the resistance you would feel against your hand's movement. This resistance force is called form drag and it will increase in magnitude as you increase the speed of your hand's movement and will also vary as you change the profile or shape of your hand as it passes through the water. In general, the larger and flatter the frontal area presented to the water, the greater the form drag.

Another contributor to the total profile drag is called SKIN FRICTION. Skin friction is literally the friction or dragging effect that the aircraft's surface has on the air (or vice versa). If the surface of the aircraft (e.g. its wings and fuselage) is very rough, the amount of skin friction will be high. Also the more surface area that the aircraft has, the greater will be the amount of skin friction.

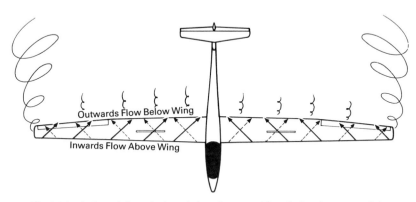

Fig 4.11   Induced drag. Induced drag is caused by air flowing around the wing tips from the relatively high pressure below the wing to the lower pressure above the wing.

INDUCED DRAG is created when the wing creates lift by causing a pressure differential. As mentioned earlier, the air will try to flow from the relatively high pressure below the wing to the relatively low pressure above the wing. Ideally, all of this moving air would be used to lift the wing as the air tries to flow from the high pressure area to the low pressure area. However, in practice, some of it takes the easy route around the wing tip, resulting in vortices of swirling air and lost energy. The larger the angle of attack, the greater the pressure differential and therefore the greater the induced drag. Unlike profile drag, induced drag increases as the airspeed is reduced.

Drag is therefore a nuisance but is itself a reaction force to the aircraft's movement through the air.

The force that moves a powered aeroplane through the air is called THRUST. Providing that the aeroplane is in STEADY or UNACCELERATED FLIGHT (that is, neither accelerating, decelerating nor manoeuvring) thrust will act in the opposite direction to drag with the same magnitude.

In an aeroplane the engine provides thrust. So what produces this force in a glider?

REPRESENTING FORCES DIAGRAMMATICALLY

Before we look at the answer to this, let us outline a way in which we can visualise the forces involved. In the diagrams used previously we have illustrated the forces of weight, lift, drag and thrust by straight lines. A

25

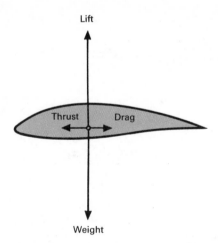

Fig 4.12   Forces in balance. In an aeroplane lift normally balances weight and thrust normally balances drag.

further inspection will show that the direction of the arrow on the line indicates the direction of the force and that the length of the line has been used to show its magnitude. (Compare the length and direction of one of the forces with those of its reaction, e.g. weight and lift.)

For simplicity, all of the forces that have been shown so far have acted vertically or horizontally. Given a force which is acting at another angle (Fig 4.13), it is possible to "resolve" this force into two components: one vertical and one horizontal (the broken lines in the diagram). For example, if two ropes were attached to an object and a force applied on one rope in the direction of V and another on the second rope in the direction of H, the effect would be similar to one force applied in the direction and with the magnitude of force R, the RESULTANT FORCE. Similarly, we can resolve force R into its vertical and horizontal components (V and H) by constructing the parallelogram shown.

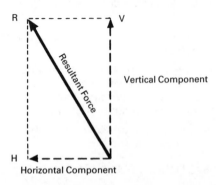

Fig 4.13   Resolution of forces. Any force can be resolved into its vertical and horizontal components or alternatively any two forces acting on an object can be replaced by one "resultant" force.

Another example of this resolution of forces is the resultant force applied by a catapult on its projectile, despite the fact that the elastic applies two angular forces.

We have dealt with the basic forces affecting an aeroplane first, as they are simpler to understand than those affecting a glider. However, they illustrate the principles of unaccelerated flight and the need to maintain forces in balance which equally affect both gliders and aeroplanes. Now that the basic rules have been set, we can concentrate on the glider and gliding flight.

From the preceding paragraphs, as with an aeroplane, a glider moving through the air can be seen to have a weight force, a drag force, and is capable of producing a lift force. Unlike an aeroplane, it has no engine to produce a thrust force to propel itself through the air. To solve this problem, the lift force is tilted forward so that it now has a horizontal component acting in a forward direction. It is this horizontal force which propels the glider in a forward direction. Fig 4.14 shows this resolution of the lift force into its vertical and horizontal components.

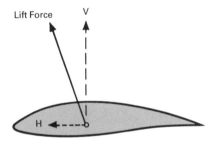

Fig 4.14   Propelling the glider forwards. The lift force can be tilted to give a horizontal component.

In order to complete the picture we need to further define the three forces which we now know affect the glider.

WEIGHT always acts vertically down.

LIFT always acts at an angle of 90° to the relative airflow.

DRAG always acts parallel to the relative airflow.

The diagram at Fig 4.15 shows the forces as defined in relation to each other.

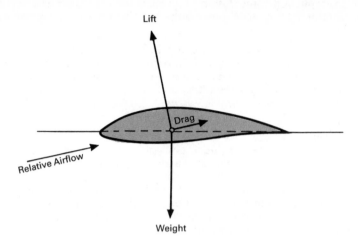

Fig 4.15 Weight, lift and drag. Lift always acts at 90° to the relative airflow. Drag always acts parallel to the relative airflow and weight always acts vertically downwards.

If we take just the lift force and the drag force (Fig 4.16), we can see that these two forces have a resultant which acts vertically upwards and it is this resultant force which balances the weight force. (Note that as the magnitude of the drag force is normally small compared to that of the lift force, it is common to refer to the resultant force simply as "lift".)

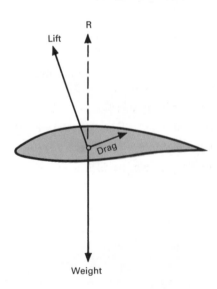

Fig 4.16 Lift and drag versus weight. The resultant of lift and drag normally balances the glider's weight.

Similarly, if we take just the lift force and the weight force, we can see that these two forces have a resultant which opposes and balances the drag force. (Fig 4.17)

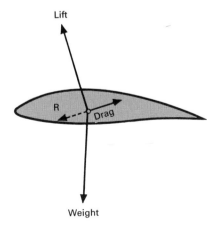

Fig 4.17   Lift and weight versus drag. The resultant of lift and weight normally balances drag.

Now, just as with the aeroplane, all of the forces are balanced and the glider is said to be in unaccelerated flight. Remember however, that if the direction or magnitude of any of these forces is changed, the balance will be temporarily upset and the glider will change either its airspeed or direction (in this case vertically). It is by making such controlled changes that we manoeuvre the glider.

Finally, if we look at the ratio between the magnitude of the lift force and that of the drag force, we have a measure of the glider's performance. The larger the lift force and the smaller the drag force then the greater the distance that the glider can fly from a given height, assuming that is, that no rising or sinking air is encountered. This LIFT/DRAG RATIO, which is also known as the GLIDE ANGLE, is typically around 30/1 for a training glider and as much as 60/1 for a high performance sailplane.

CHAPTER 5

PREPARATION FOR FLIGHT

Once airborne the glider pilot, whether training to fly solo or competing in a World Championship race, will find that he is kept busy flying the glider and making the countless decisions upon which his success in his chosen objective depends. For this reason the better prepared the pilot and the glider before the flight, the better the chances of achieving the objective during the flight.

There are many aspects of preparing for a flight, especially if the flight is an ambitious cross-country or competition flight. At this stage it is not necessary to cover the extensive preparation required for such flights. Although the items which follow would be included when preparing for more advanced tasks, they are set out here with your training and early solo flights in mind.

PERSONAL PREPARATION

Clothing

Airfields, from necessity, are open, exposed areas, often on top of hills. No-one can expect to enjoy the sport if it is cold or wet and they are inadequately clothed.

In winter, dress warmly in clothes that allow freedom of movement and wear waterproof footwear, as wearing wet shoes and socks for many hours can be a discomfort. Bear in mind however, that the glider's rudder pedals require a sensitive touch and so heavy boots may not be conducive to accurate flying. Therefore a compromise is required or even a change of footwear kept available.

In summer, the launch point may suffer from little shade and sun-burn may be the main hazard. The glider's perspex canopy magnifies the sun's effect, resulting in an over warm environment even in temperate latitudes. It is then important to dress cooly in light clothing which may even be of the long-sleeved variety to give more protection, if deemed necessary. A sun hat is also essential as the sun shining through the canopy will be felt most on the head. Some hats will also afford vital protection to the neck.

Sunglasses or shades are treated by many glider pilots as essential in their often bright environment.

Even on an early morning in summer, a heavy dew can form, causing the same footwear considerations as in winter.

As far as clothing is concerned, be practical. Do not worry about being fashionable; no-one else will!

Personal Fitness

Even the best designed, highest performance sailplane is useless without its pilot. To get the best results out of this expensive piece of hardware, the pilot has to be in reasonable condition. Now before you decide that gliding is for fitness fanatics and not for you, let me allay your fears. As long as you are fit enough to get into the glider and move the controls you will be capable of flying a glider, assuming that is, you have not been medically prohibited by your doctor from doing so. (Incidentally, there have been and still are, many a good glider pilot with physical disabilities who have been able to enjoy the sport fully.)

In this context, pilot fitness can be interpreted as "fitness to fly" on the day of the flight.

Some situations when you should not fly include:

if you have consumed alcohol in the previous 8 hours or are feeling "hung-over" from an earlier consumption,

OR

if you are taking drugs or antibiotics for any reason and your doctor has not specifically cleared you to fly,

OR

if you are suffering from a head cold or sinus complaint (such a problem may result in you not being able to equalise the pressure in your ears and can result in permanent damage to your hearing and much pain)

OR

if you are feeling in any way "under-the-weather".

GLIDER PREPARATION

Due to the fact that gliders regularly fly cross-country tasks, occasionally landing somewhere that requires them being transported back home to base, they are constructed in a manner that will allow them to be dismantled or DE-RIGGED easily into their main component parts. This de-rigging ability also allows for easy storage.

The parts that make up most training gliders are usually heavier than the equivalent parts of single-seat gliders which more often fly cross-country. It is therefore common practice to keep two-seat gliders fully RIGGED in a hangar. The rigging of a glider is dealt with in the flight manual for that individual type of glider, and you will be given instruction in the general technique of rigging, and on the peculiarities of assembling each particular type of glider, by a qualified instructor. For these reasons, rigging of the glider will not be covered here.

THE DAILY INSPECTION

Whether the glider has been rigged that day or kept in a hangar, it must receive a DAILY INSPECTION (D.I.). Club gliders are required to have a DAILY INSPECTION BOOK in which the condition of the glider is noted. When you first begin to glide, this task will be carried out by your instructor, or another pilot qualified to perform it. After you have gained some experience of gliding, you will be instructed in how to "D.I." the glider and then, after some supervision, allowed to carry out this basic, but essential task on your own.

As gliders vary so much in their detailed design, it is necessary to be briefed on the first occasion on which you inspect a new type.

The following are the important points to remember when carrying out a Daily Inspection:

- Check the Daily Inspection Book to make sure that the glider has not already been inspected previously that day by someone else and that it has not been declared unserviceable. Check also if any previous defects that have been noted, have been rectified, and if not, satisfy yourself that they are still of a type and extent that can be carried forward for later action. If you have any doubts, consult a qualified inspector.

- Make sure that the CERTIFICATE OF AIRWORTHINESS (C of A) placard and the LIMITATIONS placard are displayed in the cockpit and that the date on the C of A placard shows that it has not expired.

- Remember that the Daily Inspection is for the whole of the day. Minor defects that you find, and upon which you are willing to defer action, must not be in danger of getting worse before action can be taken. Other pilots, who may fly the glider after you, may not share your optimism of the magnitude of the defect. As a general rule **fix it before you fly it**.

- A dirty canopy or an under-inflated tyre will make the glider unserviceable and is easy to rectify.

- Establish a routine such as that shown in Fig 5.1. Methodically inspect the whole glider, both outside and inside, seeking assistance to raise wings or move controls, where necessary. Take care not to miss any areas that are difficult to see such as those underneath the fuselage.

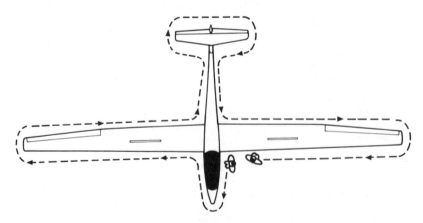

Fig 5.1   The daily inspection. Establish and follow a routine for inspecting the glider.

- Do not allow yourself to be distracted.

- Physically check that the elevator and ailerons are connected by having a colleague hold the control surface while you move the control column, thus confirming that your applied force is being transmitted to the control surface in the correct sense.

- If you find a defect which will necessitate making the glider unserviceable, never leave the glider without noting the fact in the D.I. Book, otherwise someone may fly the glider before you return with an inspector.
- If you are not satisfied with the glider's condition then declare it UNSERVICEABLE until action is taken.
- Always complete and sign the D.I. Book.

PRE-TAKE-OFF CHECKS

Once the glider is at the launch point and the pilot(s) is strapped in, there are some essential checks to be done. These PRE-TAKE-OFF CHECKS are the final check that the glider and the pilot are ready for flight. You will be formally instructed on these checks on your second or third flight and will then be expected to carry them out (with your instructor monitoring you doing them) **before every flight**. Even after you are cleared to fly solo you will be expected to religiously carry out these checks, irrespective of which glider you are flying. Such a routine is a simple but very effective method of ensuring that something vital does not get forgotten.

In order to make it easier to remember the items included in the check and their sequence, a mnemonic is used.

In the United Kingdom, and a few other countries, it is CB-SIFT-CB.

The elements of the check are as follows and how to carry out the check is explained below.

C – CONTROLS

Move the control column fully forwards and observe that the elevator deflects fully downwards. Move the control column fully backwards and observe that the elevator moves fully upwards.

Move the control column fully to the left and observe that the left aileron moves fully upwards and the right aileron moves fully down.

Move the control column fully to the right and observe that the right aileron moves fully upwards and the left aileron moves fully down.

Push the left rudder pedal fully forwards and check that the rudder moves to its maximum deflection to the left. Push the right rudder pedal fully forwards and check that the rudder moves to its maximum deflection to the right. Centralise the pedals and check that the rudder is centralised.

Operate all of the controls simultaneously to make sure that nothing is fouling their full range of movement.

If you have difficulty in observing the control surfaces as they move, enrol the assistance of a helper to confirm the amount and sense in which they move. Never settle solely for the fact that the control column moves without resistance; it may have this feel if the controls are unconnected! Always complete the control check **after** you are seated and strapped into the cockpit, otherwise you may undo your conscientious control check by subsequently strapping a control push rod or control cable to yourself!

B – BALLAST

A glider is designed to be flown by a pilot who is within a particular weight range. The upper limit of this range is normally determined by structural considerations. The lower limit of this range is determined by control considerations. It is therefore essential that, before embarking on a flight, you confirm that your weight (and that of your instructor, if present) falls in between the limits of this range.

To assist you to do this, there is a placard displayed in the cockpit which shows the range of weights permitted, along with maximum airspeed limitations. (Fig 5.2) In the case of a two-seat glider, this placard may show the permutations of weights allowed between the two occupants.

LIMITATIONS PLACARD   BGA/267/P

B.G.A. No 3366   **TYPE** ASK 13

CATEGORY: NON AEROBATIC/AEROBATIC

SEMI AEROBATIC/CLOUD FLYING

SPEED LIMITATIONS (Knots)

Auto/Winch	80	Rough Air	75
Aero Tow	80	VNE	108
Flaps	N/A	Gear Down	N/A

WEIGHT AND C.G. LIMITATIONS

Max. Wt. (dry)	1060	Max. Wt. (water)	N/A
Empty Wt.	706	Min. Solo Wt.	141
Max. Solo Wt.	242	Date Weighed	22·8·92

NOTE: Refer to flight Manual for full limitations.

Issued by J. BLOGGS   Dated 24·8·92

Fig 5.2   *The limitations placard. The glider's limitations placard will give the weights and speeds which must not be exceeded.*

Never fly in a glider if you are outside of the ballast range permitted. Even if you are only just within the lower end of the ballast range you should secure extra ballast (usually in the form of specially shaped lead bars) to the ballast points provided, in order that the cockpit load falls well within the ballast limits. In calculating your weight remember to take into account the weight of your parachute, if you are wearing one, and also check that the previous pilot has not left any unwanted ballast in place.

Each glider, even of the same type, will have a different ballast range and the ballast placard for the specific glider being flown must be consulted.

S – STRAPS

Make sure that your straps (and those of any other occupant) are secure and comfortable.

I – INSTRUMENTS

Switch on any electrics that are required and if necessary set the variometers to the desired mode. Set the altimeter to the desired datum setting. Check that none of the instruments are damaged and that they are all reading sensibly.

F – FLAPS

Exercise the flap lever through its full range of movement to make sure that the flaps are functioning and not inhibited. Set the flaps at the required setting for take-off.

T – TRIM

Exercise the trim control through its full range and set it in the position for take-off.

C – CANOPY

Close and lock the canopy. Test that it is secure by applying a gentle force on the canopy frame. In a two-seat glider with separate canopies, make sure that both canopies are secure.

B – BRAKES

The "brakes" in this case are the airbrakes (or spoilers on some older types of glider). Open them fully to check that they function properly, observing them as they extend from the surface of the wings. Close and lock them, making sure that they have fully closed and that the lever has moved fully into the locked position. (If this is a geometric lock, as opposed to a recess for the lever, you will have to push the lever firmly when in the closed position to enable the control push rods to move into the locked position.) If they are left closed but unlocked, the airbrakes will probably open during the take-off due to aerodynamic forces, with potentially disastrous results. If the glider has spoilers instead of airbrakes the check sequence for airbrakes will still apply, although often with spoilers there will be no apparent locking device. Instead the spoiler surfaces may be spring-loaded towards the closed position.

If any part of the check is not applicable to the glider to be flown (for instance many gliders do not have flaps) then do not just ignore that part of the check but instead state that they are "NOT FITTED". Provided you THINK about each part of the check, this habit will keep your checks disciplined and tidy throughout your future gliding and put you in good stead for the day when you fly a glider where that part of the check is applicable.

RELEASE HOOK CHECK

Before the first flight of the day, a release check is made to ensure that the release hook mechanism, to which the launch cable will be attached, is functioning. This check is made both with the launch cable slack and under tension. This is done simply by getting an assistant to attach and apply some force on the launch cable while you operate the release control in the cockpit. This is repeated without tension on the cable to test the release when the cable is slack. In the case of a WINCH (or BELLY) HOOK, it is also tested by pulling the cable backwards towards the tail of the glider to confirm that the automatic back-release mechanism will operate satisfactorily, should the glider overfly the winch at the top of the launch.

If the glider is fitted with separate release mechanisms for aerotow launching and wire launching, then the appropriate mechanism must be tested on each day prior to the first of that type of launch.

CHAPTER 6

THE PRIMARY CONTROLS

A glider is controllable in three dimensions. In order to define its movements we refer to the three axes shown at Fig 6.1. Each of these axes is at 90 degrees to the other two axes and all of them pass through the glider's centre of gravity.

These axes are:

The LATERAL AXIS which runs parallel with a line drawn from wing tip to wing tip.

The LONGITUDINAL AXIS which runs in the direction from nose to tail.

The NORMAL AXIS which runs up from below to above the fuselage as shown.

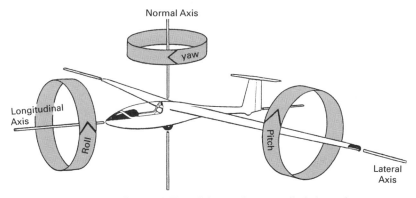

Fig 6.1   The axes of control. The glider can be controlled about three axes.

Motion about the LATERAL AXIS is called PITCHING or PITCH. This on its own would be observed by the pilot as the NOSE GOING UP or DOWN.

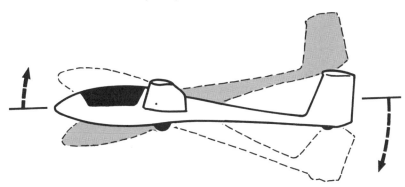

Fig 6.2   Pitching the glider.

Motion about the LONGITUDINAL AXIS is called ROLLING or ROLL. This on its own would be observed by the pilot as ONE WING GOING UP AND THE OTHER GOING DOWN.

Fig 6.3   Rolling the glider.

Motion about the NORMAL AXIS is called YAWING or YAW. This on its own would be observed by the pilot as the NOSE SWINGING TO THE LEFT OR RIGHT.

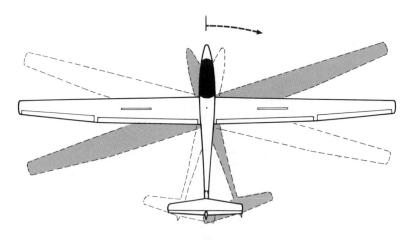

Fig 6.4   Yawing the glider.

THE MAIN CONTROLS

The ELEVATOR controls PITCH.

Moving the control column backwards causes the elevator to deflect upwards. This creates a cambered surface on the underside of the tailplane, resulting in an aerodynamic force which will cause the tail of the glider to move downwards. This in turn has the effect of raising the nose (pitching nose upwards about the lateral axis). Forward movement of the control column causes the opposite deflection and a nose down effect.

The AILERONS control ROLL.

Moving the control column to the right causes the RIGHT AILERON to move upwards and at the same time causes the LEFT AILERON to move downwards. This reduces the camber and angle of attack on the right wing (causing a reduction of lift) and increases the camber and angle of attack on the left wing (causing more lift). The combined effect is to roll the glider to the right about its longitudinal axis. A control input to the left would deflect the ailerons in the opposite direction causing the glider to roll to the left.

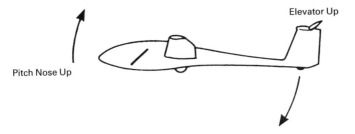

Fig 6.5   The elevator controls pitch.

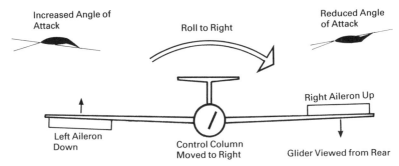

Fig 6.6   The ailerons control roll.

The RUDDER controls YAW.

Depressing the left rudder pedal causes the rudder to deflect to the left. This causes an increased camber on the right-hand side of the fin pulling the tail to the right (about the glider's normal axis) resulting in the nose yawing or swinging to the left. Similarly, right rudder would have the equivalent effect to the right.

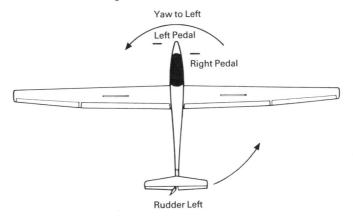

Fig 6.7   The rudder controls yaw.

It is important to note at this stage, that although we talk about the glider's nose and wings going "up" and "down ", the control surfaces and the three axes are in fixed positions **relative to the glider** and **not** to the earth's horizon. The relevant controls on the glider will therefore influence the glider relative to these axes and not directly to the earth's horizon.

AIR EXERCISE – EFFECT OF CONTROLS

The following exercise will be demonstrated by your instructor and you will then be allowed to attempt it.

THE ELEVATOR

Whilst flying at an airspeed of 45 knots with the wings level, note the position of the nose of the glider relative to the horizon. This is termed the "normal gliding attitude". If the in-flight visibility is too poor to give a clear horizon, then the amount of ground in view over the nose can be used as a reference to the glider's attitude. (Fig 6.8a)

Move the control column forwards until the nose lowers relative to the horizon or until more ground can be seen over the nose. Notice that the airflow noise increases and then settles at a higher level, as does the airspeed. The glider is now in a different attitude. (Fig 6.8b)

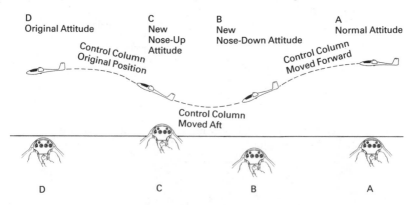

Fig 6.8   Air Exercise – the effect of elevator.

Move the control column backwards and the nose of the glider will rise and the glider will again settle in another new attitude, this time with the nose higher than the previous attitude. Less ground will be in view over the nose. The airflow noise and the airspeed will be less. (Fig 6.8c)

Return the control column to its original position and the glider will return to its original attitude. The airflow noise and airspeed will settle at their original levels. (Fig 6.8d)

For any given position of the control column in a fore and aft sense, there is a corresponding attitude and airspeed at which the glider will settle. The glider is therefore said to be STABLE in pitch.

THE AILERONS

Whilst flying at an airspeed of 45 knots with the wings level, look over the nose of the glider and note how the nose of the glider and the cockpit edge are symmetrical with the horizon. (Fig 6.9a)

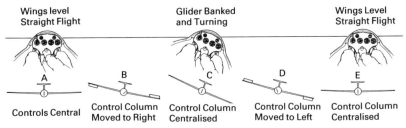

Fig 6.9   Air Exercise – the effect of aileron.

Move the control column to the right and the right wing will go down. (Fig 6.9b) It will continue to go down until the control column is moved back to the central position (or for reasons that will be discussed later, probably slightly to the left beyond central).

Once the control column is returned to this centralised position the wing will remain down and the glider is said to be BANKED. Notice the angle of the horizon relative to the nose of the glider. (Fig 6.9c) The glider will now turn in the direction of the lower wing (the direction of BANK). The larger the ANGLE OF BANK the faster the rate at which the glider will move around the turn.

To take off the bank and return to wings-level flight, move the control column to the left. (Fig 6.9d) This will raise the right wing. Then centralise the control column when the wings are level. (Fig 6.9e)

Repeat the exercise using left aileron; that is by initially moving the control column to the left.

THE RUDDER

Whilst flying at an airspeed of 45 knots with the wings level, select a feature in the distance as an aiming point. (Fig 6.10a)

Push on the right rudder pedal, keeping the wings level with aileron as you do so. Note how the nose of the glider swings (or yaws) to the right of the aiming point. However, notice that the glider is still moving towards the aiming point and that the rudder has not turned the glider or altered its direction, but merely yawed the glider. (Fig 6.10b)

Centralise the rudder pedals and the nose of the glider will swing back to the left to point in the original direction, that is, towards the aiming point. (Fig 6.10c)

From the exercise showing the effect of the rudder, it would appear that the rudder is a fairly useless device, as it does not actually turn the glider. In fact, the rudder is an essential control on a glider, as will be seen when in the next section we look at how the rudder is used to assist the primary turning controls, the ailerons, to turn the glider.

41

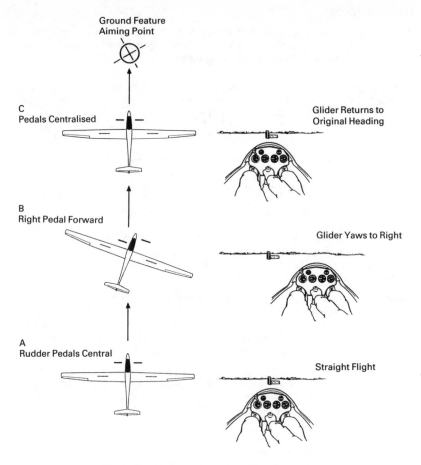

Ground Feature
Aiming Point

C
Pedals Centralised

Glider Returns to
Original Heading

B
Right Pedal Forward

Glider Yaws to Right

A
Rudder Pedals Central

Straight Flight

Fig 6.10   Air Exercise – the effect of rudder.

CHAPTER 7

TURNING THE GLIDER

The ability to turn the glider accurately is an essential skill that the glider pilot must possess. Not only are accurate turns with co-ordinated control movements necessary for directional control, but also for safety. As you will discover later, they are also the basis of the art of soaring, where an accurately flown turn may be the difference between successfully utilising a rising air current or perhaps having to land earlier than you had wished.

Turning the glider involves co-ordinating all three primary controls; the elevator, ailerons and rudder. The effect of each of the three controls has been discussed and you will have seen that, about its own axis, each control produces certain forces. These are relatively small forces which, on their own, are not sufficient to turn the glider. What they are capable of doing is tilting the much larger lift force produced by the wing in order that it will act in the direction required, e.g. forwards or backwards for a speed change or to either side to turn the glider.

In effect, we are flying the wing on its own without all the appendages such as fuselage and tail. It is the wing that does all the real work. The rest of the glider is only for seating the pilot and providing suitable levers at the end of which are the control surfaces. All these "extra bits" cause weight and drag, and the designer would be happy to do without them – if only he could! (Some designers seem to have forgotten that the whole point of the exercise is to carry the pilot and this is probably the reason why some high performance glider cockpits are ergonomically less than comfortable for all but that mythical beast known as the "average man".)

THE FORCES IN A TURN

Fig 7.1a shows the state of equilibrium of forces which we discussed previously. The force acting vertically upwards (the resultant) balances the weight force acting vertically downwards. There is no component acting sideways and therefore the glider is flying straight ahead. To initiate a turn we need to produce a horizontal force towards the centre of our intended turn. To do this we must roll the glider in order that the resultant (acting perpendicular to the wing) is tilted towards the direction of the turn. This situation and the resulting horizontal and vertical components of the tilted resultant are shown at Fig 7.1b. We now have the horizontal force that we need to turn the glider. This force is called the CENTRIPETAL FORCE.

However, having solved the problem of finding a force to turn the glider we have created another problem. The clue to this problem is in the length of the arrow representing the vertical component with which we have been left to counter the weight force. (Fig 7.1b) It has been reduced and now the vertical forces are out of balance. If this situation were allowed to persist, the glider would accelerate downwards until the airspeed increased sufficiently to cause an increase in lift (due to the increased airflow over the wings) to re-balance the weight force. This is an undesirable solution

43

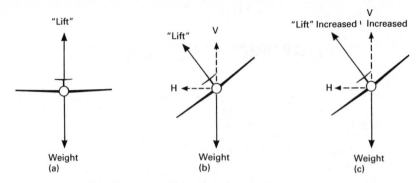

Fig 7.1   Forces in a turn. (a) The vertical force of weight is normally balanced by
the resultant of lift and drag. (b) Banking the glider tilts the resultant and causes
the glider to turn. (c) In turns, it is necessary to increase the angle of attack to
restore the vertical component to counter the glider's weight.

as it would result in the nose going down and an unwanted airspeed
change. To prevent this nose drop, it is necessary to increase the
magnitude of the vertical component of the resultant to the original level
by easing backwards on the control column. This increases the angle of
attack and, as a result, the amount of lift produced. (Fig 7.1c)

By increasing the resultant we will also increase the horizontal component,
adding to the turning force. The resulting increase in the rate of turn will
not cause a significant problem as long as the angle of bank is not
excessive. In any case, this can be nullified, if necessary, by reducing the
angle of bank slightly. In addition, asking the wing to supply an increased
force to turn the glider and maintain the attitude will require the glider to
be flown at a higher airspeed. The greater the angle of bank being used,
the greater the airspeed at which the glider must be flown. (See Chapter 8)

To summarise this far:

**In order to turn the glider, we move the control column in the direction of
the turn. We may also require a backward movement on the control
column to prevent the nose from lowering, thus maintaining the glider's
attitude and airspeed. The amount of this backward control column input
will depend on the angle of bank being used.**

AILERON DRAG

The control movements so far hopefully appear to be fairly logical, but
moving the ailerons introduces another complication, fortunately one
which can be overcome with some practice.

As already shown, when we move the control column to the right, the right
aileron is deflected upwards, reducing the angle of attack at that part of the
wing (and as a result the pressure differential between upper and lower
surfaces of the wing). This will also result in less induced drag at that wing
tip as there is less incentive for the air to escape around the wing tip to
equalise the pressure. At the same time the aileron on the left wing will be
deflected downwards, increasing the angle of attack and the pressure

differential between upper and lower wing surfaces. This creates an increase in induced drag.

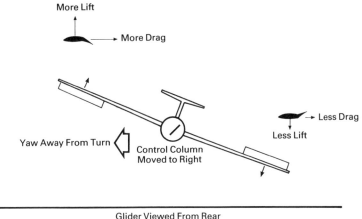

Glider Viewed From Rear

Fig 7.2   Aileron drag. On entering a turn, aileron drag will tend to cause the nose of the glider to yaw away from the direction of the turn.

The combined effect is to yaw the glider's nose away from the lower wing. This effect is known as ADVERSE YAW and the force which causes it is called AILERON DRAG.

To overcome this adverse yaw we use rudder to apply a countering yaw force in the direction of the turn. So to start a turn to the right we apply right rudder in conjunction with right aileron.

To summarise:

To turn the glider we apply aileron and rudder in the direction of the turn, applying back pressure on the control column (up elevator) to prevent the nose from lowering.

AIR EXERCISE – AILERON DRAG

The following exercise will be demonstrated by your instructor and you will then be allowed to attempt it.

Fly the glider at about 40 knots with its nose pointing at an obvious ground feature.

Apply a large amount of aileron while holding the rudder in its central position. Notice that, initially, the nose swings in the opposite direction to the aileron input.

This is known as adverse yaw and is caused by aileron drag.

Return the glider to wings-level flight with the nose pointing at the original ground feature.

To overcome the adverse yaw when aileron is applied, simultaneously push the rudder pedal on the same side as the control column movement. The nose will no longer swing away from the direction of the turn.

You should always apply aileron and rudder together when turning.

AIR EXERCISE – TURNING

The following exercise will be demonstrated by your instructor and you will then be allowed to attempt it.

The turn consists of 3 stages; entering the turn, maintaining the turn and exiting the turn. An important element of each stage is lookout.

STAGE 1 – ENTERING THE TURN

Lookout.

Look over the nose of the glider to check the glider's attitude and bank angle.

Apply bank by using aileron and rudder together.

When the bank has reached the desired angle, maintain this angle by moving the control column to a position slightly on the other side of centre from the turn direction and reduce the amount of rudder. Apply some back elevator as required to prevent the nose from lowering.

The glider is now established in the turn.

STAGE 2 – MAINTAINING THE TURN

Keep up a good lookout.

Check that the bank angle remains constant, adjusting as necessary with co-ordinated aileron and rudder movements.

Monitor the glider's nose attitude, adjusting as necessary with elevator.

STAGE 3 – EXITING THE TURN

Lookout and check that it is clear to exit the turn.

Level the wings using aileron and rudder together, and adjust the glider's attitude using elevator.

When the glider's wings are level, centralise the ailerons and rudder.

Check and re-adjust the attitude with elevator as necessary.

COMMON FAULTS WHEN TURNING

Being able to carry out an accurate turn is a crucial skill in gliding. Only by gaining this ability can you hope to become a successful soaring pilot. For this reason, it is worth looking briefly at the common faults which will ruin the accuracy of a turn.

1. **Inadequate lookout** is probably the most dangerous fault of all, and one that is easily overcome by forming a good habit from the very beginning.

2. **Not looking over the nose when entering the turn** and thereby denying yourself vital attitude information.

3. **Applying too much or insufficient rudder.** Either of these will result in the glider producing more drag and will probably have secondary effects such as rolling or pitching. Once experience is gained, you will become sensitive to the feel of a badly co-ordinated turn. Unfortunately, as the controls are very interdependent, it is not normally sufficient to simply increase or decrease the amount of rudder to correct the situation. As you will learn, even these corrections will require some co-ordination with aileron and perhaps elevator.

4. **Failing to reduce rudder once the desired angle of bank is achieved** will cause the glider to yaw and gradually lead to the bank angle increasing and possibly the nose dropping. Always reduce the amount of rudder when you "centralise" the ailerons.

5. **Failing to use definite control movements.** If you do not positively apply the aileron, it is difficult to judge how much rudder is required to co-ordinate the turn.

6. **Jerky control movements** will make it difficult to co-ordinate the rudder with aileron. Always move the controls smoothly and avoid unnecessary control inputs.

7. **Allowing the nose to drop** as a result of applying inadequate back pressure on the control column when entering the turn. Once established in the turn, any variation in the angle of bank will require a corresponding variation in the amount of back pressure necessary to maintain a constant attitude and airspeed.

8. **Unintentionally allowing the angle of bank to vary** will result in the nose attitude changing and will require a co-ordinated input of all three controls to correct the situation. When established in a turn, the outer wing will be travelling through the air faster than the inner wing, causing it to generate more lift. Therefore there will be a tendency for the bank to increase in the turn.

9. **Tensing up on the controls**, especially gripping the control column tightly and bracing your legs against the rudder pedals, is disastrous as far as accurate turning is concerned. The glider, through its controls, is trying to give you information about how well it is flying and what the air mass is doing. Strangling the controls will prevent this information reaching you. Relax and enjoy it.

10. **Chasing the readings of the airspeed indicator** will result in unnecessary pitch changes. Fly by attitude.

FURTHER TURNING EXERCISES

The following exercises can be practised once you have mastered the skill of turning the glider with reasonable co-ordination and accuracy.

AIR EXERCISE – TURN REVERSALS

Enter a moderately banked turn and once the glider is settled in the turn, reverse the direction of the turn.

After one or two turns in this new direction, reverse the direction of turn again.

Repeat the exercise, aiming to maintain the same airspeed and good co-ordination throughout the manoeuvres.

AIR EXERCISE – STRAIGHTENING ON TO A HEADING

Select a distant ground feature as an aiming point.

Enter a moderately banked turn, and once established roll out of the turn towards the ground feature.

Repeat the exercise using different angles of bank in the turn and different ground features.

AIR EXERCISE – ADJUSTING THE AIRSPEED IN TURNS

Establish the glider in a turn at 45 knots.

While turning, increase the airspeed by stages of 5 knots up to say 65 knots, allowing the airspeed to stabilise for each new airspeed.

Reduce the airspeed in increments of 5 knots while maintaining the turn, again stabilising the glider as each new airspeed is achieved.

Repeat the exercise with different angles of bank.

NOTE: If, during a steeply banked turn, the airspeed begins to increase rapidly and the glider begins a SPIRAL DIVE, it will be necessary to remove the bank with aileron and rudder before raising the nose with elevator. (See Chapter 9)

AIR EXERCISE – ADJUSTING THE ANGLE OF BANK

Establish the glider in a turn at 45 knots.

While turning, increase the angle of bank, allowing the glider to settle at this increased bank angle.

Check the airspeed and adjust it if necessary.

Return the glider to the original amount of bank and re-check the airspeed.

Repeat the exercise using different angles of bank, without exiting the turn. Your aim should be to keep the turn co-ordinated and the airspeed constant.

NOTE: If, during a steeply banked turn, the airspeed begins to increase rapidly and the glider begins a SPIRAL DIVE, it will be necessary to remove the bank with aileron and rudder before raising the nose with elevator. (See Chapter 9)

CHAPTER 8

THE STALL

The airflow over and around the wing causes the wing to produce lift which provides a force with a vertical component to counter the weight of the glider. This lift force will increase if the speed of the airflow over the wing is increased. It will also increase as the angle of attack is increased, providing the airflow over the top surface of the wing remains smooth and orderly. When the angle of attack reaches the stalling angle (typically around 15°) the airflow over the wing becomes turbulent and the amount of lift produced by the wing reduces rapidly. The wing is now stalled and the glider is said to be in a STALL. As the glider accelerates downwards due to the imbalance in the vertical forces of lift and gravity, the relative airflow meets the wing at an increasing angle and, unless corrective action is taken, the wing becomes further stalled.

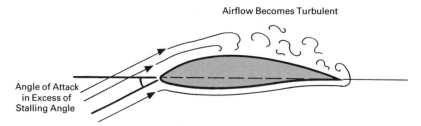

Airflow Becomes Turbulent

Angle of Attack in Excess of Stalling Angle

Fig 8.1   The stall. When the stalling angle is reached the airflow over the wing becomes turbulent and the wing is said to be stalled.

The airspeed at which the wing stalls is known as the STALLING SPEED. However, whereas the stalling angle will remain constant, the stalling speed will vary, depending on such things as the manoeuvre being carried out or the weight of the pilot. In general, the more work the wing is being asked to do (and therefore the more lift it has to produce) the greater the stalling speed. For instance, in a turn the wing is being asked to provide a turning force as well as support the weight of the glider. This extra lift is usually gained by increasing the wing's angle of attack. However, if the angle of attack is already close to the stalling angle, the extra lift must be obtained from increased airflow past the wing; that is, from increased airspeed. The greater the angle of bank used, the larger the force the wing will have to produce and therefore the greater the stalling speed. Turning with a bank angle of 45° will result in an increase of nearly 20% in the stalling speed from its normal wings-level value.

DRAG AT THE STALL

In normal (unstalled) flight the airflow over the wing is smooth and orderly. As long as this airflow remains smooth the drag produced by the wing will remain low. As the airflow becomes turbulent at the stall, the drag

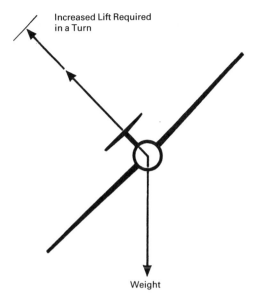

Fig 8.2   Increased stalling speed in turns. The wing is required to produce increased lift during a turn.

produced by the wing increases rapidly. This will cause the glider to lose airspeed, causing a reduction in airflow past the wing with a consequent reduction in lift.

The stall is therefore a situation where lift is insufficient to balance the glider's weight and where the amount of drag produced by the glider is large. While the glider is stalled, the pilot will not have full control of the aircraft. Altogether an undesirable state in terms of the glider's performance and one which could compromise safety.

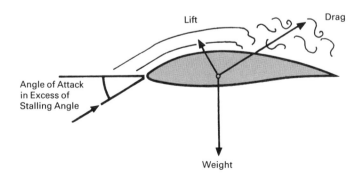

Fig 8.3   Lift and drag at the stall. When the wing becomes stalled it will produce much less lift and much more drag.

51

RECOVERY FROM THE STALL

To recover from STALLED FLIGHT it is necessary to reduce the angle of attack to a value below the stalling angle. Fortunately this is easily done by MOVING THE CONTROL COLUMN FORWARDS to lower the nose of the glider, so as to regain airspeed and thus a smooth airflow over the wing. This will result in the lift being restored and the drag being reduced. Then, when the wing has fully unstalled, the glider can be returned to a more reasonable gliding attitude.

The other option is to avoid getting near the stalling angle. With the best will in the world, this may not always be possible. It is therefore necessary to be able to recognise the approach of the stall and the symptoms when the glider is stalled, in order that a recovery can be made.

SYMPTOMS OF THE STALL

The following are the symptoms which may indicate that the glider is stalled.

1. NOSE HIGH ATTITUDE

Cause: The wing is stalled when the angle of attack reaches the stalling angle. In normal, wings-level flight the nose attitude of the glider gives an indication of whether the angle of attack is likely to be excessive.

Exceptions: Certain manoeuvres which involve high-speed entries or recoveries may result in high nose attitudes which do not necessarily mean that the glider is near the stall. The forward speed in these instances may mean that the relative airflow is still meeting the wing at an angle well below the stalling angle; for example, when pulling the glider up into a loop, in a steeply banked turn or during a wire launch.

It should also be appreciated that the glider may stall when the attitude is near the normal gliding attitude if the airspeed is low due to excessive drag, as would be caused by the airbrakes being open or excessive yaw.

2. REDUCED AIRSPEED

Cause: If the stall has occurred as a result of the nose being raised, the airspeed will decrease as the stall approaches.

Exceptions: It should be remembered that the stall occurs at a certain angle of attack and not at any one airspeed. It is possible for the wing to achieve this angle over a range of airspeeds. The actual stalling speed will depend on such factors as the glider's weight and to what extent the glider is manoeuvring.

NOTE: At any time the airspeed is low in normal flight, the angle of attack of the wing will be close to the stalling angle.

3. REDUCED AIRFLOW NOISE

Cause: If the airspeed is reduced the noise of the airflow will also be reduced.

Exceptions: If a stall occurs at a higher airspeed. (See 2 above)

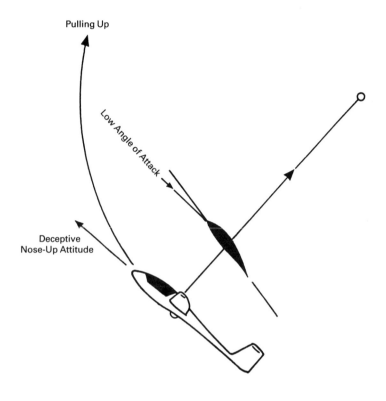

Pulling Up

Low Angle of Attack

Deceptive
Nose-Up Attitude

Fig 8.4 Attitude doesn't always indicate angle of attack. In certain manoeuvres, such as when pulling up into a loop, the angle of attack may be well below the stalling angle despite the nose high attitude.

4. BUFFET

Cause: As the airflow over the wing becomes increasingly turbulent the aircraft may "tremble". In more severe cases, this may manifest itself as a "buffeting" especially if the turbulent air is flowing past the tailplane and elevator. When this happens, the buffeting may be felt through the controls. This buffet can be a useful warning of the onset of the stall.

Exceptions: Whether buffet is present and obvious depends a lot on glider design and the way the stall is approached. Some gliders do not display buffet such that it can be a useful warning of the onset of the stall.

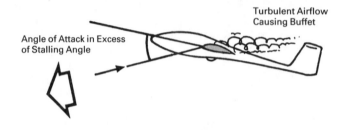

Fig 8.5   Buffeting at the stall. The turbulent airflow from a stalled wing may cause noticeable buffet.

5. REDUCED CONTROL RESPONSE

Cause: As the wing reaches the stalling angle the airflow over the trailing edge of the wing is the first to become turbulent, gradually moving forwards to become turbulent over the larger part of the wing, if the stall is deep enough. As the ailerons are situated at the trailing edge of the wing, they will not be able to function effectively due to this disrupted flow. The elevator and rudder will also lose some of their effect if the airspeed reduces significantly. This is due to the reduced airflow over the control surfaces, although the effect may not be as much as that felt on the ailerons. (However, as the wing is not capable of producing its usual quota of lift, it is pointless asking the elevator to increase the wing's angle of attack further to raise the glider's nose or prevent it from dropping.)

Exceptions: In recent years designers have become more adept at designing gliders which maintain aileron response well beyond the point of the stall. Impressive as this is, the aileron response at the stall, even on these gliders, is still obviously diminished, and the amount of adverse yaw created when the ailerons are used at the stall increased, thereby increasing the danger of the glider entering a spin.

6. UNUSUALLY AFT CONTROL COLUMN POSITION

Cause: Given that the glider is stable in pitch, for any one control column position in steady flight, there is a corresponding angle of attack. Eventually, experience will make you aware when the control column feels uncomfortably far back.

Exceptions: An aft control column position may also occur when the glider is being wire launched without the wing being near the stalling angle, but in all other circumstances an aft position of the control column can be taken as an indication of a large angle of attack and therefore a warning of a potential stall.

7. INCREASED RATE OF DESCENT

Cause: Due to the breakdown of the smooth airflow over its upper surface, the wing is not producing enough lift to give a large enough vertical component to counter the glider's weight. This imbalance causes the glider to accelerate downwards, that is, height is lost rapidly.

Exceptions: On rare occasions, if the stall occurs when the glider is in an up-current of air, which is rising at a high rate, the glider's instruments may not show a rate of descent because a net rate of climb may still exist. This situation will probably be short lived.

8. NOSE DROP

Cause: As the angle of attack is increased, the centre of pressure moves forward towards the leading edge of the wing. At the point of the stall the centre of pressure moves swiftly back towards the trailing edge of the wing. Depending upon the position of the centre of gravity, this aft movement of the centre of pressure may cause a nose-down tipping effect which appears to the pilot as nose drop.

Exceptions: This effect depends largely on the glider's design, its loading and how the stall is approached. It is therefore not displayed by some gliders. Typically, those gliders which do not exhibit nose drop will "mush" or "wallow" with the nose just above the normal gliding attitude and a high rate of descent.

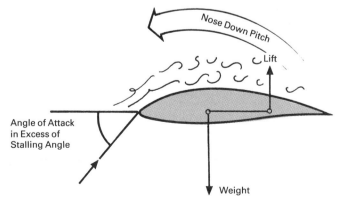

Fig 8.6   Nose-drop at the stall. As the stall occurs, the centre of pressure moves aft, often resulting in the nose dropping.

NOTE – It should be appreciated that, although the nose of the glider may have dropped, this does not necessarily mean that the wing has unstalled itself. The angle of attack may still be greater than the stalling angle due to the glider's high rate of descent. Recovery action will still be required.

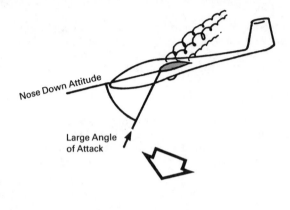

Fig 8.7   The need for stall recovery action. Although the stall may have caused the glider's nose to drop, the high rate of descent may still mean that the angle of attack is above the stalling angle.

9. WING DROP

Cause: If one wing reaches the stalling angle before the other, lift at that wing will decrease and drag will increase. As a result, it will become further stalled and drop, relative to the other unstalled (or less stalled) wing.

Exceptions: This symptom depends largely on the design of the glider's wing, the flight conditions, and on whether there is any yaw present as the stall is approached.

As seen, some of these symptoms may not be present at the stall, depending on such factors as glider design, flight conditions and the type of manoeuvres being flown. Others may occur in some manoeuvres even though the glider is not near the stall. The first six symptoms can also therefore serve as warnings of an approaching stall, while increased rate of descent, nose drop or wing drop, together with lack of effectiveness of the elevator, are very definite symptoms of the stall. The important point is that you learn to look for and recognise any of these warnings or symptoms, and if it is suspected that you are approaching the stall, or are stalled, initiate the recovery drill immediately.

Although most gliders display docile stalling characteristics, stalled flight normally involves height loss. This, combined with the reduced control response and the possibility of the nose or wing dropping (or both) make the inadvertent stall potentially dangerous, especially if it occurs close to the ground where there may not be sufficient height to recover.

It is therefore essential to fly the glider in such a manner as to prevent the possible occurrence of a stall in such situations. This is normally done by maintaining a lower nose attitude and a higher indicated airspeed than would normally be necessary were the ground not so close. Despite these precautions, workload and other distractions can cause potential stall situations. For this reason, stall recognition and recovery forms a major part of the glider pilot's training and, after some practice, most glider pilots should feel happy with their ability to control the glider near, in and on recovery from the stall.

AIRMANSHIP CHECKS

Before carrying out any manoeuvre which will involve either a large loss of height or a high rate of descent, a series of checks must be made to ensure that the manoeuvre can be carried out safely. These checks are remembered by the mnemonic H-A-S-S-L-L, the elements of which are listed and enlarged below.

H – HEIGHT   Check that sufficient height is available to carry out the manoeuvre and still return to the airfield.

A – AIRFRAME   Confirm that the glider is cleared for the manoeuvre and check the maximum airspeeds permitted. Set the flaps as required.

S – STRAPS   Check that those of each occupant are tight.

S – SECURITY   Check that there are no loose objects in the cockpit.

L – LOCATION   Check that the glider is not above a built-up area or in controlled airspace.

L – LOOKOUT   Carry out well-banked turns in both directions to ensure that there are no aircraft below or near your glider.

AIR EXERCISE – STALLING

The following exercise will be demonstrated by your instructor and you will then be allowed to attempt it.

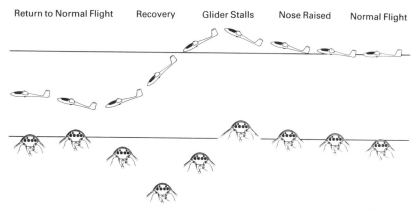

Return to Normal Flight   Recovery   Glider Stalls   Nose Raised   Normal Flight

Fig 8.8   Air Exercise – stalling.

57

Airmanship checks – HASSLL.

From straight flight, gradually and continuously raise the glider's nose until the various symptoms of the stall are observed.

When the glider becomes stalled, **recover by moving the control column forwards until flying airspeed is regained. Then return the glider to the normal gliding attitude**.

Repeat as necessary with different rates of entry until each of the symptoms of the stall has been observed.

THE INCIPIENT SPIN

We have just considered wing drop as a possible symptom indicative of the stall. At the point of the stall, the dropping of a wing may lead to a SPIN and as a result, the initial roll and subsequent rotation is often called the INCIPIENT SPIN.

At the point at which the wing drops, there will also be a tendency for the glider to yaw towards the lowering wing, and for the nose to drop. If no action is taken, and especially if the control column is held aft, the incipient spin may well develop into a FULL SPIN.

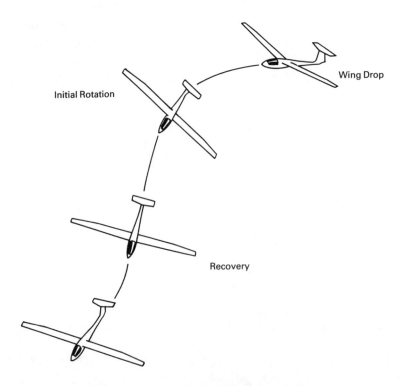

Wing Drop

Initial Rotation

Recovery

Fig 8.9   The incipient spin. Flight path of a glider entering and recovering from an incipient spin.

To prevent this occurrence and to recover from the incipient spin, you should move the control column forwards to unstall the wing. After doing so, normal control will be regained and the wings can be levelled with aileron and rudder, and the glider returned to a normal gliding attitude.

Until you have unstalled the wing, you should resist the temptation to raise the dropping wing by using aileron. To do so will risk increasing the angle of attack over the outer part of the stalled wing as the aileron goes down, thus further stalling that wing.

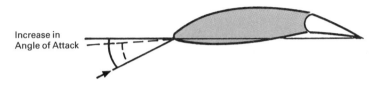

Increase in Angle of Attack

Fig 8.10   Use of aileron at the stall. Attempting to raise a stalled wing with aileron may only stall that wing further.

Application of the rudder to the side away from the dropping wing ("opposite rudder") will prevent a large yaw from developing; yaw which if unchecked would cause two undesirable effects:

a)   the high drag caused by the glider's subsequent skidding sideways would cause a further loss of airspeed, thus aggravating the situation, and

b)   yaw present at the stall will assist the glider in entering a full spin. (See Chapter 9)

Thus correct use of the rudder in this situation can have a powerful "anti-spin" effect. This is something which may be important if the stall has occurred at a low height.

However, it must be realised that applying opposite rudder will not unstall the wing, nor will it raise it. **The primary recovery action must be the unstalling of the wing by moving the control column forwards.** Indeed, to apply rudder without moving the control column forwards could aggravate the situation and potentially cause the glider to enter a spin in the opposite direction to the initial wing drop.

Therefore if a wing drops at the stall, the recovery action should be:

1. **Move the control column forwards** (applying sufficient rudder if yaw is observed)

2. **Regain flying airspeed**

3. **Level the wings**

4. **Return to a reasonable gliding attitude**

At which point the incipient spin becomes a full spin is difficult to say. Usually the glider will have completed at least three quarters of a turn before full spin recovery techniques become necessary.

The recovery from the full spin is dealt with in the next chapter.

AIR EXERCISE – INCIPIENT SPIN

The following exercise will be demonstrated by your instructor and you will then be allowed to attempt it.

Airmanship checks – HASSLL.

Begin a turn which has a small angle of bank and too much rudder.

Gradually and continuously raise the glider's nose until the glider stalls and the inner wing drops.

When this happens, recover by moving the control column forwards to regain airspeed.

After the airspeed has increased and full control regained, ease out of the dive and return to a reasonable gliding attitude.

AIR EXERCISES – FURTHER STALLING DEMONSTRATIONS

Throughout your training, you will be given other air exercises, in the form of demonstrations, which are intended to increase your awareness of the stalling characteristics of gliders. These will also show you the importance of co-ordinated control inputs as regards safety.

Typically these will include demonstrations of:

- The fact that, at the stall, the elevator will not be capable of raising the glider's nose until after the recovery drill has been carried out.

- The fact that the stalling speed is increased when the glider is turning.

- The fact that the stalling speed will be increased when the glider is subjected to increased loading or "g", such as when it is pulling out of a dive.

- The fact that the stalling speed will be greater when conventional airbrakes are opened.

THE SENSATION OF REDUCED "g"

As the control column is moved forwards to recover from the stall, you may encounter a feeling of "weightlessness". This is a result of moving the control column forwards, either too rapidly, or too much.

The human body is designed to operate under the influence of the earth's gravity. That is, we are subject to a constant acceleration of 1g. In a tight turn, or as the glider's nose is pulled upwards, this "g" force is increased slightly and you feel this as being pushed more firmly into your seat. In fact, while this sensation is being experienced, you will feel as if you weigh more that your normal weight. This is not an uncomfortable feeling.

If on the other hand, you were to push the control column forwards suddenly (even while in level flight), the opposite sensation would be felt. The glider would be flying downwards, away from you. This would reduce the effect of gravity felt and this sensation is known as reduced "g". This sensation is similar to that which you experience if you drive too fast over a humpback bridge. It can easily be mistaken for a falling sensation, and as a result, many people find this sensation unpleasant.

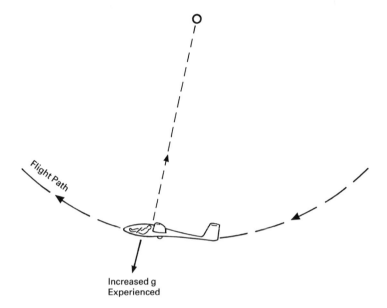

Fig 8.11   Positive "g". Positive "g" Makes the pilot feel as if he/she is being pulled into the seat.

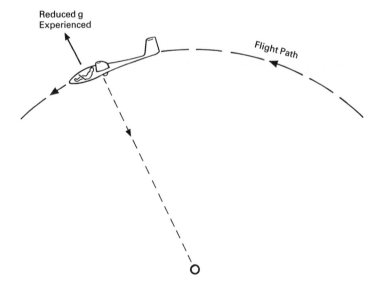

Fig 8.12   Reduced "g". With reduced "g'"the pilot is being "thrown out" of the glider.

The danger is, that if you move the control column forwards sharply at any time (for instance to recover from a stall), then reduced "g" may be felt and the sensation of falling may be mistaken for the glider stalling or being further stalled. If you then move the control column further forwards to recover from this wrongly perceived "stall", the reduced "g" sensation will intensify. If all of this occurs close to the ground, there is a very great risk of the glider striking the ground in a steep nose-down attitude.

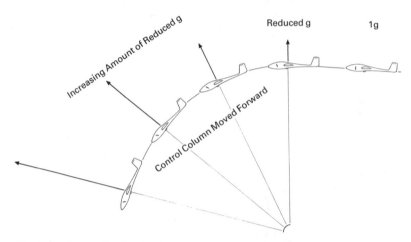

Fig 8.13   Forward control column movements and reduced "g". The more the control column is pushed forwards, the greater the sensation of reduced "g".

It is therefore essential that, if a sustained or an increasing amount of reduced "g" is experienced, you realise that the glider is NOT stalled. Sustained or increasing reduced "g" is caused by over control. The feeling will cease if you stop pushing forwards on the control column and, if necessary, return the glider to a normal attitude.

AIR EXERCISE – REDUCED "g"

The following exercise will be demonstrated by your instructor and you will then be allowed to attempt STAGE 3.

STAGE 1

Airmanship checks – HASSLL.

From an airspeed of 55 knots pull the glider up into a 30° climb.

Allow the airspeed to diminish gradually and the glider to stall fully.

As the glider stalls, note that there is little or no sensation of weightlessness.

Recover from the stall.

STAGE 2

Airmanship checks – HASSLL.

Repeat the pull up into the same angle of climb from an airspeed of 55 knots but this time BEFORE the glider stalls, move the control column forwards positively and you will feel a pronounced sensation of reduced "g". Observe however that the controls are still effective and that the glider is **not** stalled.

Return to level flight.

STAGE 3

While flying in straight flight, move the control column forwards sharply *by a small amount* and note the sensation of reduced "g".

Return to normal flight.

To summarise: Reduced "g" is **NOT** a symptom of the stall and can be induced at any time the glider is pitched nose down suddenly.

CHAPTER 9

THE SPIN

One wing dropping as a result of it being stalled to a greater extent than the other wing may result in a sequence of aerodynamic events which, if not prevented, can place the glider in a SPIN.

When a glider is in a spin, it may be rotating about all three axes at the same time (that is, pitching, rolling and yawing simultaneously). The spin could result in a very nose-down attitude or a relatively flat attitude. The rate of rotation and the attitude will vary depending on the way in which the spin is entered and also on the individual glider and its cockpit loading. The airspeed will be low and the airspeed indicator will not give reliable information. In all spins, rapid height loss is the major problem and makes spinning at low levels a dangerous event. For this reason, your training will cover spin recognition, recovery and avoidance. The most important point to remember about spinning, is that it is a form of stalled flight and therefore, if situations that result in the glider's wing (or any part of it) becoming stalled are avoided, then the glider cannot spin. Also, although the recovery from the spin will be dealt with for all stages of a spin, it cannot be over-emphasised that, as the wing is stalled during the spin, the need to reduce the angle of attack by moving the control column forwards to unstall the wing, is an essential part of the recovery.

AUTOROTATION

Autorotation can be regarded as the sequence of events which causes the glider to become established in a spin.

In normal (unstalled) flight, any dropping of a wing is dampened by the lift created as the relative airflow meets the down-going wing at an increased

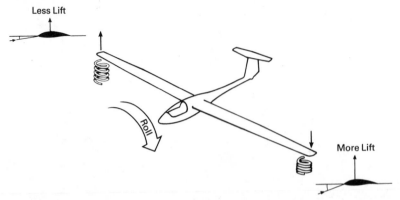

Fig 9.1   Roll dampening. In normal flight there is a resistance to rolling caused by the increased angle of attack of the down-going wing and the reduced angle of attack of the up-going wing.

64

angle of attack. The resulting reduced angle of attack at the up-going wing adds to the dampening effect thus resisting the rolling motion.

However, if the wing is already close to the stalling angle, any increase in the angle of attack of the down-going wing will cause it to become stalled and lift will be lost, instead of gained, at that wing. As a result the anti-roll tendency will not exist, and rolling due to autorotation will become the dominant tendency.

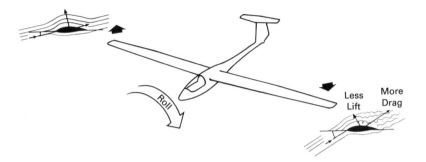

Less Lift

More Drag

Roll

Fig 9.2   Autorotation. At the stall the down-going wing becomes more stalled and the rolling and yawing tendencies increase.

If we assume that the left wing has reached the stalling angle before the right wing, the left wing will produce less lift and more drag than the right wing. This will result in the left wing dropping and slowing down, causing it to meet the relative airflow at an increasing angle. This will increase the angle of attack further and stall the wing even more. This will again cause the wing to drop further, with an ever increasing angle of attack.

On the other hand, the glider's right wing, which is not yet stalled, will be caused to rise, reducing the angle at which it meets the relative airflow and thus reducing the angle of attack. It will therefore continue to produce more lift and less drag than the left wing.

The result of the differing roll effects at either wing, is to roll the glider towards the left wing. As this happens, the nose will also pitch downwards as the wing becomes more stalled, and the increase in drag at the left wing will cause the glider to yaw towards that wing.

These events will occur quite swiftly, unless recovery action is taken, and will continue until the glider establishes itself in what could be loosely regarded as a stable situation known as the spin. Even once the spin has reached this stage, the glider's rate of rotation and attitude may change without the glider exiting the spin. Once established in the spin, the glider may rotate at around 5 times a minute, losing 400 feet or more per rotation. Although this description deals with the wing in general, it is the stalling of the outer part of the wing, and especially the wing tip, which will lead to the most rapid autorotation. Unfortunately, the instinctive reaction to the dropping of the glider's nose and wing, (that is, using elevator and aileron to prevent these events) will aggravate the situation and increase the possibility of the glider entering a full spin.

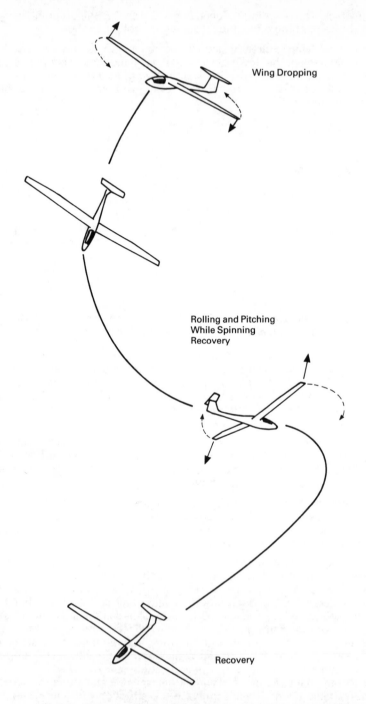

Wing Dropping

Rolling and Pitching
While Spinning
Recovery

Recovery

Fig 9.3   The spin. Flight path of a glider spinning and recovering.

SITUATIONS WHICH MAY CAUSE AUTOROTATION

As mentioned previously, for autorotation to occur, one wing must reach the stalling angle before the other, or stall more than the other. This can occur in many situations, the most common of which are:

1. THE PRESENCE OF YAW WHILE FLYING CLOSE TO THE STALL

If the glider is yawed while flying close to the stall, the wings will momentarily be flying at different airspeeds. As both wings are descending at the same rate (that of the glider), any change in forward speed of the wings will result in the wings meeting the relative airflow at different angles of attack. The forward moving wing will increase airspeed and reduce its angle of attack, whereas the rearward moving wing will have its airspeed reduced, thereby increasing its angle of attack.

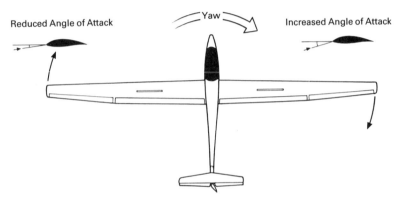

Fig 9.4   The danger of yawing at slow speed. Yawing causes different airspeeds and angles of attack at either wing and at slow airspeeds could result in a spin.

If the angle of attack is close to the stalling angle, before the yawing movement occurs, then the yawing action may increase the angle of attack of the rearward moving wing to the stalling angle. This will cause the wing to stall and allow autorotation to begin.

Such yawing may be caused intentionally, by applying rudder, in order to induce a spin for training purposes, or while practising aerobatics. On other occasions, it can be caused by inadvertently mis-co-ordinating the controls, resulting in too much rudder being used.

A common situation where such mis-co-ordination can occur is when turning the glider. As the turn is entered, there is a need to apply rudder as the ailerons are moved, in order to overcome aileron drag. Too much rudder will result in an excessive amount of yaw, thus satisfying one of the requirements which may stall the inner wing of the turn.

Another variation of mis-co-ordination which may cause the inner wing to stall as the turn is entered, is to not reduce the amount of rudder once the desired angle of bank for the turn is achieved. The result will again be too much rudder, and therefore yaw, again leading to the potential stalling of the inner wing of the turn.

2. SHALLOW TURNS

Over-ruddering is more likely in shallow, rather than well-banked turns, because the small amounts of aileron required to establish such turns require very little rudder, thus making it more difficult to judge the amount of rudder required to balance the entry into the turn. Another problem is that a shallow turn will not turn the glider very quickly and therefore leads to a subconscious desire to "increase the rate of turn" using rudder. Applying excessive rudder will yaw the nose of the glider in the direction of the turn, giving the false impression of a higher rate of turn. This is due to the increase in yaw created and not an increase in the rate of turn. Given that the amount of back pressure on the control column needed to maintain the attitude in the turn will also be small in a shallow-banked turn, the risk of spinning is increased relative to that in a well-banked turn, which will demand more positive co-ordinated control inputs.

Although in an earlier section, it was mentioned that the stalling speed increases as the bank in the turn increases, the risks of spinning a glider in a shallow-banked turn are still greater than in a well-banked turn. This is shown at Fig 9.5, where it can be seen that the inner wing of the turn must be at a higher angle of attack than the outer wing. This is because, once established in the turn, the descent rate of both wings must be the same, but the forward speed of the outer wing must be greater to enable it to cover the same amount of turn as the inner wing in the same period of time.

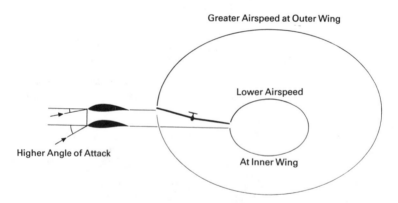

Fig 9.5   Spinning from a shallow turn. In a shallow turn the inner wing tip will be at a larger angle of attack than the outer wing tip.

On the other hand, if the bank angle during the turn is moderate or high, then the distances covered by each wing tip will be more similar to each other than during a shallow turn, as will be their respective airspeeds and angles of attack. (Fig 9.6)

3. GUSTS

In both thermic and turbulent conditions, there will be frequent changes in the direction of the relative airflow, which will momentarily alter the angle of attack of either or both wings. If the glider is being flown close to the stall when such a gust is encountered, the stalling angle may be reached and the wing may stall as a result. If this stall only affects one wing (or part of a wing), or if there is any yaw present, the wing will drop and autorotation may occur.

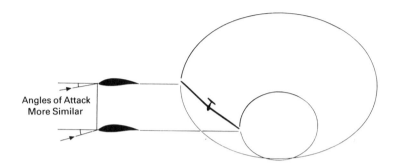

Angles of Attack
More Similar

Fig 9.6   *Steeper turns are safer. In a steeper turn the angles of attack of both wing tips will be more similar than in a shallow turn.*

Generally, such gusts will be of such short duration that the wing will not remain stalled long enough for a spin to develop, unless the pilot aggravates the situation by raising the nose or attempting to use aileron to prevent the wing from dropping.

Once below 700 feet or so, adopting an increased airspeed will greatly reduce the risk of stalling or spinning at heights where turbulence is greatest and inadvertent stalling or spinning is dangerous.

RECOVERY FROM THE SPIN

To recover from a full spin, the following procedure should be used.

1. **Apply full opposite rudder (opposite to the direction of rotation)**

2. **˙Pause**

3. **Ease the control column forwards until the rotation stops**

4. **Centralise the rudder**

5. **Ease out of the dive and return to a reasonable gliding attitude.**

Note that while some gliders will require the whole of the recovery procedure to recover from a spin, many gliders will not. Some will start to recover as soon as the controls are moved to a central position. Others may stop rotating when opposite rudder is applied. The "pause" at stage 2 need only be a slight hesitation but may be essential in some gliders, especially those with "V" type tails.

Despite the different spin recovery habits of some gliders, only the full recovery procedure shown above can guarantee recovery on all types of glider. Even if a particular type of glider requires less than the full recovery, it is still essential to ensure that the glider will not re-stall and spin, by easing forward on the control column to reduce the angle of attack.

69

When the glider has stopped spinning, it will be in a steep nose-down attitude. This will result in a rapid increase in airspeed which should be monitored as the glider is returned to a reasonable attitude, otherwise the airspeed may exceed the maximum airspeed permitted. If a high airspeed is likely, the glider should be gently, but positively, eased out of the dive and in an extreme case the airbrakes may need to be used to prevent excessive airspeed. In the event of airbrakes having to be used, they should be closed and locked as soon as the glider's attitude and airspeed become less extreme, so as not to risk re-stalling the wing as the nose is raised.

AIR EXERCISE – SPINNING

The following exercise will be demonstrated by your instructor and you will then be allowed to attempt it.

STAGE 1 – ENTRY

Airmanship checks – HASSLL.

Enter a turn using only a small amount of bank.

Gradually increase rudder while keeping a constant angle of bank with aileron, easing the control column backwards as you do so.

As the wing stalls (and drops) push the into-turn rudder to full deflection and pull the control column fully back.

Hold the controls in these extreme positions until you intend recovering.

STAGE 2 – RECOVERY

Apply full opposite rudder (followed by a slight pause).

Ease control column forwards until the rotation stops.

Centralise rudder.

Ease out of the dive.

SPIRAL DIVES

Many gliders, especially some training gliders, are reluctant to enter a spin. As well as making it difficult to train student pilots to recognise and recover from spins, this characteristic will often result in the glider entering a SPIRAL DIVE rather than a spin, or in some cases, exiting from the early stages of a spin into a spiral dive.

The SPIRAL DIVE consists of the glider rolling and pitching nose downwards until an excessive amount of bank and a very nose-down attitude exists. The spiral dive will result in attitudes and bank angles similar to those present in a spin, although it must not be confused with a spin.

The major difference between the two phases of flight is that during the spiral dive the glider is flying and is NOT STALLED. As a result, the airspeed will be increasing rapidly due to the nose-down attitude and any attempt to reduce it by moving the control column backwards will only result in the spiralling turn being tightened, due to the excessive bank which exists, and a resultant increase in the 'g' force experienced.

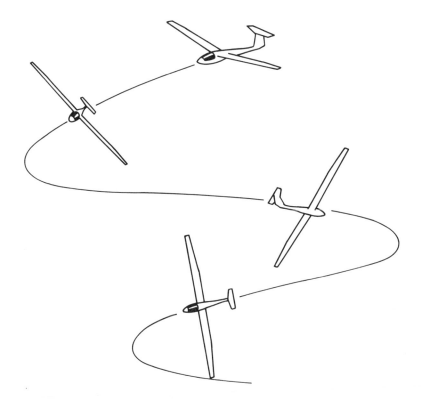

Fig 9.7   The spiral dive.

Experience will soon enable you to differentiate between a spin and a spiral dive and thus take the appropriate recovery action. Basically, if the amount of 'g' being experienced and the airspeed is increasing, the glider is in a spiral dive NOT a spin.

It is the resulting high airspeeds and the high rate of descent which are the greatest dangers of the spiral dive.

In order to recover from a spiral dive, you must

- **Ease the control column forwards slightly to prevent excessive 'g'**

- **Reduce the angle of bank with aileron and rudder**

and then

- **Ease out of the dive and return the glider to a reasonable attitude.**

71

Consideration should always be given to opening the airbrakes well before the airspeed becomes excessive and care taken not to use large control deflections when the airspeed is high.

Apart from failed attempts to spin the glider, entry into a spiral dive may come from bad co-ordination, and loss of control during cloud flying or aerobatics.

AIR EXERCISE – RECOVERY FROM A SPIRAL DIVE

The following exercise will be demonstrated by your instructor and you will then be allowed to attempt it.

STAGE 1 – ENTRY

Airmanship checks – HASSLL.

Enter a steeply-banked turn, allowing the bank to continue to increase, but without moving the control column backward to maintain the glider's attitude.

Allow the glider's nose to lower of its own accord, and the airspeed to increase.

As the airspeed increases so too will the angle of bank.

STAGE 2 – RECOVERY

Firstly, relax any back pressure on the control column.

Take off the bank with aileron and rudder.

When the bank has been reduced (or when the wings are level) ease back on the control column to reduce the airspeed and regain normal flight.

AIR EXERCISES – FURTHER SPINNING DEMONSTRATIONS

Throughout your training, other air exercises in the form of demonstrations will be given which are intended to increase your awareness of the spinning habits of gliders and to show you the importance of co-ordinated control inputs as regards safety.

Typically these will include demonstrations of –

- The fact that the glider is less likely to spin when performing a well-banked turn as opposed to a shallow turn.
- The fact that misuse of rudder, especially over-ruddering in a turn at low airspeeds, can cause the glider to spin.
- The fact that a forward movement of the control column at the point of entry into a spin will prevent the glider spinning.

CHAPTER 10

THE TRIMMER

Once you have mastered the primary controls and how to use them to maintain attitude, direction and to turn the glider, you will be introduced to the TRIMMER and shown how to TRIM the glider.

WHY THE GLIDER NEEDS A TRIMMER

The amount of force that the pilot needs to apply to the controls of the glider is quite small. However if a constant force has to be applied for any length of time this can become tedious. This can lead to relaxation of the muscles from time to time, resulting in the amount of force varying, with subsequent changes of control input to the glider.

Fortunately, when in straight flight, the natural position for the ailerons and rudder is in the centre, and normally no control force is required to maintain this position. Even when turning, the ailerons and rudder will not need to be held in a constant non-central position for long periods, as even in a sustained turn there will be a need for adjustments.

Unlike the ailerons and rudder, the elevator will not spend any length of time in its central position. If the control column is moved forwards slightly and held in a new position, the glider's nose will lower and the glider will take up a new attitude. The airspeed will increase and settle at an airspeed which corresponds to this new attitude. For any one position of the control column there will be a corresponding attitude and airspeed. Any change of the position of the control column forwards or backwards of this position will cause the attitude and airspeed to alter. The problem is that a force needs to be applied to the control column to maintain this position or else the control column (along with the elevator and the attitude) will return to a position of its own choice. This force has to be applied constantly by the pilot.

Apart from being tiresome, the constant need to exert a force on the control column, as well as leading to inaccuracies in flying, makes it difficult to carry out other tasks such as map reading and photography. The ideal would be to relieve this force by somehow fixing the control column in the desired position. The trimmer is designed to do just that. It does so by applying the same amount of force as the pilot would to counter the tendency of the elevator to return to its own natural position.

HOW THE TRIMMER WORKS

There are various designs of trimmer, all of which are easy to use after a little practice. All of these design variations work on different principles, although they all achieve the desired result.

TAB TRIMMER

The trimming device often used is an aerodynamic surface called a TRIM TAB. This is a small control surface which is situated on one or occasionally both sides of the elevator and forms part of the elevator's trailing edge. When the trimmer control knob in the cockpit is set correctly, the trim tab will be in a position where it creates an aerodynamic force (similar to a small lift force) which acts directly on the elevator surface, keeping it in the desired position. When this occurs, the force being applied to the control column (and through the control runs to the elevator) by the pilot will be relieved by the force supplied by the trim tab, maintaining the control column position and the glider's attitude.

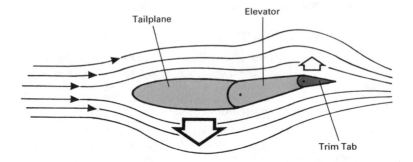

Fig 10.1   How a trim tab works. The airflow around a deflected trim tab creates a force which holds the elevator in the desired position.

As you can see from Fig 10.1, to hold the elevator in an upward position the trim tab needs to be deflected downwards. This will create an increased camber over the trim tab area and thus an aerodynamic force which will act upwards, keeping the elevator in the desired position. The trim tab will always require to be moved in the opposite direction to the elevator to achieve its purpose.

SPRING TRIMMER

In its simplest form the trimmer is a spring device which holds the control column in the desired position by the force exerted by a spring. As well as being simple, this type of trimmer, the SPRING TRIMMER, also has the advantage that the control linkage is on, or close to, the control column, thus avoiding the need for lengthy control runs to the elevator. There is also a performance bonus with this type of trimmer over gliders with a tab trimmer as it does not require aerodynamic control tabs which invariably produce drag. The spring trimmer is more common on modern gliders than the tab trimmer.

ANTI-BALANCE DEVICES

Some gliders which have very light control forces employ a device known as an anti-balance tab. This aerodynamic surface acts in the opposite sense to a trim tab in that it gives the controls artificial "feel" to make controlling the glider easier. An anti-balance tab moves in the same direction as the control surface thus increasing the control force necessary in the cockpit. When fitted to a glider's elevator, an anti-balance tab may be combined with a trim tab in such a way that it can be used to trim the glider. This is done by allowing it to be adjusted so that no force is felt through the control column when the glider is being flown at the correct attitude and airspeed for the selected control column position.

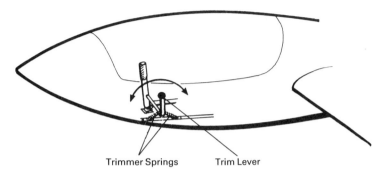

Trimmer Springs   Trim Lever

Fig 10.2   The spring trimmer. The springs of a spring trimmer supply a force which keeps the elevator in the desired position.

HOW TO USE THE TRIMMER

The main point to remember is that trimming the glider is all about removing the fore or aft force that the pilot is required to exert on the control column. Providing that the glider is in steady flight, for any one attitude there will be one position of the control column. Only by holding the control column, and therefore the attitude, constant can the force required be assessed. It is therefore necessary to maintain a constant attitude while trimming. **You cannot trim accurately if the attitude is changing.**

Sequence of trimming:

1. Select the nose attitude which you think will give you the required airspeed.

· 2. Allow the airspeed to settle and then check that it is the chosen airspeed. If it is not then readjust the attitude and check the airspeed again once it has settled at the new value. (Repeat as necessary.)

3. While holding the attitude constant, assess the force required on the control column.

4. Move the trimmer control knob in the same direction as the force you are having to apply until there is no longer any force required to hold the control column in a constant position. (In other words, if you are having to push forward on the control column, then move the trimmer knob forwards.)

5. When you believe you have relieved the control force on the control column, momentarily release the control column, watching the glider's attitude as you do so. If the attitude remains constant then you have trimmed the glider successfully. If the attitude changes then you will have to reselect the attitude and start all over again.

Trimming may sound tedious but after some practice the routine will, like many of the other skills involved in flying a glider, become an almost subconscious act. In the early stages and at times when the workload may be high, trimming will save you having to struggle to maintain attitude. Never put up with control forces when you can trim them out. Even in phases of flight where the time available may not allow you to trim the glider accurately, adjusting the trimmer until the control force is light (as opposed to non-existent) may be enough to improve your flying accuracy and reduce the workload.

Trimming is normally considered as a practice carried out in straight flight and indeed there is little point in retrimming every time you make a turn to change direction. However, unlike the pilots of most aircraft, as a glider pilot, you will spend quite long periods of time in turns as you attempt to use the rising air currents known as THERMALS. As discussed earlier, there is a requirement to exert a backward force or pressure on the control column in turns, and this applies especially to the steeper banked turns commonly used when thermalling. You will therefore find it useful to trim the glider when turning for any length of time. The technique involved is the same as for straight flight, using the attitude as a reference as before. Remember, however, that if you have trimmed in the turn, when you level the wings to exit the turn, the nose of the glider will want to rise unless a forward force is applied to the control column to maintain attitude. This force will need to be removed by retrimming.

Later, when you begin soaring and cross-country flying, you will find that regular airspeed changes are made both in straight flight and in turns. It is then that having learned a good trimming technique pays off.

SETTING THE TRIMMER BEFORE TAKE-OFF

In order that the glider does not become airborne with large out-of-trim control forces which could result in the glider being difficult to control, the trimmer should be set before take-off. Without airflow over the tailplane and elevator, it is not possible to trim the glider accurately from "feel" as in flight. Setting the trimmer for take-off can therefore only be done approximately. Also as the airflow over the tailplane and elevator will increase throughout the first part of the launch as the glider accelerates, the forces required on the controls will also change, adding to the inaccuracy of the initial trimmer setting.

To give the pilot a rough idea of where the trim knob should be set for take-off, there will be a datum marked which will normally correspond to a "neutral" setting.

The best setting relative to this datum will vary depending on whether the glider is to be launched by aerotow or wire launch. Typically, the trim setting for aerotow will be forward of that required for wire launch. If in doubt about the best setting for take-off, set the trim knob at the datum position and you can always adjust it once airborne.

The trim setting of a glider also depends on the weight of the pilot. The heavier the occupant, the further back the trim knob will have to be. Normally you will be briefed on the most suitable position for the trimmer in a particular glider and launch situation. On future flights you will be able to decide the best trim setting from your own experience.

AIR EXERCISE – TRIMMING

STAGE 1

Fly the glider with the wings level at a constant airspeed.

Sense the force necessary on the control column to maintain a constant attitude and airspeed.

Move the trimmer in the same direction as the applied force until the force on the control column is removed.

Release the control column momentarily and, if the glider is correctly trimmed, the attitude should not change.

If the attitude changes, repeat the trimming exercise from the beginning.

STAGE 2

Adjust the attitude and adopt a new airspeed.

Once the airspeed is constant, sense the force required to maintain it and move the trimmer until the force has been removed.

Release the control column to check whether the glider is correctly trimmed.

CHAPTER 11

THE AIRBRAKES

The modern glider is an incredibly efficient machine. It is designed to conserve its energy and does so very well. "Energy, what energy?" I hear you ask. The glider's energy can be quantified in two ways, either as height (potential energy) or as speed (kinetic energy). Both types of energy are interchangeable; if you raise the glider's nose then the glider gains height but the airspeed reduces, with the reverse effect occurring when the nose is lowered. The glider is designed so that its energy wastes away as slowly as possible. The rate at which the glider dissipates its energy is a measure of its performance. The slower it does so then the higher the performance. Drag wastes energy and therefore the more drag produced by the glider, the more inefficient it is and the lower its performance.

In CHAPTER 4 it was pointed out that one measure of the performance of the glider can be expressed as the ratio of the lift produced by the glider relative to the drag produced, and that this ratio is the same as the glide angle. Any reduction in lift or any increase in the drag will reduce the glider's performance. Normally, the aim is to keep the glider flying as efficiently as possible but there are occasions when we need to reduce the glider's efficiency, such as when we want to land or lose height without gaining airspeed.

In order to "dump" excess energy at times like these, gliders are fitted with controls called AIRBRAKES or SPOILERS (and exceptionally a DRAG PARACHUTE or TAILCHUTE).

HOW AIRBRAKES WORK

Given that a particular glider flying an approach at an airspeed of around 50 knots (a typical approach speed) will have a glide angle (or a lift/drag ratio) of 40 to 1, the angle of approach would be very shallow, making it difficult to judge.

40

1

Fig 11.1   40:1 glide angle. Approaching with a 40:1 glide angle makes landing difficult and would require a large airfield.

Also, due to the low drag of the glider and the resulting low rate at which it loses energy, it would be very difficult to land, requiring a very large landing area.

Opening the airbrakes on the glider causes large flat surfaces to project perpendicularly from each wing into the airflow. When extended, these airbrakes increase the drag dramatically and disrupt the airflow over part of the wing thus reducing the lift produced.

Fig 11.2   How airbrakes work. Opening the airbrakes disrupts the airflow creating a large amount of drag.

The ratio of lift to drag is therefore reduced, as is the glide angle, steepening the angle of approach and making the glider easier to land in smaller areas.

Fig 11.3   5:1 glide angle. Airbrakes can be used to reduce the glide angle to around 5:1.

The amount of airbrake can be varied over the complete range, between fully closed and fully open, giving an infinite number of settings and allowing the glide angle to be adjusted to match the approach path required.

Once on the ground after a landing, the drag created by opening the airbrakes fully will assist in slowing the glider down. This will also result in less lift from the wings, making the wheel brake more effective as the glider's weight will then give the main wheel better ground contact.

Apart from their use as an approach aid, some airbrakes have another, less used purpose, that of "speed limiting" or DIVE BRAKES. Providing that the airbrake surface is large enough, the airbrake can be used to limit the airspeed of the glider should control be lost while cloud flying or carrying out aerobatic manoeuvres. The drag produced by the airbrakes is profile drag and as this drag increases rapidly as the airspeed increases, the airbrakes can be used to limit the airspeed to a value that is within the structural limits permitted by the glider's design. This speed limiting effect usually will operate up to a certain angle of dive (typically about 45 degrees) and if required for this purpose, the airbrakes should be opened well before the limiting airspeed for their operation is reached. This airspeed will often be the same as, or close to, the maximum airspeed at which the glider is permitted to fly.

The position on the wing and the design of the airbrakes on many types of glider will result in a tendency of the airbrakes to extend of their own accord when unlocked from the closed position. This "suck open" effect can be quite pronounced and means that care must be exercised when operating the airbrakes, not to extend them too much, or else an excessive loss of height may occur. The operating force required to close the airbrakes is normally greater than that required to open them. This design problem makes it essential that when operating the airbrakes, you keep your hand on the airbrake control lever to maintain the airbrake setting selected. When not required, the airbrakes must be locked in the closed position.

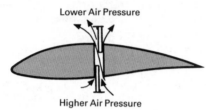

Fig 11.4   *Why airbrakes "suck" open. Most airbrakes, if left unlocked, will tend to "suck" open due to the pressure distribution around the wing.*

Opening the airbrakes will result in several less obvious side effects.

The increase in drag caused when the airbrakes are opened will cause a decay in airspeed. Depending upon the power of the airbrakes, the amount of airbrake selected and the rate at which they are opened, this airspeed reduction may be slight or dramatic, often without a corresponding attitude change. It is therefore essential to monitor the airspeed closely when using the airbrakes, and to realise that any adjustments in the amount of airbrake are likely to require an adjustment to the glider's attitude to maintain the chosen airspeed. This attitude correction is achieved, as in all flight situations, with the elevator.

The fact that most airbrakes disrupt the airflow over part of the wing effectively results in less wing area to support the glider's weight. A smaller wing area means that the stalling speed is increased. This increase (of up to 5 knots with large airbrakes), coupled to the tendency of the airbrakes to cause an unintentional airspeed reduction, results in the need to select an airspeed for the approach which gives a safe margin above the normal stalling speed.

With some airbrakes, especially more powerful ones, buffeting may be felt as the disrupted airflow streams off the wing. This buffeting is nothing to be concerned about and may even, in some instances, act as a useful warning that the airbrakes are extended. It should not be confused with the buffeting sometimes experienced at the stall. If in doubt, a glance at the airspeed indicator should confirm that the glider is not stalled.

SPOILERS

Having described how airbrakes function, and discussed the implications of their use, we can now look at how spoilers differ. Most gliders these days have airbrakes as opposed to spoilers. However, many of the older designs of glider and some motor gliders, which you may fly, will have spoilers.

Unlike airbrakes which extend vertically from slots in the upper surface (or often both upper and lower surfaces) of the wing, spoilers are hinged surfaces which, when closed, lie flush with the upper surface of the wing. They are hinged along their forward edge in such a way that, when operated, they protrude upwards into the airflow. As they only come close to being perpendicular to the wing's surface when fully open, they are less efficient than airbrakes, depending as much on reduction of lift as the creation of drag to reduce the glide angle. In order to increase their efficiency at "spoiling" lift they tend to be situated further forward than airbrakes thus breaking up the airflow near the thickest part of the wing, that is, where most of the lift is produced.

Fig 11.5   How spoilers work. Spoilers disrupt the airflow and cause a reduction in the lift produced by the wing.

The smaller amount of drag produced by spoilers makes them useless as speed limiting devices, and indeed as the lift produced by the wing increases with airspeed, they become less efficient with excessive airspeed.

Spoilers are normally spring-loaded towards the closed position. This prevents the need to guard against them being "sucked" open, but when using them they must be held in the selected position or they will close of their own accord.

The different mechanism and situation of spoilers from that of airbrakes creates their own variation of secondary effects.

As less drag is caused when spoilers are opened than when airbrakes are used, there will be less tendency for airspeed to reduce. However, as lift is being disrupted over part of the wing, the stalling speed will still be increased.

The change of lift distribution as the spoilers are opened may cause the nose to lower. This effect may be enough to counter any slight reduction in airspeed, but on most gliders it will result in an increase in airspeed which must be prevented by stopping the nose from lowering with elevator.

DESIGN HYBRIDS BETWEEN AIRBRAKES AND SPOILERS

Airbrakes, and to a lesser extent spoilers, of the types described so far are common equipment on most gliders. Very occasionally you will come across a variation of design which falls between the two types in the way in which the actual control surface operates e.g. the Blanik and IS 29 gliders.

Because of their design, the operating characteristics of these airbrakes will fall somewhere between airbrakes and spoilers, but the use of them will remain the same for approach control. Whether or not they are speed limiting depends on the individual design.

TRAILING EDGE AIRBRAKES

This type of airbrake is common on medium and high performance single-seat gliders but does not appear on the type of gliders on which you are likely to be trained. Basically the control surface is a hinged surface which forms part of the trailing edge of the wing. Operating the airbrake control in the cockpit rotates this surface to protrude above and below the wing, producing a large amount of drag. Due to the large control surface area, these airbrakes are very effective and are normally speed limiting. Sometimes this control surface is designed only to provide drag, but often it will be incorporated with a flap system which is used to improve performance at other times in flight. Due to this fact, and also because having an understanding of how flaps affect the flight of a glider will help you appreciate the operation of this type of airbrake, these will be covered in the section describing flaps.

TAILCHUTES

With the advent of gliders made from glass fibre, designers achieved a considerable performance leap as the new material allowed thinner, smoother wings with new, low drag wing sections. In what seems an obsession with performance, they forgot that even the highest performance sailplanes would still have to land eventually. In so doing they omitted to put airbrakes on at least one design of glider. (More likely the truth is that they did not want to ruin the smooth airflow around the beautifully efficient wings they had created.)

The answer seemed simple. Produce the drag required by deploying and dragging a small parachute from the glider's tail. Thus the era of the tailchute came about.

Fig 11.6   The tailchute. A deployed tailchute will increase the drag dramatically.

The tailchute is housed in a small compartment in the base of the rudder. It is operated by pulling a release in the cockpit. When deployed it is a very effective drag producer and has a dramatic effect on the glider's glide angle and also, if you are not careful, on the glider's airspeed. When deployed it will also give a strong speed limiting effect.

Now the bad news! Once operated the tailchute obviously cannot be re-used until it is re-stowed in the rudder compartment. It can however be jettisoned if its effect is causing an undershoot. If it is jettisoned outside of the airfield boundaries this will mean, at best, a search of the land below the approach, possibly involving a short walk or swim, or perhaps some tree-climbing. At worst it involves the cost of a new tailchute and housing. These facts, coupled with the fact that full deployment without tangling of the shrouds depends on its being dry and sensibly stowed, resulted in tailchutes being installed mainly as speed limiting devices on gliders which also had airbrakes for approach control.

You are unlikely to encounter a glider with a tailchute in your basic training, but the use of them is dealt with in APPENDIX 3 in case you come across such a glider later.

AIR EXERCISE – THE AIRBRAKES

Fly at 50 to 55 knots and gradually open the airbrakes to their full extent, noting any force necessary to control their opening.

Hold the airbrakes open for a second or two and observe the increase in the rate of descent and any attitude or airspeed change that they cause.

Close and lock them and note the force required for this operation.

Try the operation of the airbrakes at various airspeeds and note the forces required for their smooth operation.

CHAPTER 12

LANDING THE GLIDER

To many students the ability to land the glider is treated as the ultimate challenge and this, to some extent, unfortunately results in this phase of flight being over-rated in terms of difficulty. That is not to say that your first unassisted landing is not an achievement of which to be proud. Even the most experienced pilot can occasionally make a misjudgment or suffer a momentary lapse of concentration which causes a landing to be somewhat less than a textbook manoeuvre.

When it comes to the landing, gliders are very forgiving of mistakes. Training gliders especially are well-designed for their role and will withstand all but the heaviest arrival on the ground. With this in mind and secure in the knowledge that your instructor's "undercarriage" is closer to the glider's undercarriage than yours, you should be able to attempt your first landings without apprehension.

The landing is often thought of as the moment at which the glider makes contact with the ground. While strictly speaking this is probably true, for training purposes the landing can be defined as encompassing all of that part of the flight from the lower part of the approach to the point when the glider finally comes to rest after touchdown. The landing therefore can be said to consist of four parts as follows:

1. The last part of the APPROACH.

2. The ROUND OUT.

3. The HOLD OFF.

4. The GROUND RUN.

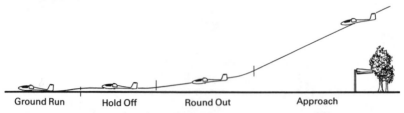

Ground Run   Hold Off   Round Out   Approach

Fig 12.1 Stages of the landing. The landing consists of 4 distinct stages.

THE APPROACH

The APPROACH is the last part of the flight into the airfield when the glider is lined up with the landing area in the direction of landing. In order to be able to attempt your first landings you will have to be able to fly the approach, keeping the glider flying in a straight line (known as the glider's TRACK) towards the landing area. For this reason your instructor will allow you to attempt your first landings only after you have mastered the ability to turn the glider and maintain a track. Another requirement of the approach is that the glider is flown at a preselected airspeed (the APPROACH SPEED) in order that the glider can maintain a safe margin above the airspeed at which it can be expected to stall.

The approach therefore requires the ability to maintain DIRECTIONAL CONTROL and AIRSPEED CONTROL.

DIRECTIONAL CONTROL is achieved in the normal way, by co-ordinated movements of the ailerons and rudder. At first you may find that maintaining the desired approach track seems more difficult than maintaining a similar track towards a ground feature while flying at much higher altitude. The main reason for this is that at the lower heights involved on an approach, any diversion from the chosen track over the ground is much more apparent and becomes more so, the closer you are to the ground. On your first attempts at landings this may in turn result in you applying control movements which are too large, in an attempt to place the glider back on the correct track. In addition to this desire to over-control, the glider will probably be flying at a higher airspeed than that used during normal training exercises. The increased airflow past the control surfaces will make them more sensitive, increasing the problem of over-controlling. The answer to this problem is to (a) relax and (b) stop moving the controls as much. (The chances are that if you are moving the controls constantly you are often cancelling the preceding movement **before it has had an effect**.)

Another hindrance to directional control is our old enemy, AILERON DRAG. In CHAPTER 7 (and on your early flights) it was shown that there is a need to co-ordinate aileron and rudder in order to overcome the tendency of the nose of the glider to swing away from the direction of the turn as aileron is applied. Whereas your turns may be perfectly co-ordinated when executed at 2000 feet, the small adjustments required on the approach (perhaps changing direction through as little as 10° or less) require more subtle co-ordinated inputs. In addition to any actual divergences from track, any lack of co-ordination on the approach will aggravate the apparent divergence. Again, relaxing will help, so as not to brace your legs on the rudder pedals or grip hard on the control column; also take care not to over-control. Remember that every time you move the ailerons, you also need to move the rudder. Would it not be easier to move the ailerons less and thus reduce the amount of co-ordination required?

AIRSPEED CONTROL during the approach is, as during any other phase of flight, achieved using the elevator. However, whereas changes in the glider's attitude can still be a reliable indication of the tendency of the glider to change airspeed, the changing perspective as the ground is approached makes regular monitoring of the airspeed indicator more important.

The airspeed selected for the approach will vary depending on the weather conditions prevailing but should always give adequate margin above the stalling speed. This will give good control response and allow for manoeuvring without the risk of stalling the glider. In the early stages it is reasonable to nominate a target approach speed and allow a narrow band of not more than two knots on either side of the target airspeed. It is also important not to exceed the upper limit of this airspeed band, as excessive airspeed and the resulting increased control response will make it more difficult to control direction and the later stages of the landing, as well using up more landing area. With some practice you should be able to maintain the chosen airspeed with more accuracy.

Lastly, the glider's rate of descent on the approach is controlled by using the airbrakes. While you are attempting to master landings your instructor will use the airbrakes to control the rate of descent, leaving you to concentrate on the use of the primary controls. This means that, until you have mastered the basic technique of landing the glider, you should not concern yourself with how much of the landing area you use up during your landing, as you have no control over this. Let your instructor deal with that aspect while you concentrate on the technique of doing smooth landings. For this reason the airbrakes are dealt with in the next chapter.

THE ROUND OUT

The ROUND OUT starts when the point is reached on the approach to reduce the glider's rate of descent in order that the glider, instead of descending towards the ground, flies parallel to, and just above the ground. When this has been achieved the round out has been completed.

The round out is achieved by raising the nose of the glider with the elevator; that is, moving the control column backwards. This movement is gradual. If the control column is moved too rapidly the glider's nose will be raised too high and the glider will climb away from the ground instead of flying parallel to it, airspeed will be lost, and unless corrective action is taken, a stall will occur. If the control column is moved backwards too slowly, the glider's rate of descent will not be reduced sufficiently, resulting in the glider flying onto the ground at too high an airspeed, possibly causing it to bounce back into the air.

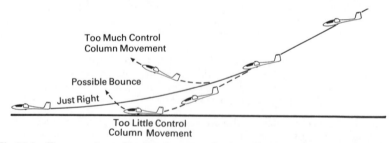

Fig 12.2   The round out. Moving the control column backwards too much during the round out will cause the glider to climb away from the ground, whereas too little movement will risk striking the ground.

The best way therefore to round out is to move the control column gradually, while watching the rate at which the ground is coming up to meet the glider. If it is approaching too fast, then move the control column backwards at a slightly faster rate. If it appears not to be rising towards the glider at a reasonable rate then stop the control movement for a second or so. As the glider loses airspeed, the lift produced by the wing will also diminish and the glider will start to sink towards the ground again. You can then start the backwards movement of the control column again. Only in the exceptional situation of the glider climbing away from the ground in a very nose-up attitude will it be necessary to level the glider by moving the control column forward and even then, only with the utmost care so as not to strike the ground.

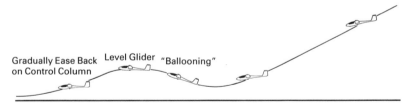

Fig 12.3 "Ballooning" whilst landing. Ballooning on round out can normally be corrected by returning the glider to a level attitude and then recommencing the backward control column movement once the glider again starts to descend.

The round out can be regarded as involving two aspects; a skill aspect and a judgement aspect. The physical act of moving the control column is the skill aspect of rounding out. The judgement aspect is made up of decisions such as when to start rounding out and whether to increase the rate of control movement or reduce it. This will come quickly with experience and to help you in your initial attempts, your instructor will prompt you when to begin the round out and the rate at which to move the control column. This will allow you to gain the necessary skill before you are allowed to attempt to judge the round out for yourself.

As for guidance as to when to begin the round out, this is best judged by watching the example your instructor sets and gaining a mental picture of what the point of round out looks like. This is because this judgement is based on perspective; that is, how the landing area and the features around it are viewed in relation to each other, and how this view is changing (Fig 12.5). As you will have gathered by now, the landing is a part of the flight where things are changing fairly rapidly, and therefore to try to pinpoint a certain height at which to begin the round out would be meaningless. Another problem is that we all have different ideas of distance and height. This judgement is therefore best gained from experience; firstly that of your instructor by way of demonstration, then by responding to his prompts and finally from the results you personally achieve from judging the round out yourself.

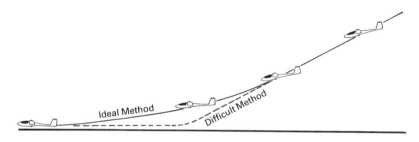

Fig 12.4 Round out technique. The safest round out is one which starts early and continues gradually. Leaving the round out late means that large and sudden control movements become necessary.

87

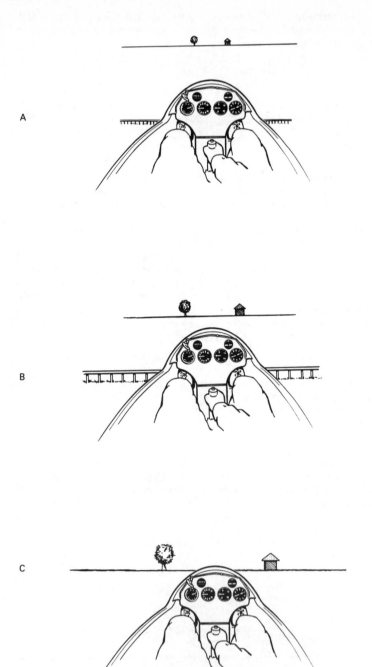

Fig 12.5   *Judging the point of round out. The point of round out is judged by the changing perspective of the landing area.*

One clue that may help you is the fact that the round out begins much higher than many people think. Indeed, ideally it begins early and continues gradually, rather than at the last moment when the ground is close creating the need for sudden, large control movements. (Fig 12.4)

Up to the point where the round out is started, you will have been looking at the landing area and monitoring the glider's airspeed. At the point of round out, look forward, well up the airfield ahead of the landing area. This will help you, as the changing perspective of the ground will be more obvious when viewed with peripheral vision, thereby making judgement easier. Staring at the point on the ground immediately ahead of the glider will reveal only a blurred image and will almost always result in the glider flying into the ground rather than a smooth landing.

THE HOLD OFF

The HOLD OFF comes after the glider's flight path has been converted from a descent, to a flight path parallel to, and just above the ground (that is, the round out has been accomplished). It consists of the glider literally being held above the ground at or near the height established at the end of the round out, and prevented from landing. This may sound strange when the whole aim of the exercise is to land the glider, however there are good reasons for holding off the impending touchdown. What we are trying to achieve when we land the glider is, in effect, a controlled stall. If this is achieved the glider will settle onto the ground at the minimum airspeed possible, thus reducing both the distance required to lose the last bit of airspeed as it rolls along the ground before stopping, and the stresses placed upon the glider (and its occupants) if the ground is rough. Another advantage is that in the event of the glider's wheel hitting a piece of bumpy ground on touchdown, the glider is unlikely to become airborne again as the wing is stalled (or to put it another way, the glider does not have flying speed).

In order to maintain the height during the hold off, the control column is progressively moved backwards. Trying to fly level will result in the airspeed reducing which, in turn, will diminish the lift being produced by the wing. To prevent the glider sinking the control column is moved backwards to increase the angle of attack of the wing, thus restoring the lift to the required value. The airspeed will continue to reduce and the angle of attack must be continually increased to restore the lift. Eventually the angle of attack will reach the stalling angle and the glider will stall. As all this is happening within a couple of feet of the ground, the onset of the stall results in the glider settling gently onto the ground. The glider has now touched down.

During the hold off, care must be exercised so as not to over-control, otherwise the glider may increase its height from the ground (known as BALLOONING). This situation will again be aggravated if the airspeed on the approach is too high. In most circumstances where the glider is held off too high, it is sufficient not to allow the nose of the glider to rise too much. Only in extreme cases should the nose be lowered and then only with the utmost care so as not to fly onto the ground.

THE GROUND RUN

The GROUND RUN after the touchdown is just as important as the other phases of the landing. Once the glider has settled onto the ground it must still be controlled until it has come to a complete stop. Your aim during the ground run is to keep the glider travelling in the direction chosen for the landing. Unfortunately, as the glider's airspeed decays, so too does the effectiveness of the controls, making it necessary to use increasingly larger control deflections to maintain control.

Now that the glider is on the ground, directional control is achieved by using the rudder alone and the wings are kept level for as long as possible using the ailerons. This is one of the few situations where the controls are used in an unco-ordinated sense. Failure to keep the wings level could result in a wing tip touching the ground. If this occurs while the glider is still travelling forwards, it can cause the glider to swing uncontrollably around the lowered wing tip, in what is known as a GROUND LOOP. Such an event can cause significant and sometimes serious damage to the glider.

During the ground run the elevator is used to keep the glider in the correct attitude, usually with the tail held firmly on the ground. This will give the glider maximum drag at the tail thus improving its directional stability and the increased drag will help slow the glider down.

No attempt should be made to steer the glider to either side of the landing direction except for reasons of safety or to avoid obstructions. In such cases, and during any field landing, the wheel brake should be used to stop the glider as soon as possible.

AIR EXERCISE – LANDING

STAGE 1

Your instructor will demonstrate the need to maintain airspeed and direction on the approach, the point at which the round out should begin, and the control inputs required to achieve a good round out, hold off and ground run.

STAGE 2

You will be allowed to attempt the landing technique demonstrated using the primary controls, while your instructor controls the rate of descent with the airbrakes. At this stage your instructor will prompt you, when the time is right to start easing back on the control column to begin the round out.

STAGE 3

Having mastered the amount of control input necessary for the round out and hold off, you will be allowed to judge the point of round out and attempt the whole landing technique yourself. (Your instructor will still help by operating the airbrakes until your landings are good enough for you to be shown how to use the airbrakes.)

CHAPTER 13

THE APPROACH

In the previous chapter we considered the very last part of the approach as part of the landing. This was necessary in order to encompass the beginning of the landing technique, that is, the round out. In this chapter, we will cover the whole approach and all of the various aspects involved in controlling it. We have already discussed how to control both the glider's airspeed and direction on the approach. The other vital parameter which must be controlled, is the rate of descent.

To recap:

Directional control on the approach is maintained in the normal way, that is, with co-ordinated aileron and rudder inputs in order to keep the glider tracking along the desired approach path.

Airspeed is controlled by using the elevator to adjust the attitude as necessary, thereby maintaining a preselected airspeed until the beginning of the round out.

The rate of descent is controlled by using the airbrakes.

To enable you to give your full concentration to the technique of landing the glider, the airbrakes will, up to this stage, have been applied as necessary by your instructor. Having demonstrated your ability to land the glider, you will be shown when and how to use the airbrakes to increase the glider's rate of descent, thus enabling you to land the glider at your chosen point.

The first requirement is to decide where you wish to touchdown. This decision will normally be made as you fly towards the general area in which you have chosen to land, be it within your base airfield or, when you are more experienced, another airfield or even in a farmer's field. In the early stages of training you will be landing back on your base airfield and so the touchdown area can be defined before take-off.

Having selected the area where you wish to touch down, select a feature over which you will fly on the approach and which is a short distance from the touchdown area.

This feature is called the REFERENCE POINT and is used to judge the glider's approach angle. (Fig 13.1)

This is how the reference point is used:

Once the glider is lined up on the approach and flying at the selected approach speed, the position of the reference point in the canopy or its relative position to the canopy frame is noted. As long as the relative position of the reference point remains constant, the glider is following an approach path which will take it to the reference point. (Fig 13.2)

If the reference point is moving downwards relative to the canopy, then the glider is following an approach path which will take it to a position beyond

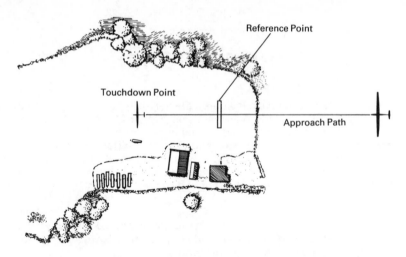

Fig 13.1   *The reference point. The reference point, which will be used to judge the height on the approach, is a point on the ground, a short distance from the touchdown point, over which the glider will fly on the approach.*

the reference point (or to put it another way, overflying the reference point). This means that the rate of descent must be increased to steepen the approach angle. This is done by extending the airbrakes. (Fig 13.3)

If you select the correct amount of airbrake, the reference point will appear to stop moving down the canopy. It will take up a new constant position which will be lower than its original position relative to the canopy.

If too much airbrake is applied, the reference point will move upwards relative to the canopy and the amount of airbrake will need to be reduced to lessen the rate of descent and the approach angle. (Fig 13.4)

Again, when the correct airbrake setting is used the reference point will remain in a constant position relative to the canopy, although this position will now be higher up the canopy.

Fig 13.2   *Correct approach. If the reference point does not move relative to the canopy then the correct amount of airbrake is being used.*

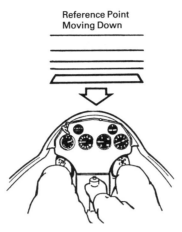

Fig 13.3   Overshooting on the approach. If the reference point is moving downwards relative to the canopy then too little airbrake is being used.

To summarise:

The decision whether or not to apply airbrake is made by monitoring the relative movement of the reference point.

The correct approach path will result in a constant reference point position relative to the canopy; that is, neither moving upwards nor downwards.

Too shallow an approach (an overshooting situation) will result in the reference point moving downwards relative to the canopy. Increase airbrake.

Too steep an approach (an undershooting situation) will result in the reference point moving upwards relative to the canopy. Reduce airbrake.

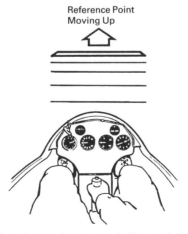

Fig 13.4   Undershooting on the approach. If the reference point is moving upwards relative to the canopy then too much airbrake is being used.

There may even be occasions when no airbrake is required on the approach and therefore you should avoid getting into the habit of opening the airbrakes as soon as you turn onto the approach track. The decision to use airbrake must always be a considered judgement, because to dump height thoughtlessly could leave the glider in an irretrievable undershoot situation. Closing the airbrakes reduces the glider's rate of descent; it will not increase your height.

If the air is smooth and the wind is light there will be an airbrake setting which, once found, will take the glider down an approach path to the reference point. In the early stages of training, once the glider is at the point of round out, the airbrake setting can be kept constant and the landing completed using only the main controls, thus making the landing easier to accomplish. However, if there is any danger of the glider undershooting the landing area or if the airspeed has decayed, you must be ready to reduce the amount of airbrake. Should you misjudge the round out and the glider balloons back upwards into the air, you should consider whether it might be necessary to close the airbrakes. If the airspeed has started to decay, closing the airbrakes will prevent it reducing too rapidly and give you more time to sort out a landing further up the landing area.

Later, when you are more adept with the controls, and are more confident at landing the glider, you will be able to make adjustments to the amount of airbrake during the round out and hold off in order to achieve more precise landings. Note that, as the glider is rounded out, the reference point should be ignored because it will soon disappear under the nose of the glider and the glider will land somewhere beyond the reference point. You should not expect to touch down at the reference point, hence the reason for selecting a point or feature on the ground some distance before the desired landing point as the reference point.

It is more likely that, as the glider descends, it will pass through air which is rising or descending at different rates and will also encounter different wind strengths. This will mean that although an airbrake setting may be found which keeps the reference point in a constant relative position initially, the changing air mass will result in the glider diverging from the desired approach path. In this case the amount of airbrake will need to be constantly re-assessed and adjusted as necessary, almost on a trial and error basis. Again, when ready to round out it will be helpful, in the initial stages of training, to maintain a constant airbrake setting if airspeed and glider position permit.

It is important to realise that, in order to maintain the approach angle using the reference point technique, the glider's attitude must remain constant. If the attitude varies either intentionally (for instance, to correct the airspeed) or unintentionally, then the reference point will move relative to the canopy. So as not to act upon these false indications, movement of the reference point should be ignored momentarily while the glider's attitude is changing.

Lastly, remember that although many gliders have airbrakes which are powerful and create enough drag to influence the glider's airspeed, it is still the elevator which is used to control the attitude and airspeed on approach. Airbrakes should only be used to control the rate of descent. Keeping this point in mind will stand you in good stead for the day you convert on to a higher performance glider with less efficient airbrakes than your training glider, when good airspeed control will be essential.

AIR EXERCISE – APPROACH CONTROL USING THE AIRBRAKES

STAGE 1

Select a suitable feature or point to be used as a reference point.

Establish the glider on an approach which begins further back from the landing area and higher than normal.

Once established on the approach, fly the glider towards the landing area with the airbrakes closed.

Notice that the reference point is moving down relative to the glider's canopy; that is, the glider is overshooting the landing area.

STAGE 2

Apply FULL airbrake and notice that the reference point is now moving upwards relative to the glider's canopy; that is, the glider is now undershooting the landing area.

STAGE 3

Adjust the airbrake setting until the reference point remains in a constant position relative to the canopy.

Once this situation is achieved the glider will be descending towards the reference point.

At the point of round out, disregard the reference point, look well ahead, and land the glider using the technique learned previously. (If you are safely inside the airfield with sufficient airspeed at the point of round out, you should be able to land without further adjustment of the airbrakes.)

CHAPTER 14

THE EFFECT OF THE WIND

Up to this point little mention has been made of the effect that the wind has on the glider. The reason for this is simplicity. Most of the exercises we have covered up until now have dealt with the control of the glider, on which the wind normally has little or no effect. The exception is the approach to land and the actual landing of the glider, where the ground becomes an essential part of the act. Even during your early attempts to land the glider, the wind will not be a serious consideration, for the simple fact that, if there is any significant wind, your instructor will not be able to allow you to attempt your first landings.

Now that you have gained some idea of how to control the glider, it is time to discuss the effects that the wind has on the glider, be they good or bad.

WHAT IS WIND?

Before it is possible to study the wind's effect on the glider's flight, it is necessary to understand what wind actually is. Without going too deeply into the meteorological aspects, wind can be described as a mass of air which is moving relative to the earth's surface, or, if you like, across the ground. When we talk about a mass of air, we are talking about a very large quantity of air, perhaps thousands of feet deep and hundreds of miles across. Admittedly, localised winds occur but even these make the glider appear like a model motor-boat in a very large river. The only difference is that the glider is surrounded by this huge parcel of air and not floating upon it. Despite this difference, the boat/river analogy holds good in many ways.

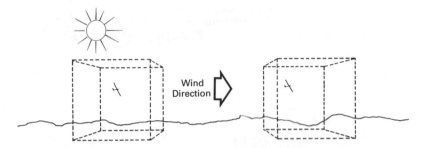

Fig 14.1   The wind and the glider. The glider is flying in a huge mass of air which, if there is any wind, is itself moving across the ground.

ASSESSING THE WIND STRENGTH AND DIRECTION

There are many tell-tale signs which give an indication of the wind direction. The most obvious of these are visual clues such as the direction in which smoke from fires and chimneys is being blown. These will give the direction of the wind at ground level. The direction in which cloud shadows are crossing the ground will give an idea of the wind direction at the level of the cloud base. The way in which the glider is drifting in turns will give an idea of the wind direction at the glider's altitude.

The speed of the wind is slightly more difficult to estimate from observation, but can be judged by the behaviour of some of the features mentioned above. Smoke, for example, will rise less vertically if a strong wind is blowing. A windsock will also be more horizontal in a stronger wind. The speed at which the cloud shadows drift across the ground will be directly related to the wind speed at cloud base, just as the wind at the glider's altitude will affect the drift rate of the glider.

THE EFFECT OF WIND ON THE CONTROLS

The parcel of air in which the glider is flying, is all around the glider. If, for a moment, we go back to basics and assume that this parcel of air is stationary, (that is, there is no wind and the glider is said to be flying in STILL AIR) then the controls will respond normally to the pilot's inputs. A radio controlled, model boat on a calm pond, when instructed to turn left or right will do so.

If the boat is on a fast flowing river and the signal to turn left is given, it will still turn left, despite the flow of the river. The river's flow is having no effect on the boat's controls. They still respond in the same way, in this case by swinging the front of the boat to the left as desired. The direction in which the front of the boat is pointing is called the boat's HEADING.

Similarly, the glider's controls will continue to act normally even when the air mass in which it is flying is moving; in other words when there is a wind blowing. Moving the controls to turn the glider, or to raise or lower the nose, will have the desired effect and, as in still air, the glider's heading or airspeed will change accordingly. The wind does not affect the glider's control response in normal flight.

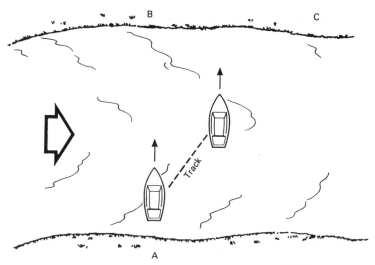

Fig 14.2   Drift. A boat crossing a fast flowing river will drift downstream.

THE EFFECT OF WIND ON THE GLIDER'S TRACK

To continue with the boat analogy, if our boat sets off to cross a fast flowing river, pointing the boat directly across the river will not achieve a direct crossing (from A to B in Fig 14.2).

The current will cause the boat to reach the far shore further downstream at position C. The medium on which the boat is travelling is moving and the boat is obliged to move with it and, despite its forward motion, the result is the deflected route from A to C. This achieved route is called the boat's TRACK.

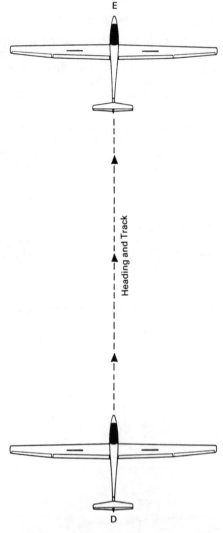

Fig 14.3   Track and heading. When there is no wind a glider's track over the ground will be the same as its heading.

Similarly, a glider pilot flying in STILL AIR from position D to position E in Fig 14.3 will point the nose of the glider towards E. (That is, the glider's HEADING will be towards E.) As there is no wind the glider's TRACK will also be from D to E.

If, on the other hand, there is a wind blowing from the left, (that is, the parcel of air in which the glider is flying is moving from left to right) the glider's TRACK over the ground will be deflected to the right. In this case, the glider will track towards position F. (Fig 14.4)

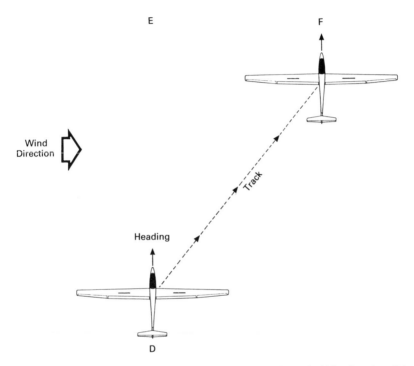

Fig 14.4   *Wind causes the glider to drift. When there is a wind blowing the glider will suffer drift. Its track will no longer be the same as its heading.*

The pilot can counter this DRIFT by altering his heading towards the direction from which the wind is blowing; in this example to the left. The end result will be a TRACK towards position E. This corrected HEADING will depend on both the wind speed and the glider's airspeed. (Fig 14.5)

THE EFFECT OF WIND ON A CIRCLING GLIDER

A glider circling in STILL AIR, at a constant airspeed and angle of bank, will inscribe a circular path in the sky. Because there is no wind, this will also be a circular TRACK over the ground. On the other hand, if there is any wind, the glider will be blown downwind. The shape of the circles flown relative to the ground will be elongated as the glider turns downwind, and shortened as it turns into wind. During the part of each turn which is across the direction of the wind, the glider will be drifted downwind.

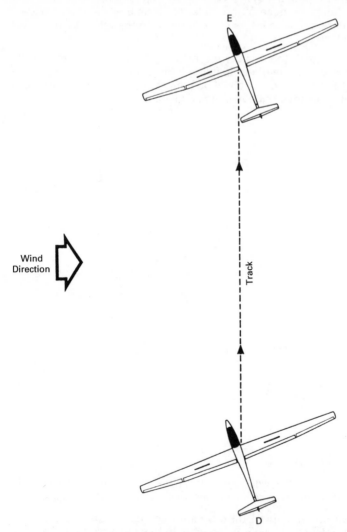

Fig 14.5   *Correcting for drift. The desired track over the ground can be achieved by pointing the glider's nose slightly into wind.*

AIRSPEED VERSUS GROUNDSPEED

Despite the fact that the wind has an effect on the glider's track, it must be remembered that the glider, as well as flying in this moving air mass, is also flying *through* it. In other words the glider has speed relative to this air mass; its airspeed. Up to now, when speed has been mentioned, it has almost always been airspeed to which we have been referring. This is because all of the aerodynamic surfaces, such as the wing and the controls, rely on this relative airflow passing over them to function. Without airspeed the glider will not fly.

100

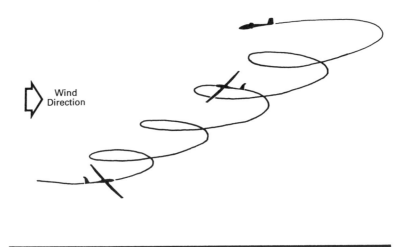

Fig 14.6   Wind effect on a circling glider. When circling a glider will drift downwind.

If there is no wind, the glider would fly over the ground at the same speed as its airspeed. Flying into wind at the same airspeed would result in a reduced groundspeed whereas flying downwind at the same airspeed would increase the glider's groundspeed.

THE EFFECT OF WIND ON THE APPROACH ANGLE

We have already described the glide angle as the distance which the glider can fly from a given height, assuming that is, that no rising or descending air currents are encountered during this glide. This means that from any given height, a particular glider will be able to cover a corresponding distance over the ground, *assuming that is that there is no wind to affect the glider's progress.*

If any wind is present it will result in the glider being able to cover a greater or smaller distance over the ground, from the same height. When we consider the distance covered over the ground in a certain period of time, we are dealing with groundspeed. We have seen that groundspeed increases when there is a tail wind and reduces in a headwind. During the period of time in which the glider is descending from a specific height, its groundspeed will determine how far it will travel over the ground. Since a tail wind will give a higher groundspeed, the glider will be capable of covering more ground with the height available.

For the same reason, a headwind will reduce the amount of ground that can be covered from a given height.

It is vital, for safe approach planning, to have an understanding of the effect that the wind has on the distance the glider can cover over the ground. Enough height must always be available to allow a safe approach to be flown. If insufficient allowance is made for the prevailing wind then there is the danger that the glider may not have sufficient height to reach the landing area.

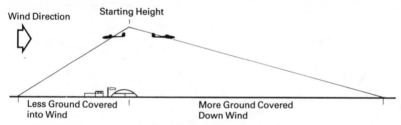

Fig 14.7   The wind's effect on ground distance covered. A glider will be able to cover more ground when flying downwind than it would if there were no wind. Flying into wind will reduce the distance that can be covered.

THE EFFECT OF THE WIND ON TAKE-OFF

When the launch of a glider begins, the glider must be accelerated until it achieves an airspeed in excess of its stalling speed. When this airspeed is reached the wing will produce enough lift for the glider to begin to take-off. In zero wind conditions this means that the groundspeed at take-off will equal the airspeed (and therefore the stalling speed) before the glider becomes airborne. During the period of time when the glider is being accelerated, it will be travelling up the runway. A certain length of runway will therefore be required to achieve a take-off.

If the glider is launched into a headwind, the airspeed required for take-off will be achieved at a lower groundspeed. The wind can be regarded as giving the glider a start by the value of the wind speed, since it is a certain airspeed that the glider requires for take-off, and the wind is supplying some of this even before the glider starts moving. As the groundspeed required is less, the glider will need to use up less runway while accelerating to take-off airspeed.

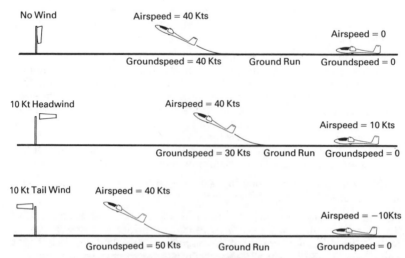

Fig 14.8   The wind's effect on the take-off distance. A headwind will reduce the take-off distance required over that required in no wind conditions. A tail wind will increase the take-off distance required.

Taking-off with a tail wind would have an adverse effect because a groundspeed equivalent to the wind speed would have to be achieved before the airspeed even starts to increase. The acceleration to take-off airspeed would take longer and a much longer ground run would be required.

As it takes longer for the airspeed to build when launching with a tail wind, the controls will take longer to become effective, making it more difficult to maintain direction and keep the wings level. Taking-off with any significant tail wind component should therefore be avoided if at all possible.

Whether the glider is launched by aerotow or wire launch will have a bearing on the rate of acceleration to take-off airspeed, but there are many other factors which influence the distance of runway required, such as slope, surface and if the launch is by aerotow, any obstacles which have to be cleared. Suffice to say that the wind only affects the take-off of the glider as far as airspeed is concerned while it is still connected to the ground. In the case of a wire launch, this will include the whole time that the glider is being launched, as it is still attached to the ground by the launch cable.

If the glider is being launched by aerotow, then the stalling speed and the climbing speed of the tow-plane will influence the take-off distance required. Once the tow-plane and glider combination is airborne, then the wind only affects the launch in terms of track and angle of climb. The angle of climb can be regarded as following similar rules to glide angles over the ground (only in ascent rather than descent) with better angles of climb being achieved into stronger winds due to the lower groundspeeds. A more shallow climb angle will be experienced if a tail wind exists.

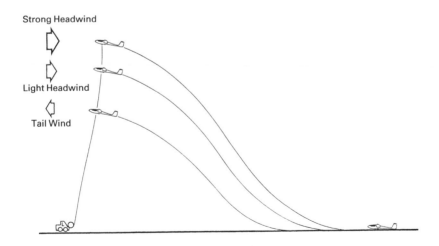

Fig 14.9   The wind's effect on wire launch heights. A greater launch height will be achieved when launching into a headwind as opposed to launching in calm conditions. Reduced launch heights will result if launches are made with a tail wind component.

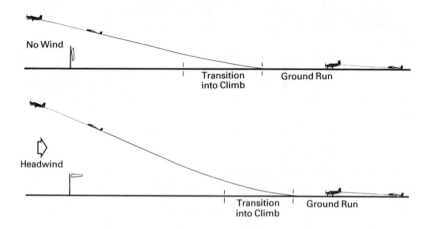

Fig 14.10   The wind's effect on an aerotow launch. When aerotowing, launching
into wind will result in a steeper climb gradient than launching in calm
conditions.

THE EFFECT OF THE WIND ON LANDING

Just as with the launch of a glider, the wind has an effect on the landing
distance required.

The rules are essentially the same as for take-off. Into-wind landings
require a smaller landing area than is necessary in calm conditions.
Landing with a tail wind will require a larger landing area. The reasons for
the difference in the length of the required landing distance is mainly due
to the wind giving a decreased groundspeed when approaching into wind,
thus less runway is used up in the hold off and ground run stages. Using
the same reasoning will show why landing downwind will use up more
runway.

Apart from the advantages of being able to land in a smaller space, landing
into wind will have other advantages.

For a start, if the glider is landing on uneven ground, the reduced
groundspeed at the point of touchdown will reduce the stresses on the
glider and on the pilot's "unsprung parts".

The fact that the glider's control surfaces depend on air flowing over them
in order for them to function means that as the glider decelerates, its
controls will become less effective. In calm conditions the pilot may even
lose the ability to maintain direction and keep the wings level before the
glider finally comes to rest after landing. If there is a headwind on landing
then the glider's airspeed will be greater than its groundspeed. As a result,
even in light headwinds, there may still be enough control effect to
maintain control until the glider has come to a stop. In moderate to strong
winds the chances are that the wings may be kept level even after the glider
has stopped completely at the end of its landing run.

Landing downwind will have the opposite effect in that control on the ground run may be lost well before the glider has come to rest.

As if the reasons given so far were not enough for avoiding, whenever possible, a downwind landing, there is one other trap into which the unwary pilot must not fall. We now know that approaching and landing with a tail wind will involve the glider's *groundspeed* being greater than its airspeed. Remember that the glider will stall at a certain airspeed. Because the landing is being carried out with a tail wind, the visual impression you will receive from external references, such as the ground, will be one of excess airspeed. Unless the temptation to reduce this high groundspeed is resisted, the glider may end up flying too slowly for the round out, resulting in a stall or a heavy landing. The answer to this dilemma is firstly to appreciate the fact that there is a tail wind, and secondly, monitor the airspeed as often, and as late, on the approach and landing as possible.

Lastly, although landing into wind has numerous advantages over landing with a tail wind, most gliders flown sensibly can cope with reasonable tail winds on landing. There will also be some exceptional occasions when a downwind landing will be the safer option. Such situations will be covered and explained when they become pertinent to the exercise being covered.

CROSSWINDS ON LANDING

When the wind is blowing across the direction of approach and landing, a CROSSWIND is said to exist. Gliders generally can tolerate quite strong crosswinds, but they do affect the glider in the following ways:

On the approach, and during the round out and hold off, the glider will suffer from the tendency to drift to one side by the wind. This creates the need to point the glider's nose slightly into wind so that the glider's track is down the approach path. This is done by turning the glider (using co-ordinated controls) until the heading is such that the glider is following the desired track, and then levelling the wings as is normal after a turn. As the glider will be flying sideways relative to the ground, the pilot must align the glider with the runway direction immediately before touchdown. This is achieved by applying rudder to swing the glider until the nose is pointing down the runway, whilst keeping the wings level with the ailerons. Failure to do so will result in a sideways landing and will place extra stress on the glider, in particular the main wheel assembly. (Fig 14.11)

An alternative to this CRABBING (or TRACKING) method of maintaining track is to approach with the windward wing held lower than the other wing, countering any tendency to turn by applying opposite rudder. With gliders which have a low set wing and a large wingspan, care must be taken not to touch a wing tip at the point of landing. Many pilots use a combination of both the crabbing approach technique and the wing down technique at the same time. (Fig 14.12)

Once on the ground, any crosswind will tend to swing the glider so that its nose is pointing into wind, that is, at an angle to the landing direction. This effect, known as WEATHERCOCKING, is caused by the wind striking the rear fuselage and fin which present a larger surface area behind the main wheel (which on the ground is the pivot point) than the relatively small cockpit area in front. Surprisingly, this effect can be just as pronounced in

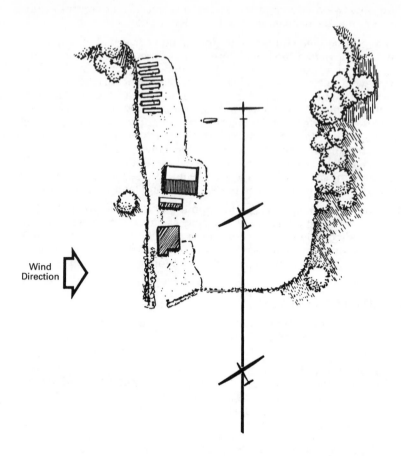

Wind Direction

Fig 14.11 Crosswind landing – crabbing method. The crabbing technique of approaching with a crosswind. Just before touchdown the glider is aligned with the landing direction by using rudder.

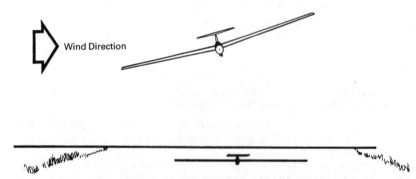

Wind Direction

Fig 14.12 Wing-down crosswind landing technique.

light crosswinds as in stronger ones, especially if the glider's centre of gravity is behind its main wheel; in other words if the glider is tail heavy even with the pilot on board. The swing tendency will be aggravated if there is any tail wind component which will reduce control effectiveness further. In an extreme case, such a swing can cause the glider's wing tip to touch the ground, resulting in the glider pivoting about the wing tip and being damaged.

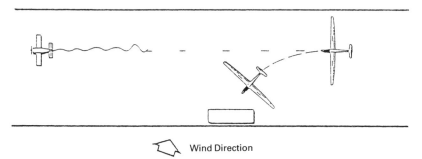

Wind Direction

Fig 14.13   Weathercocking may result in the glider swinging to the windward side.

Fortunately, most gliders have adequate controls to maintain direction after landing, up until the point when the glider has almost stopped at the end of the ground run. It is as this point is approached that the weathercock effect is most likely during the landing phase. You should try to anticipate any possible swing by taking note of the wind direction (windsock, drift, etc.) and be prepared to use large amounts of rudder to maintain direction and as much aileron as necessary to keep the wings level. Gliders which have a tailskid may have increased directional stability on landing if the tail is held firmly on the ground with elevator after landing. This is especially true if the surface of the landing area is soft earth or grass, whereas tail wheels will have more effect on a concrete or other hard-surfaced runways.

In crosswind conditions, landing close to obstructions such as vehicles and other aircraft should be avoided.

CROSSWINDS ON TAKE-OFF

Crosswind take-offs should be treated with the same respect as when landing in similar conditions. On the ground run, the tendency of the glider to weathercock is the main problem, especially on aerotow launch, where the initial acceleration and the rate at which the flying controls become effective is often poor. A clear take-off run, with adequate clearance to either side in case of a swing is essential. Take-offs should never be accepted if there are any obstructions anywhere near the projected take-off path.

Once airborne the only crosswind consideration is that of drift. The degree to which drift will affect the launch depends not only on the crosswind strength but also on the type of launch. The effect of drift on the launch will therefore be covered in the separate sections on aerotow and wire launching.

All in all, crosswinds do not cause much difficulty for the glider pilot as long as their effects are anticipated. Many gliding sites are restricted to a single runway operation and therefore have to cope regularly with crosswinds on both take-off and landing. Pilots from such sites tend to learn the necessary techniques for safe crosswind operation almost subconsciously as a part of their normal training. As a result, they often benefit from the confidence that the possession of such handling skills can give. Pilots from larger sites which have the ability to operate more often into wind, find that crosswind training has to be covered as a specific exercise.

TURBULENCE

The air in which the glider flies may be smooth or it may be TURBULENT. The term TURBULENT describes an air mass where there are localised variations from the general flow of air. These variations of airflow, which are very often of short duration and can occur in any direction, are known as GUSTS. Such turbulence may be anything from light to severe in degree. This rough air effect may be caused by ascending or descending air due to convection but more often turbulence is associated with strong winds or a combination of both these factors.

The fact that the wind strength is moderate or strong does not necessarily result in turbulence. However if the wind is blowing across obstructions such as mountains, hills or even trees and buildings, these can cause the air mass to become turbulent as the airflow is retarded and distorted as it attempts to flow around them. As a general rule such turbulence reduces as height is increased and the ground's influence is left behind.

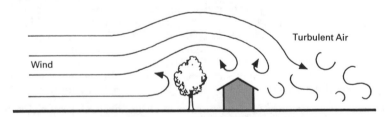

Fig 14.14   Obstructions causing turbulence. Turbulence can be the result of the wind blowing over obstructions such as buildings.

The modification of the airflow caused by large obstructions such as mountains may last for a hundred miles or more downwind of the source, whereas the effects from smaller objects like buildings and trees can be felt up to a mile or more downwind. Glider pilots from sites situated on top of, or immediately downwind of a hill, are usually well aware of the turbulence caused as the wind flows over the edge of the hill sometimes causing severe turbulence, sinking air and even the reversal of the main wind direction.

As far as the glider pilot is concerned, turbulence will often be an aid to finding rising air currents. At other times turbulence may be a forewarning that large amounts of sinking air may be encountered. In such conditions, if you are sensible, you will allow for the possible loss of height which may make a return to the airfield or chosen landing area beyond the best glide

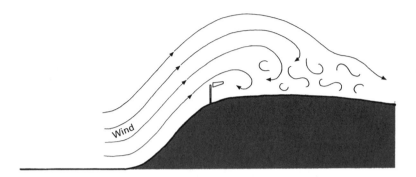

Fig 14.15   Curl over at a hilltop airfield. Hilltop sites are prone to turbulence as
the wind curls over the crest of the hill.

angle achievable. If the approach has to be made over trees or buildings, flying a higher approach will reduce the risk of encountering increased turbulence and sinking air downwind of the obstruction.

Another problem involving turbulence comes from the fact that on many gliders which have a large wingspan, the rate of roll available may be poor. This, together with the fact that some gusts may cause a tipping effect which is at a higher rate than can be countered by use of aileron, makes turbulent conditions closer to the ground more hazardous. The main safeguard against this lack of control response is to fly at an increased airspeed, thereby adding to the control effectiveness. In turbulent conditions, however, too much airspeed will result in you getting a rougher ride and in any event the airspeed must be kept below the MAXIMUM ROUGH AIR SPEED displayed on the limitations placard in the cockpit.

Severe turbulence can be unpleasant to fly in, and even the most seasoned pilot will prefer to be safely on the ground in these conditions. Fortunately such turbulence is usually found only at low altitudes, in the lee of hills and mountains or in certain extreme meteorological conditions, such as large thunderstorm clouds. It may often result in the cancellation of flying activities and even if flying does continue, is almost certain to prevent early training and restrict solo flying to more experienced pilots.

WIND GRADIENT

The slowing down of a moving air mass caused by obstructions and by friction with the ground itself is greatest close to the ground. In windy conditions the result is a rapid increase in wind speed with height.

This WIND GRADIENT is at its steepest, close to the ground and reduces as height from the surface and the guilty obstructions increases.

The effect of the wind gradient on the glider, which can be pronounced, especially when the wind is strong, is best explained by an analogy.

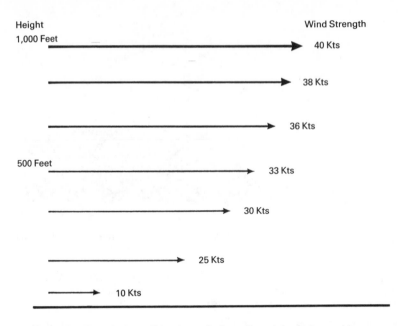

Height	Wind Strength
1,000 Feet	40 Kts
	38 Kts
	36 Kts
500 Feet	33 Kts
	30 Kts
	25 Kts
	10 Kts

Fig 14.16   The wind gradient. In a wind gradient the wind speed increases rapidly with height.

You may have seen or heard of the stage trick where the performer snatches a tablecloth from beneath a setting of cups and saucers. If he is lucky, the crockery will remain set on the table while he waves the tablecloth with toreador aplomb (to the amazement, or perhaps disappointment, of the audience). The physics of the trick are simple, even if his success was not. The cups and saucers possess mass. Any object with mass suffers from inertia. (Inertia is the reluctance of any object to change what it is doing, be that moving at a certain speed or standing still. It is due to inertia that a lot of power is required to accelerate a train, and similarly why it takes some stopping once it is going fast.) Our performer was relying on the fact that, as he snatched the tablecloth away, the crockery's inertia would keep it stationary. The cups and saucers simply did not have enough time to accelerate like the tablecloth.

A glider has inertia which causes it to try to maintain a constant speed *relative to the ground*. When it descends quickly through a steep wind gradient, the glider is travelling down through air which is itself travelling at a reducing speed. As the wind speed drops off, the glider's inertia will cause the airspeed to reduce in an attempt to maintain the constant groundspeed.

If airspeed reduces, so too will the lift produced by the wing. This will create an imbalance in forces and cause the glider to descend more rapidly through the wind gradient which, remember, is getting more severe as the glider gets lower. As the glider loses airspeed and descends faster, it will be meeting the relative airflow at an ever increasing angle of attack. If you are not careful, the glider's angle of attack may be at or close to the stalling angle even

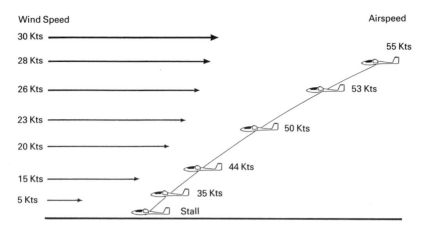

Fig 14.17   The wind gradient's effect on the glider's airspeed. As the glider descends through a marked wind gradient, there will be a tendency for the glider's airspeed to reduce.

though the attitude looks normal for the approach. The result may well be a stall or a heavy landing before, or as you attempt the round out.

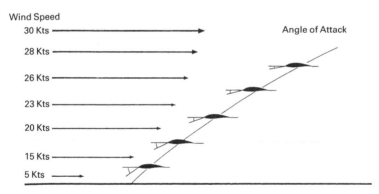

Fig 14.18   Increased angle of attack due to the wind gradient. As the glider descends through the wind gradient, any reduction in airspeed and subsequent reduction in lift will result in the glider meeting the relative airflow at an increasing angle.

As the glider descends at an increasing rate through the wind gradient, the glider will not only be losing airspeed but will also be following an approach path which will meet with the ground short of the landing area. If you attempt to correct this situation by raising the nose of the glider, you will accentuate the problem by reducing airspeed and groundspeed still further. The only action available will be to **CLOSE THE AIRBRAKES** to reduce the rate of descent and if height allows, **LOWER THE GLIDER'S NOSE** to maintain or even restore airspeed. Some wind gradients will be so steep that, once encountered, even lowering the glider's nose considerably will not restore the desired approach speed. (Fig 14.19)

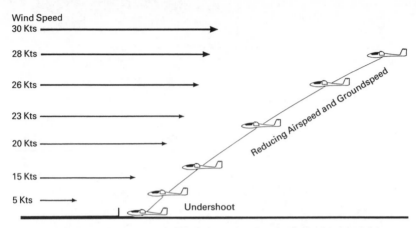

Fig 14.19   The wind gradient causing an undershoot. The high rate of descent
caused by the wind gradient can result in an undershoot.

The situation described is one that is best avoided and the only way to do
so is to:

a)   Anticipate the presence of a wind gradient in strong winds, taking into
account the wind direction and the terrain around the landing area.

b)   Allow extra airspeed at the beginning of the approach. Perhaps as
much as 10 or 15 knots in some cases and monitor the airspeed
indicator regularly.

c)   Begin the approach higher and closer to the landing area than normal.

d)   Avoid large amounts of airbrake during round out. (Remember that
the wind gradient is most pronounced lower down and that the faster
you descend through it, the more pronounced its effect.)

e)   Plan to land well into the landing area. (Do not worry about using up
too much runway; remember that in strong headwinds you will stop
in less distance.)

f)   Do not confuse the rapid rate of descent on the approach on windy
days with ordinary descending air. Gliders tend to fly through ordinary
"sink", but wind gradient effect goes all the way to the ground.

Probably the most dramatic effect of the wind gradient, and certainly just
as dangerous as the loss of airspeed on the approach, is the effect which
the wind gradient has on a steeply banked glider. A glider making a turn
will have one wing tip lower than the other. In a steeply banked turn the
lower wing tip may be as much as 30 to 40 feet below the upper wing tip.
In strong wind gradient conditions, such a turn made into wind (as when
turning on to the final approach) will mean that each wing is in a different
wind speed band and that there is a different speed of airflow over each
wing. This may mean as much as 10 to 15 knots more airspeed at the upper
wing tip of a glider which has a large wingspan.

The faster airflow over the upper wing will be producing more lift than the
reduced airflow over the lower wing. This will result initially in a tendency
to over-bank, possibly followed by difficulty in levelling the wings at the

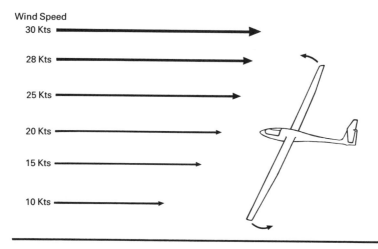

Fig 14.20   *Turning in a wind gradient. A wind gradient can make it difficult to control a steeply-banked glider.*

end of the turn, as the reduced airflow over the lower wing may result in aileron control being inadequate to counter the tipping effect of the wind gradient.

Again the only safeguard against this effect is avoidance. In addition to the previous advice on preventing wind gradient problems, never allow yourself to get into a position where you have to carry out a low turn, *especially* in windy conditions.

Launching in wind gradient conditions also has its problems and although these are very similar to those discussed above, they will be dealt with in the chapters on launching.

SOARING WINDS

Now before you decide that only a madman would want to fly in any wind stronger than a breeze, we will end this chapter with a brief look at a couple of good reasons for flying in windy conditions.

The fact that the wind is deflected upwards when it meets a hill or mountain allows the glider pilot to use this rising air to keep his glider aloft for long periods. In its simplest form this is called HILL SOARING and is the easiest type of soaring to master. Generally the stronger the wind, the stronger the rising air currents.

A further effect which hills and mountains have on a moving air mass occurs after the wind has passed over the high ground. If meteorological conditions are favourable, the whole air mass will be caused to follow a waving motion which may continue for 100 miles or more downwind of the ridge and up as high as 50,000 feet. Again the glider pilot can use these air currents to climb to considerable altitudes, in what can be beautifully smooth, fast-rising air. Once you have discovered this type of soaring, known as WAVE SOARING, you will gladly go gliding in a gale!

113

CHAPTER 15

WIRE LAUNCHING

WIRE LAUNCHING is the name given to the group of launch methods which employ a very long steel cable and launch vehicles which, unlike the tow-planes used when aerotowing, remain on the ground throughout the launch. Wire launching includes winch, car and reverse pulley launching.

WINCH LAUNCHING

Despite the first impression which many people get from watching a winch launch from the ground, winch launching is not as dramatic a method of launch as it looks. Neither is it difficult to master, with much of the success of the winch launch (measured in terms of height gained by the end of the launch) depending as much on the winch driver and the equipment as the skill of the pilot.

That is not to say that the pilot's technique is not crucial in gaining the best possible height from the launch. The way in which the pilot handles the glider during the launch will not only be reflected in the height achieved, but also on the safety of the glider in the event of the launch cable breaking or the winch itself failing.

The best way to cover the components and techniques of winch launching is to start at the beginning and follow the various stages of the launch to the point of release at the top of the launch.

CONNECTING THE LAUNCH CABLE

With the glider lined up at the launch point and after the pre-take-off checks have been completed, the launch cable is attached to the glider.

The end of the launch cable is fitted with specially designed attachments for winch or car launching.

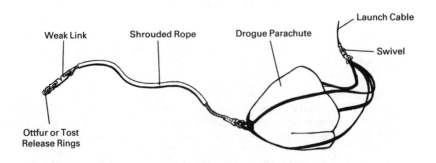

Fig 15.1   The glider end of a winch launch cable.

114

The two steel rings at the end of the assembly, which are common to all methods of launch, are designed to fit into the glider's release hook. (These rings are known as OTTFUR or TOST rings, depending on their design.) The rope attaching the rings to the parachute should be long enough so as to avoid any possibility of the parachute becoming tangled with the glider's nose skid or wheel should the glider over-run the rope slightly at the beginning of the launch. The rope itself, which will also act as a shock absorber, will be protected or stiffened with a plastic shroud to prevent it fouling the glider in such an event. The parachute, which will remain closed during the ascent, is included in the system to deploy after the glider releases the cable at the top of the launch, thus giving the winch driver time to wind in the cable evenly and under some tension. A WEAK LINK, designed to break if the load on the cable exceeds a pre-determined value, is included in the assembly to prevent excessive loads being placed on the glider during the launch. This weak link may be colour coded to show its strength. Different types of glider require different strengths of weak link to be fitted and the colour coding assists this matching.

Only at the request of the pilot is the cable attached to the glider. To do this the pilot calls "Cable On" and pulls the cable release knob in the cockpit. An assistant inserts the smaller of the two rings at the end of the cable into the release mechanism and calls "Close". After the cable has been attached and tested with a gentle pull on the rope to confirm that the ring is secure and yet free to move within the release hook, the assistant can announce that the cable is "On and Secure". Once the helper has moved away from in front of the glider, and the take-off path is clear, the launch can begin.

LAUNCH SIGNALS

The launch can only be initiated by verbal instructions from the launch point controller.

Only when the pilot is ready to be launched should he/she allow the launch cable to be attached, as the acceptance of the launch cable is recognised by the launch point controller as the pilot's "go-ahead" for the launch to begin. In two-seat gliders, it is essential that both pilots have agreed that they are ready for launch before the request to attach the launch cable is made.

The cable should never be attached without the permission of the pilot, for instance, by using any external mechanism (such as on the Bocian or Pirat gliders) or the automatic back-release mechanism.

On seeing the cable is attached the launch point controller will assume charge of the launch and give the following calls to the pilot and the person responsible for signalling to the winch driver.

"ALL CLEAR ABOVE AND BEHIND?"

The launch point controller is expected to check that there is nothing occurring behind the glider, and therefore out of sight of the pilot, before confirming that it is "all clear above and behind". The most likely reason for delaying the launch at this point is if a glider is landing or likely to overfly the launch point, or perhaps if someone is standing too close to the glider's tail. Only if it is clear should the launch commence.

"TAKE UP SLACK"

This command instructs the signaller to signal the winch driver to slowly take the slack out of the launch cable so as not to jerk the glider when launch power is applied at the winch. Once this has been achieved the cable will be taut and any further pull from the winch will result in the glider moving forwards.

"ALL OUT"

This is the last command necessary from the launch point controller to commence the launch. Once the signal resulting from this instruction has been received by the winch driver, power is applied at the winch and the glider is accelerated down the runway and into the air.

"STOP"

All of the preceding commands must come only from the launch point controller. However, there is one command that can be given by *anyone* who sees a problem or perceives a danger in allowing the launch to commence. That command is "STOP". On hearing someone shout "stop" the signaller will give a "stop" signal to the winch and the pilot should release the launch cable from the glider, thus preventing the launch from continuing.

When the launch point controller calls out a command, the signaller should repeat the call and start signalling to the winch driver. This has the effect of confirming to the pilot that the required signal is being given thus reducing the need for the pilot to look to see if this is the case. It will also warn everyone at the launch point that a launch is taking place. Hopefully, in this way anyone who was dreamily thinking of going for a stroll in front of the glider or for a chat with its occupant will be alerted.

In practice, the launch point controller may also be the signaller. Even when this is the case, the commands being sent to the winch driver should still be called aloud.

The bat and light signals used at gliding clubs in the United Kingdom are listed below.

Command	Bat Signal	Light Signal
Take up slack	Bat waved from side to side in front of body.	Repeated flashes of light of one second duration with three seconds rest between each flash.
All out	Bat waved from side to side above head.	Repeated quick flashes with one second rest between each flash.
Stop	Bat held stationary, vertically above head.	Light held on.

When you consider that the winch is over half a mile away from the glider, you will understand that it is unlikely that even the Chief Flying Instructor's voice will be heard at such a distance. It is therefore necessary to have some method of relaying the pilot's commands to the winch driver. The usual method of doing this is to use either a signalling bat, or a system of flashing lights. Occasionally a radio or telephone link is used to back up such visual signals, but the problem of engine noise and interference usually makes such systems unsuitable as the primary signalling method. (Such a system must still allow a stop signal to be heard clearly, even when the winch is running at maximum power.)

THE LAUNCH

The launch itself can be regarded as consisting of the following stages:

1. The GROUND RUN.
2. The INITIAL TAKE-OFF.
3. The TRANSITION INTO THE CLIMB.
4. The FULL CLIMB.
5. The RELEASE.

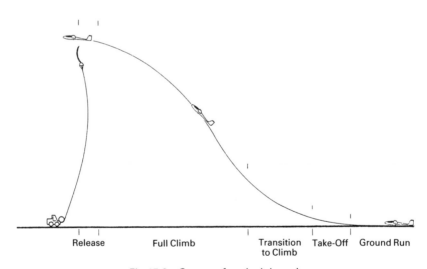

| Release | Full Climb | Transition to Climb | Take-Off | Ground Run |

Fig 15.2 Stages of a winch launch.

THE GROUND RUN

After the "All Out" signal has been given, the glider will begin the ground run, the first part of the launch. The acceleration will be quite rapid and as a result the airspeed and control response will increase quickly. At this stage, you should be ready to prevent the glider leaping into the air in an uncontrolled climb, should the acceleration caused by the winch be too great. With this in mind, the control column should be held forward until the initial acceleration is seen to be reasonable.

During the ground run, which may only last a few seconds if a powerful winch is used, you must keep the wings level using aileron, maintain direction with rudder, and get the glider running along on its main wheel using the elevator.

If there is any crosswind present, you may have to counter any tendency of the glider to swing to either side of the take-off direction by applying as much rudder as necessary. If the glider does start to swing and the rudder proves inadequate to prevent this divergence, you should release the launch cable immediately. Only by doing so can the glider be stopped from gaining the extra speed and momentum which can result in a violent swing. As such a swing can develop rapidly, you should be ready for such an event and keep a hand near (or preferably on) the cable release knob as the launch begins. (This requirement is the reason why hand signals from the pilot should not be used to initiate the launch.)

THE INITIAL TAKE-OFF

The glider will soon become airborne and tend to gain height even in a level attitude. Allow the airspeed to increase to a safe value before allowing the glider to adopt the climb attitude, preventing it, if necessary, from climbing too steeply in the early stages. The ease with which this is achieved will depend on both the power of the winch and the position of the cable release hook relative to the glider's centre of gravity.

A powerful winch will not take long to accelerate the glider and the glider can transition into the climbing attitude as soon as it reaches a reasonable height and has a safe airspeed. A less powerful winch will take longer to provide a safe airspeed for the climb and you may need to keep the glider in an attitude close to the take-off attitude for a longer period, until the required airspeed is achieved.

If the cable release hook is situated well back (close to the glider's centre of gravity) there may be a tendency for the glider to pitch steeply nose up shortly after leaving the ground, thereby adopting the full climb attitude far too soon and before a safe airspeed is reached. This must be prevented. This problem will be lessened if the cable release is further forward.

From the above you will have realised that there is a need to have a high respect for airspeed monitoring. You may think that the airspeed would take a lower priority during the launch as the winch is supplying the forward power. You would be wrong! Let us look at why.

From the understanding you should now have of the stall (Chapter 8) you will know that the angle of attack of the wing must be kept below the stalling angle or else the glider will stall. Your first impression of a winch launch may suggest a very large angle of attack (of say around 70° or 80°). However, as the stalling angle of the wing is typically around 15°, this first impression cannot be correct. The mystery is solved when you recall that the angle of attack concerns the relative airflow and that this has nothing to do with the horizontal.

Fig 15.3 shows the relative airflow and the angle of attack during a winch launch. Notice that the angle of attack is quite small as the glider is not travelling horizontally but upwards at an angle.

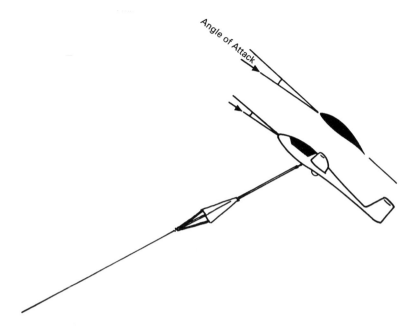

Fig 15.3   The angle of attack during a winch launch.

As the attitude during the launch will vary and is nowhere near the "normal gliding attitude" you will not be able to refer to nose attitude in the same way as during normal flight. Neither will attitude be a good measure of having a safe margin from the stall. The only reference you will have which relates to relative airflow is the glider's airspeed. Each type of glider will have an optimum airspeed for winch launch. This airspeed will lie somewhere between the minimum safe airspeed (as dictated by the likely stalling speed) and the maximum airspeed allowed on the launch, which will be displayed on the limitations placard in the cockpit.

This minimum safe airspeed will be somewhat higher than the airspeed which would give a safe margin over the stalling speed in free flight. This is due to the fact that the same wing area is being asked not only to support

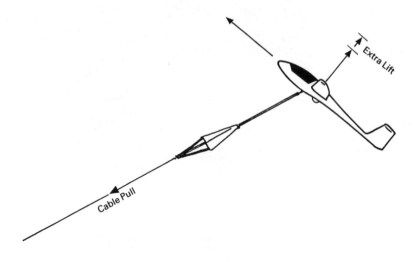

Fig 15.4   Increased stalling speed during a winch launch. The wing is required to produce extra lift during a winch launch, resulting in an increased stalling speed.

the glider's weight, but also the considerable weight of the cable and to some extent the pull from the winch. The glider's stalling speed on the winch launch will therefore be somewhat higher than that during free flight.

The minimum safe airspeed will also give an essential reserve of airspeed in case the power from the winch to the glider is cut suddenly, such as would happen if the launch cable breaks. This extra airspeed will allow you to lower the nose of the glider before the onset of a stall which, if allowed to occur, could have disastrous consequences due to insufficient height being available to effect a recovery.

THE TRANSITION INTO THE CLIMB

Once a safe airspeed and height have been achieved, you can gradually ease the glider into the full climbing attitude, monitoring the airspeed as you do so. It is during this transition that the winch driver is most likely to misjudge the power required from the winch, resulting in the glider having too much or too little airspeed. Also at this point the winch and launch cable are being subjected to a large increase in loading. As a result the transition into the climb is the most likely (and most critical) phase of the launch to have the cable break or a launch failure.

The winch driver judges whether the correct power is being applied mainly by watching the way in which the glider is climbing. If the glider is not adopting a reasonable climbing attitude, the winch driver will assume that insufficient airspeed is being achieved and will increase the winch speed. If you delay the transition into the nose-up attitude of the climb unnecessarily, the end result may well be excessive airspeed due to the winch driver receiving the wrong impression. It is therefore essential that you transition from the attitude at take-off to the climb attitude as soon as it is safe to do so. Otherwise the launch may be too fast and in an extreme case may have to be abandoned to avoid exceeding the maximum winch launch airspeed.

THE FULL CLIMB

The greatest part of the launch occurs with the glider in the full climb attitude. During the full climb, you should attempt to maintain the climbing attitude, only adjusting it if the airspeed dwindles. As the glider nears the top of the launch, the pull of the cable is becoming more vertical and there will be an increased tendency for the nose of the glider to be pulled down from the climbing attitude. To counter this, increased back pressure will be required on the control column.

Depending upon the release hook position, there may also be a tendency for the nose to oscillate up and down slightly, as the top of the launch is approached. This was once thought to be the tailplane stalling, but it is in fact caused by the bow in the cable increasing and decreasing in size, causing variations in the pull being exerted on the glider, with the tailplane trying to compensate for this by taking up the slack in the cable. The initial cause is probably either an unintentional change in pitch angle or a variation in the winch speed. (Fig 15.5)

Should this "hunting" begin, relaxing the back pressure on the control column momentarily may reduce it, but cancelling it completely is an art not a science.

If the cable release hook is near the glider's centre of gravity, the tendency of the nose to be pulled down may not be significant and the elevator control forces will probably be light throughout the launch. The "hunting" tendency in pitch is less likely to be present when such an aft release hook is in use.

During the climb you can check that the wings are level by having an occasional glance at the wing tips. If drift due to wind has to be countered, then one wing can intentionally be held lower than the other. This causes the glider to slip sideways through the air towards the lower wing and

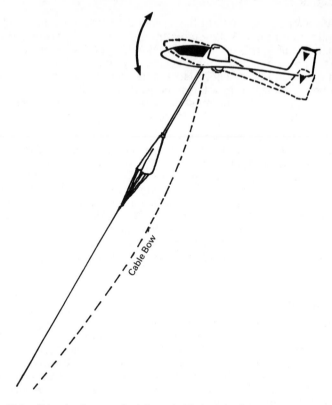

Fig 15.5   "Hunting" on a winch launch. The nose of the glider may oscillate up
and down near the top of the winch launch. Relaxing the backward pressure on
the control column usually stops this.

although sideslipping in this way will reduce the overall height gained on
the launch, if done correctly it will keep the glider in a reasonable position
relative to the runway.

At some airfields, dropping the cable far off of the runway may be
hazardous to third party property and in these circumstances the winch
driver will be forced to curtail the launch if you are not correcting for drift.
Despite this it is preferable not to start correcting for drift until the glider
has settled into the full climb.

THE RELEASE

The top of the launch can be recognised in several ways. You may
recognise that the glider is overhead the winch by reference to the ground
features abeam the winch, or the fact that the rate of climb has reduced
considerably. More often than not, the signal that you have reached the top
of the launch will come from the winch driver, who will cut the power of
the winch. This curtailment of the launch will appear as the airspeed
reducing, and the nose wanting to pitch up.

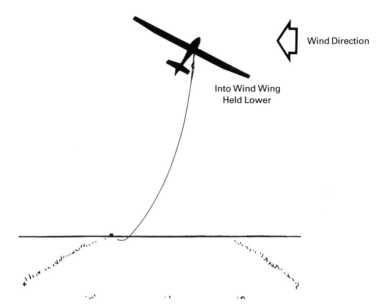

Wind Direction

Into Wind Wing
Held Lower

*Fig 15.6   Correcting for drift on a winch launch. To correct for drift on a winch
launch the into wind wing should be held lower than the other wing.*

Often, as the top of the launch is reached, the cable back-release
mechanism will operate and the cable will automatically be released from
the glider. As well as the resulting loss of pull from the winch, this event
can be clearly heard.

Whether or not the cable releases automatically, when you decide that the
glider is at the end of the launch, the nose of the glider must be lowered
and the cable release knob pulled twice to leave no doubt that the cable
has released.

Lowering the nose of the glider before pulling the release knob means that
a manual release is achieved with less tension on the cable and avoids
loops of cable arriving at the winch and potentially causing problems
during subsequent launches.

After release, the attitude can be readjusted and the glider trimmed. If a
retractable undercarriage is fitted, retracting it should be left until after
releasing the cable at the top of the launch.

LAUNCHING IN A WIND GRADIENT

If the glider is to be launched into a wind gradient the airspeed will increase
quickly and the initial climb will be very rapid. In such conditions it is
difficult for the winch driver to judge the glider's airspeed until the glider
has passed through the worst of the wind gradient, where the wind speed
is more constant. During this early part of the launch the glider should not
be climbed steeply, for if the cable breaks or the launch otherwise fails, the
glider may find itself having to begin a descent through the wind gradient
with insufficient airspeed.

The possibility of a cable break is much increased if a strong wind gradient is present, because the rapid increase in the glider's airspeed increases the loading on the cable. The only safe way to launch through a wind gradient is cautiously and never steeply.

TOO FAST SIGNAL

If the glider's airspeed is approaching the maximum airspeed allowed during a winch launch, you can signal this fact to the winch driver by yawing the tail of the glider from side to side by applying alternate rudder. This "too fast" signal should only be given after lowering the nose slightly, as it is unwise to apply large amounts of rudder with the glider still in the full climb attitude. If the cable were to break while the glider is in this high nose-up attitude, with yaw being applied at the same time, the glider is well set up to find itself not only stalled but, even worse, in a spin. Generally, the "too fast" signal should not be given at too early a stage of the launch, thus allowing the winch driver time to adjust the winch speed after the transition into the climb has been made.

It should be remembered that this signal should be given as the airspeed is approaching the maximum launch airspeed permitted and not when the placarded airspeed limit is reached or exceeded. If the limiting launch airspeed is reached, you should lower the nose, release the cable and abandon the launch.

CAR LAUNCHING

Car launching is very similar to winch launching and in general the same signals, techniques and considerations apply. However, there are some subtle differences which are important to recognise, especially if you are trained on winch launch and are converting to car launch or vice versa.

The main difference is in the initial acceleration. Unlike the winch, which only has to accelerate the glider, the tow car also has to accelerate itself. The result is a more sedate launch in the initial stages where the ground run will be longer, as will be the period before the transition into the full climb can be made. Given that a long enough runway is available, the car launch can achieve almost the same height as a winch launch. This is due to the glider not actually arriving overhead the tow car to the same extent or as early as it would on a winch launch. This is because, unlike the winch, the car is moving forwards all of the time and the length of cable remains the same. There is therefore less "pull down" tendency as the top of the launch is approached, and so, unlike the winch launch, where the amount of height gained during the last part of the launch is relatively small, on a car launch, the glider can still achieve a good rate of climb late in the launch.

REVERSE PULLEY LAUNCHING

Reverse pulley launching, generally used where a hard surfaced runway is available, but is not long enough or wide enough to allow straight car launching, gives a launch which has some of the characteristics of both a winch launch and a car launch.

Its similarities with car launching mean that initial acceleration is slower than winch launching, creating a need for a more gentle transition into the climb. The "pull down" and "pitching " tendencies at the top of the winch launch are present since the pulley system around which the cable runs is in a fixed position at the end of the runway, creating an increasingly vertical pull as the launch nears its end.

SUMMARY

Whichever of the wire launch methods is used, each has its own advantages and disadvantages and often the system chosen will be forced upon the operation by circumstance.

All of these methods can produce reliable, satisfactory launching, providing good care is taken of the launch equipment. When it comes to that part of your training requiring special attention to approaches and landings, wire launching is most cost effective and has the advantage of allowing repeated attempts without incurring the higher costs of aerotows.

Lastly, when you are at the stage of learning to fly a wire launch, you can gain a great deal when you are on the ground by watching other gliders as they climb on the launch. Subsequent discussion with your instructor can give you a better idea of what you are trying to achieve during your launches.

AIR EXERCISE – WIRE LAUNCHING

STAGE 1

Your instructor will demonstrate how to fly the wire launch.

STAGE 2

Your instructor will fly the first part of the launch and once the glider is established in the climb, you will be allowed to take control and attempt the rest of the launch and the release.

STAGE 3

You will be allowed to attempt the whole launch.

CHAPTER 16

AEROTOW LAUNCHING

AEROTOW LAUNCHING (or AEROTOWING) is the name given to pulling the glider into the air behind an aeroplane (known as the TOW-PLANE or simply the TUG). The two aircraft are coupled by a rope, called the TOW-ROPE.

Fig 16.1   The versatile aerotow launch. An aerotow launch can deliver the glider to a particular part of the sky at a chosen height.

Aerotowing has several advantages over wire launching. Whereas wire launching is ideal for landing-related training exercises which do not require great launch heights, aerotowing can guarantee a choice of launch height, providing cloud and controlled airspace permit. This makes aerotowing ideal for exercises which require height (such as stall or spin recovery training) or a reasonable practice time (as do the early handling exercises).

With an aerotow, the tow-plane can deliver the glider to a chosen part of the sky, perhaps miles from the home airfield, and place it in an area of rising air. There is even the added advantage that a glider can be fetched back to its own airfield (or RETRIEVED) from a landing away from base at another airfield or even from a farmer's field by aerotow.

Aerotowing is therefore a very versatile method of launch and one which every glider pilot should seek to learn, even if this means visiting another gliding club which uses this method of launch in order to do so.

THE TOW-PLANE

The tow-plane, being a powered aircraft, will be of a type approved by the national aviation authorities as being suitable to perform this task. As a result, its pilot will have to hold a licence which entitles him or her to operate this type of aeroplane. The only modification which the towing aircraft must have is a special release mechanism fitted at its tail. This mechanism allows the tow-rope to be connected to the tow-plane. It also allows the tow-rope to be released by operating a control in the tow-plane's cockpit. The tow-plane will also be fitted with a mirror so that its pilot can observe the glider.

CONNECTING THE TOW-ROPE

Once the glider has been lined up and the pre-flight checks have been completed, the tow-rope can be attached to the glider.

The tow-rope assembly is much simpler than the assembly at the end of a winch or car launch wire, and consists mainly of a rope which is around 180 feet (55 metres) long. The two steel rings at the glider end of the rope are of the same type used for wire launching. There will also be a similar set of rings at the other end of the tow-rope to allow it to be attached to the tow-plane. The assembly is completed by the inclusion of suitable weak links, which prevent excessive loads being transmitted to either the glider's release hook fittings or to the tow-plane.

The smaller of the two steel rings is attached to the glider's release hook, which may be the same hook as is used for wire launching. However, on many gliders a specific release hook is fitted for aerotowing. This mechanism, if fitted, will be situated further forward than the wire launch release hook and should be used, as it will make the glider easier to fly on the aerotow launch. The technique for connecting the tow-rope is the same as for the winch launch, described in the previous chapter.

LAUNCH SIGNALS

The acceptance of the tow-rope being attached to the glider will be taken by the launch point controller as the pilot being ready to launch. On seeing that the cable is attached and that the area in front of the glider is clear, the launch point controller will give the calls which will begin the launch.

The commands and signals which begin an aerotow launch are identical to those given to start a wire launch. (See Chapter 15.) As with wire launching, only the launch point controller can initiate the launch by issuing the verbal commands "All Clear Above and Behind", "Take Up Slack" and "All Out". These commands must be given loudly and clearly.

Any person suspecting that the launch cannot be carried out safely should shout "Stop", at which point the launch should be terminated and the pilot should release the tow-rope from the glider.

No signals should be given if the path in front of the tow-plane and glider is not clear or if there are any objects which will become a hazard if the glider swings to one side on take-off.

The launch point controller's commands are normally relayed visually to the tow-plane pilot. This is achieved by a signaller near the glider (often the same person who is supporting the wing) who will relay the command to a forward signaller, who is positioned well forward and to one side of the tow-plane. These signals are the same as those used for wire launching, but as the distances involved are much less, the signallers can use arm movements instead of bats.

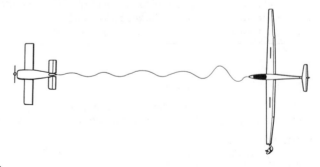

  Forward Signaller

Fig 16.2   The aerotow launch point.

Light signals or a radio link may be used as a relay to the tow-plane pilot instead of a forward signaller. The arm and light signals used in the United Kingdom are shown below.

Command	Arm Signal	Light Signal
Take up slack	Arm waved from side to side in front of body.	Repeated flashes of light of one second duration with three seconds rest between each flash.
All out	Arm waved from side to side above head.	Repeated quick flashes with one second rest between each flash.
Stop	Arm held stationary, vertically above head.	Light held on.

If a radio link is used, it should be operated by launch point personnel and not directly between the glider pilot and the tow-plane pilot. It is unwise that the glider pilot transmits directly to the tow-plane pilot as this has the following implications which may be detrimental to safety:

a)   The glider pilot's commands will not be heard except by the tow-plane pilot. Therefore persons near the glider are not warned that a launch is beginning.

b) The glider pilot can do without fumbling for or trying to stow a microphone as the launch begins.

c) If the glider is jerked at the beginning of the launch, its pilot's hand would be better employed operating the cable release than holding a microphone.

THE LAUNCH

The launch itself can be divided into five distinct stages.

1. The GROUND RUN

2. The TAKE-OFF

3. The TRANSITION INTO THE CLIMB

4. The CLIMB

5. The RELEASE

THE GROUND RUN

The first part of the aerotow launch is the GROUND RUN. During this stage the glider will be accelerated relatively slowly to its take-off airspeed. During the early part of the ground run, the controls will be very unresponsive, requiring large control inputs in order to keep the wings level, and the glider running in a straight line behind the tow-plane. At this stage the elevator may not be capable of lifting the tail (or the nose, depending on the glider) in order to balance the glider on its main wheel. The person holding the wing tip is invaluable at this stage and should be capable of running several paces while supporting the wing.

As the glider accelerates, the controls will become more effective and the wings can be maintained level with aileron and the glider kept in line behind the tow-plane with rudder. These control inputs will be independent of each other and unco-ordinated until the glider leaves the ground. The elevator will soon become effective and the glider can easily be kept running along the ground on just its main wheel.

During the ground run, do not hesitate to use as much rudder as is necessary to prevent any tendency of the glider to swing to either side. If a swing should occur, or if a wing should drop onto the ground, you should release the tow-rope immediately. Ideally, you should keep your hand on the cable release knob until full control has been achieved, and the possibility of a ground loop has passed.

THE INITIAL TAKE-OFF

Once the glider is travelling fast enough, it will become airborne. You will find that little or no control input is necessary to achieve this, providing the glider has been kept running on its main wheel during the latter part of the ground run.

With most tow-planes, the glider will become airborne before the tow-plane. It is necessary to prevent the glider from climbing away from the ground until the tow-plane itself becomes airborne and starts to climb. At this stage the glider should be kept within a few feet of the ground, but you should not attempt to keep it too close to the ground, as this is unnecessary and can prove difficult. From the moment the glider is in the air, co-ordinated control inputs will be required to keep the glider in position behind the tow-plane. Any drift experienced due to the effects of wind must be countered using co-ordinated control movements.

From this stage onwards, it is essential that your full concentration is focused on the job in hand, that is, following the tow-plane. Do not allow yourself to be distracted. There will be lots of time later for closing noisy fresh air vents, fiddling with instruments and retracting the undercarriage.

The tow-plane will continue to accelerate until it reaches its take-off airspeed. This acceleration will result in the glider's controls becoming increasingly responsive, and the glider's wing producing more lift. The resulting tendency of the glider to climb must be prevented, for at best, it will prevent the tow-plane from getting airborne, and at worst could pull the tow-plane's tail upwards causing its propeller to strike the ground.

Fig 16.3   The take-off on aerotow. The glider will often become airborne before the tow-plane. Don't allow the glider to get too high.

Even after the tow-plane has left the ground, it must continue to accelerate to an airspeed at which it can climb safely. This will mean that the controls of the glider will continue to increase their sensitivity and you will have to be careful not to over-control, especially in pitch. This phase of the launch will not last long and soon the tow-plane will start to climb. You must anticipate this and be ready to follow the tow-plane into the climb. If you are slow to react when the tow-plane starts its climb, do not worry. Just take your time and try to follow it. Never rush to get back up behind the tow-plane, as it is all too easy to overdo the control input required, resulting in the much more dangerous situation of going too high above the tow-plane or a series of overcorrections suitably called PILOT INDUCED OSCILLATIONS (PIOs).

Fig 16.4   Aerotowing – combination just airborne. Once both the tow-plane and glider are airborne, maintain position behind the tow-plane.

THE FULL CLIMB

Once the combination is established in the full climb, the aim is to keep the glider in position behind the tow-plane. The lateral position is maintained using co-ordinated aileron and rudder inputs. Due to the higher airspeed on aerotow, the controls will be more sensitive than in slower, free flight, and so only small control movements will normally be required.

The vertical position of the glider relative to the tow-plane is best judged by referring to the tow-plane's position relative to the horizon. The glider should be kept in a position where the whole of the tow-plane appears to be slightly above the horizon. This is known as the NORMAL TOW POSITION. In this position the glider will be flying just above the turbulent air of the tow-plane's PROPELLER WASH (often referred to as the TOW-PLANE'S SLIPSTREAM).

Fig 16.5   The normal tow position. In the normal tow position the glider is just above the tow-plane's propeller wash.

You will soon get used to this position and what it looks like. In bad visibility, where no distinct horizon can be seen, you can confirm that you are in the correct position by moving the glider down until you can feel the tow-plane's propeller wash and then reposition the glider back up slightly.

The glider being in too low a position creates no problems for the tow-plane pilot. There is a huge margin for manoeuvre from the normal tow position downwards to a position well below the tow-plane's propeller wash. (Fig 16.6)

On the other hand, if the glider gets too high, then this situation can quickly become critical, for at an early stage you will lose sight of the tow-plane and the risk of pulling the tow-plane's tail upwards exists. This TOW-PLANE UPSET, as it has become known, can result in the tow-plane pilot losing control of his aircraft completely. This event is even more likely if the glider rapidly goes into too high a position. Due to the dangers

131

involved for the tow-plane, it is essential that, if you lose sight of the tow-plane, or if you are diverging upwards rapidly above the normal tow position, you RELEASE THE TOW-ROPE IMMEDIATELY.

Given that the glider is only slightly high, the normal position can be regained by gently easing the glider downwards until once again in the correct position to the tow-plane

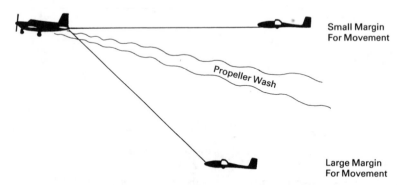

Fig 16.6   Margins for vertical movement behind tow-plane. You can manoeuvre downwards a long way without causing problems for the tow-plane pilot but getting high can quickly become hazardous.

TURNING WHILE ON AEROTOW

During the full climb, the tow-plane pilot will normally make a series of gentle turns, in order to keep the glider within gliding range of the airfield. As the tow-plane turns, you should follow it by banking the glider's wings to approximately the same angle as the tow-plane's wings. If you find that the glider is tending to turn faster than the tow-plane (that is, inside of the tow-plane's turn) then the glider's nose can be pointed slightly towards the tow-plane's outer wing tip. All of these turns should be made with co-ordinated control movements, remembering to take care not to over-control.

THE EFFECT OF TURBULENCE

Any turbulence encountered during the aerotow will be seen to affect the tow-plane first and so the behaviour of the tow-plane can act as an advanced warning of what you can expect a couple of seconds later. Should a gust cause the tow-plane to rise or descend rapidly, do not over-react by chasing the tow-plane, as the glider will soon fly into the same gust. Chasing such divergences can lead to problems if, for instance, the glider having moved up to maintain its position behind the tow-plane, then hits the same updraught which lifted the tow-plane originally, thus causing the glider to be in too high a position. The problem is compounded if the tow-plane simultaneously encounters a neighbouring downdraught, leaving the glider in an even higher position relative to the tow-plane.

Fig 16.7   Turning on aerotow. When turning, match the glider's bank with that of the tow-plane.

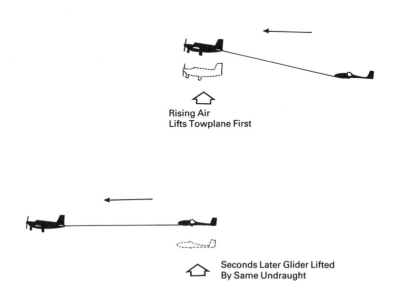

Rising Air
Lifts Towplane First

Seconds Later Glider Lifted
By Same Undraught

Fig 16.8   Encountering rising air on aerotow. Don't overreact if the tow-plane flies through rising air – the same updraught will soon affect the glider.

133

REGAINING POSITION AFTER A LATERAL DISPLACEMENT

While getting high behind the tow-plane is critical, losing position to the left or right of the tow-plane's centre-line is less of a worry, providing that is, that this lateral displacement does not become extreme. Should the glider become slightly displaced to the side (e.g. to the left) then, provided the wings are kept parallel to the tow-plane's wings, there will be a tendency for the rope to pull the glider back towards the central position. As the glider approaches the desired position, a small amount of bank may have to be applied momentarily to the left, to prevent the glider overshooting the central position.

A larger displacement to either side will require the glider to be banked towards the central position, until the glider moves back towards this desired position. As this position is approached, the bank will need to be reversed momentarily to prevent the glider overshooting the central position.

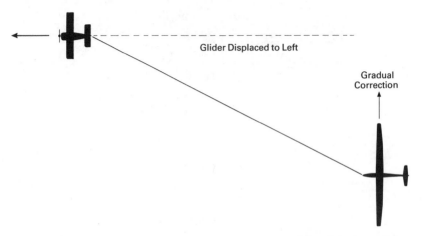

Glider Displaced to Left

Gradual Correction

Fig 16.9   Correcting lateral displacement on aerotow. If the glider becomes displaced to one side, gentle control movements are all that are normally required.

If the glider is out of position both laterally and vertically, do not attempt to adjust both at once. Firstly, stabilise the glider and then adjust its vertical position. Once that has been stabilised, gently remove the lateral displacement. Never rush any corrections or you may start a sideways oscillation which will make life difficult.

Should the glider's lateral displacement be very large, or increase to the extent that any bow forming in the tow-rope could come close to any part of the glider, the tow-rope should be released immediately.

THE RELEASE

The glider pilot is normally responsible for determining the height at which the release of the tow-rope takes place. When you decide that you wish to release the tow-rope, you should follow this sequence of events.

1. Lookout
2. Normal position behind tow-plane
3. Pull release and observe tow-rope go
4. Clearing turn
5. Adjust airspeed and re-trim
6. Orientate

1. Lookout

As the release sequence will involve a turning manoeuvre, the need for a thorough lookout is essential. A good tow-plane pilot will attempt to take the glider to an area where rising air is likely to be found. This is also likely to be an area full of other gliders.

2. Normal Position Behind Tow-plane

Ideally, the release should be carried out while the glider is in the normal tow position. However, this is not essential and in the event of sight of the tow-plane being lost, or any other emergency or extreme position occurring, you should release the tow-rope immediately irrespective of the glider's position relative to the tow-plane.

3. Pull Release Knob and Observe Tow-rope Go

To release, the cable release knob should be pulled and the tow-rope seen to have detached before any manoeuvre is started. It does not matter if the tow-rope is slack or taut just before release. No attempt should be made to increase the tension on the tow-rope before releasing.

4. Clearing Turn

The glider should begin a climbing turn as soon as the tow-rope has been seen to have become detached from the glider. The purpose of this turn is to increase the clearance from the steel rings at the end of the tow-rope, and also to make it clear to the tow-plane pilot that the glider has released. It also has the advantage of converting excess airspeed into height.

This turn does not need to be a complete 360° turn. In fact, a well-banked turn taking the glider just off to one side is better, because as well as fulfilling the two aims mentioned, such a turn also allows the tow-plane to be kept in sight and will not result in the glider speeding off downwind if the wind is strong. The direction of this turn may be subject to local or national rules, but in the United Kingdom, it is at the glider pilot's discretion. (This allows for joining other circling gliders and hill soaring traffic.)

If you have been trained on wire launching only, your instinctive action on releasing the cable will be to lower the glider's nose. DO NOT LOWER THE GLIDER'S NOSE, or else you may catch up with the end of the tow-rope and have a close encounter with the steel release rings. Do not worry about stalling, as, unlike the wire launch release, the airspeed will be adequate or even excessive at the moment of release from the aerotow.

5. Adjust Airspeed and Re-trim

Once clear of the tow-plane, the glider can be settled to its new airspeed and re-trimmed. Should a retractable undercarriage be fitted, it is at this point that it should be retracted.

6. Orientate

After the release, it is necessary to orientate yourself, so that you know exactly where the airfield is. Normally, for training and local soaring, the tow-plane pilot will have kept the glider close to or upwind of the airfield. If, on release, you cannot immediately see the airfield or recognise a local feature, then just be patient, make sure that you are not flying the glider too fast, and, if there is a wind of any strength, that you are not flying downwind. Once you have time to get your bearings, you will probably see the airfield. Do not forget to look immediately below and behind the glider as this is a typical blind spot where airfields hide from early pilots! On a hazy day, the glare from the sun may make the airfield difficult to see if it is in the direction of the sun. As on these low visibility days there is usually little wind, it may help to fly a short distance into sun, as the airfield may be just out of sight as a result of glare. Once you are looking away from the sun, it will be easier to see ground features which are further away.

TOW-ROPE LENGTHS

The length of the tow-rope used will vary from one gliding club to another. The recommended minimum length in the United Kingdom is 150 feet, (46 metres) although longer tow-ropes are advised, as they make aerotowing easier and safer.

This is because it is the angle of the force exerted on the tow-plane by the glider which can cause problems. This angle will be reached with smaller lateral or vertical displacements from the ideal towing position with shorter tow-ropes. With longer tow-ropes, the glider can be further out of position without reaching a critical angle to the tow-plane.

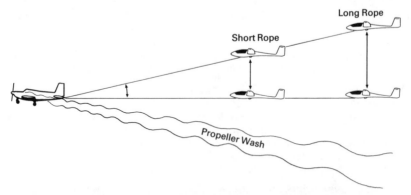

Fig 16.10 The effect of tow-rope length when aerotowing. The longer the tow-rope the greater any displacement can be without causing the tow-plane pilot problems.

LOW TOW POSITION

The normal tow position, with the glider being flown above the tow-plane's propeller wash, is one of two tow positions in use. The second is called the LOW TOW POSITION, where the glider is flown in a position below the tow-plane's propeller wash. This position, which is a more stable situation than the normal tow position, is used in some countries as the standard aerotowing technique (most notably Australia).

To place the glider in the low tow position from the normal tow, the glider is simply moved down through the turbulent air of the tow-plane's propeller wash into the calmer air below. A considerable forward force on the control column will be required to hold this position and if it is to be maintained for any length of time, forward re-trimming will be necessary.

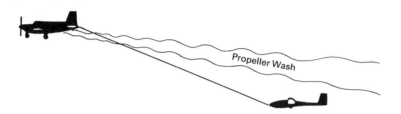

Fig 16.11   The low tow position. In the low tow position the glider flies just below the tow-plane's propeller wash.

As an exercise in aerotow handling, the low tow position can be approached from the normal tow by flying around the tow-plane's propeller wash without allowing the glider to come into contact with this turbulent air. When this exercise is continued to place the glider back in the normal tow position by flying the glider all the way round the tow-plane's propeller wash, it is given the name BOXING THE TOW.

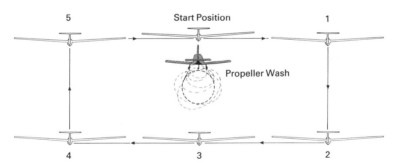

Fig 16.12   "Boxing the tow" involves flying the glider around the tow-plane's propeller wash.

Whether aerotowing is the first method of launch which you are taught, or whether you convert to it after mastering wire launching, you will find that before you become adept at it, you must be able to control the glider reasonably well in free flight. For this reason it is normally taught much later than you might expect. Do not worry if your instructor delays allowing you to attempt some of the aerotow until after you have done quite a few flights, as the better your general handling, the easier you will find aerotowing. This is because aerotowing is, in effect, formation flying, albeit with the formation tied together. The secret of successful aerotowing is to concentrate totally on the tow-plane and anticipate what it will do next. Remember, that if it starts to bank, a turn will follow and that any gust which the tow-plane encounters will soon affect the glider.

AIR EXERCISE – AEROTOW LAUNCHING

STAGE 1

Your instructor will demonstrate how to fly the aerotow launch including how to regain position behind the tow-plane, the position of the tow-plane's propeller wash and the release procedure.

STAGE 2

Your instructor will fly the first part of the launch and once the glider is established in the climb, you will be allowed to take control and attempt the rest of the launch and the release.

STAGE 3

Your instructor will allow you to attempt more of the launch until eventually you will be allowed to attempt the whole launch.

STAGE 4

Having mastered the whole of the aerotow launch, you will practise manoeuvring the glider out of position and then returning it to the normal towing position. Eventually, as an exercise in controlling the glider while on aerotow, you will be expected to manoeuvre the glider all the way around the tow-plane's propeller wash.

CHAPTER 17

CIRCUIT PLANNING

You now know that in order to land the glider accurately, it is necessary to fly an approach, which will allow you to keep the glider tracking towards the landing area, and also to make the final adjustments to your rate of descent. To enable you to do this, you firstly must fly the glider into a position from where you can begin the approach.

The route you take to this point must satisfy the following criteria:

- It must keep you within easy gliding range of the landing area, bearing in mind, that the glider can only travel a certain distance from a given height. (This distance will of course, be dependent on any wind present.)

- It must allow you to keep the landing area in view for the maximum period possible.

- It must allow for other traffic and make your intentions clear to other aircraft.

- It must result in the glider being lined up with the approach path. This should be achieved by the time the glider is no lower than twice the height of a tall tree.

The route which fulfils these requirements is called the CIRCUIT and consists of 3 sections or LEGS. (Fig 17.1)

1. The DOWNWIND LEG

2. The BASE or CROSSWIND LEG

3. The APPROACH

Before it is possible to fly a circuit, you must decide where you intend to land. Only once you have decided where exactly you intend to land, can you decide where the circuit will begin, as all of the decisions and adjustments to track will be made with direct reference to your landing area. **Your landing area will be your prime reference when judging your progress while flying the circuit.**

During training, the landing area will probably be a familiar part of your own airfield, but later it may be on a strange airfield or part of a farmer's field. For this reason it is important that, from your first attempts at planning a circuit, you concentrate on your position and height relative to the landing area and not to any familiar local features. Such secondary features will include roads, villages or farms, or even the upwind end of the runway on which you may be landing. In order to illustrate this requirement, the diagrams given in this section deal with a landing area in an irregular shaped field.

Due to the fact that a landing away from base will involve a landing area which is higher or lower than your own airfield, height while flying the circuit should be judged visually, and not read from the altimeter, whose datum will have been set to either airfield level or sea level and not relative

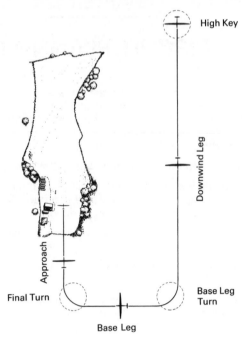

Fig 17.1   Typical circuit pattern.

to your new landing area. The altimeter is also a relatively inaccurate instrument, with a lot of mechanical lag. For this reason, you will find that the best way to judge height in the circuit is by the changing appearance of familiar objects, such as buildings and trees. This is especially so as the glider gets lower and height judgement becomes critical.

These two habits, if formed early in your training, will be invaluable later in your gliding, when you fly cross-country or inadvertently land away from base.

While flying in the circuit, you will be able to assess the general wind direction and its likely effect on the glider during the approach and landing. This can be done, not only by observing local indicators such as windsocks or smoke, but also the way in which the glider is drifting as you try to fly the downwind and base legs.

PLANNING AND FLYING THE IDEAL CIRCUIT

Having selected your landing area you can fly the glider to the beginning of the DOWNWIND LEG. Ideally, the downwind leg will begin some distance upwind of the landing area and well to one side.

You may occasionally hear a pilot talking about the HIGH KEY POINT. This is just another name for the starting point of the downwind leg. The downwind leg will take the glider on a track which is parallel, but in the opposite direction to the approach and landing direction.

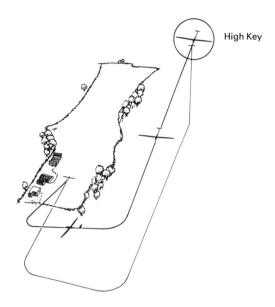

High Key

Fig 17.2   The high key point. Position of the high key point relative to the landing area.

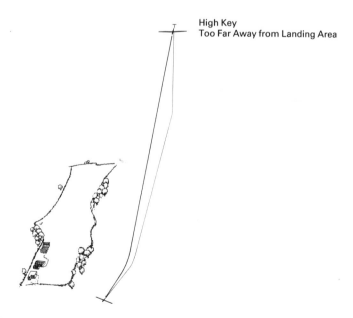

High Key
Too Far Away from Landing Area

Fig 17.3   High key point too far away. Starting the downwind leg too far from the landing area will risk the glider running out of height before reaching the landing area.

Beginning the downwind leg too far from the landing area will risk the glider running short of height before reaching the chosen landing area.

Starting the downwind leg too close to the landing area will reduce the time available to prepare for the landing and will result in the landing area going out of sight behind the glider at an early stage.

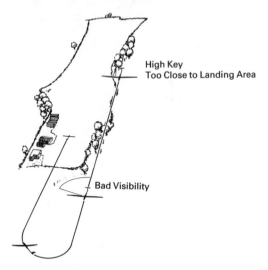

Fig 17.4   High key point too close. Starting the downwind leg too close to the landing area will reduce the time available for track adjustments and result in the landing area disappearing behind the glider at an earlier stage.

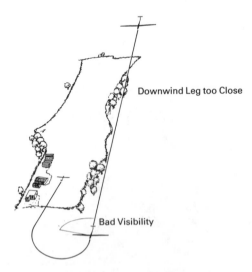

Fig 17.5   Downwind leg too close. Flying the downwind leg too close in will reduce the time available for track adjustments and result in the landing area disappearing behind the glider at an earlier stage.

Flying too close a downwind leg will also make the landing area difficult to see and can reduce the time for manoeuvring at the lower (downwind) end of the circuit, potentially creating the need for low, tight turns.

A downwind leg flown too far out will again risk the glider not having enough height to reach the landing area.

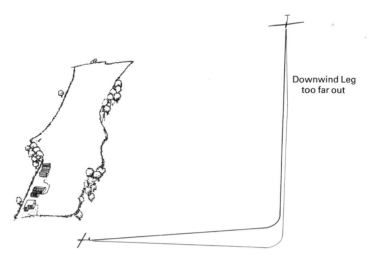

Downwind Leg too far out

Fig 17.6   Downwind leg too far out. Flying the downwind leg too far out will risk the glider running out of height.

While heights for starting the downwind leg can be suggested, such heights are totally dependent on the starting point chosen, the glider's performance, the weather conditions prevailing and perhaps even terrain and local rules. For this reason, any heights given here should be regarded as approximations and will only apply to that mythical beast, "the ideal circuit".

DOWNWIND CHECKS

Once established on the downwind leg, you should begin preparing yourself and the glider for the landing. This is normally done by carrying out a series of checks covering vital, pre-landing actions. These are usually remembered by a mnemonic. Different clubs prefer different downwind checks and you will be taught and expected to use the downwind check which is used at your club. Whichever downwind check is used should serve you well even on the more advanced gliders which you may eventually fly, and will include essential actions, such as lowering retractable undercarriages, setting flaps and jettisoning water ballast.

Ideally, you should have completed your downwind checks by the time the glider is passing the landing area on the downwind leg. Doing so will leave the glider ready for the approach and trimmed to a safe approach speed, leaving you to concentrate more on flying the final part of the circuit. Such workload management will reduce your workload at a time when decision making and flying the glider demand most of your attention, and will contribute to the safety of your flight.

The airspeed should be adjusted to the approach speed before this point. Doing so will give a reasonable margin above the stalling speed and increase the glider's control response. The higher airspeed will reduce the time spent in any rising or descending air which you might fly through, thus reducing its effect. Also, as some height is always lost with any airspeed increase, the height remaining after the adoption of the approach speed will be the height available for manoeuvring. This makes it easier to assess the glider's rate of descent and plan the rest of the circuit.

A good habit to get into after you have retrimmed the glider, is to place your left hand on the airbrake lever, so as not to go fumbling for it at the busiest part of the approach. If the air temperature outside the glider has been below freezing, then checking that the airbrakes are not frozen shut, by opening them slightly is a good idea. If you do need to do this check, make sure you lock the airbrakes closed again, or else they may suck open – perhaps unnoticed.

For convenience, the point on the downwind leg at which the glider is abeam the landing area is often called the LOW KEY POINT. Although the name is not important, the significance of its position is. The low key point is the point where the glider's height is becoming critical, and the decisions you make from this point onwards must be well thought out. Typically, you will be passing the low key point at around 500 feet, if your circuit planning is going well.

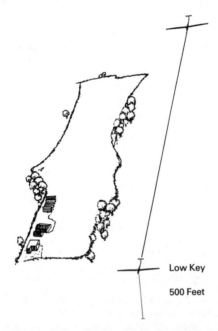

Low Key

500 Feet

Fig 17.7   The low key point. The low key point is abeam the landing area and typically the glider will be at around 500 feet at this point.

The low key point is also the point on the downwind leg where your view of the landing area will be increasingly restricted as the landing area moves behind the glider's wing, making judgement of the height required to reach the landing area more difficult. Should you encounter any rising air at or after this point you should not attempt to manoeuvre in the hope of using it to extend your flight time. Any such manoeuvring could leave you in a poor position for the subsequent approach, should you fail to gain height. Your actions may also be hazardous to other circuit users.

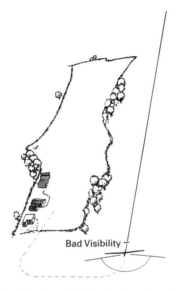

Bad Visibility

Fig 17.8   Lower end of the circuit. After the low key point is passed the pilot's view of the landing area will generally deteriorate.

The downwind leg is completed when the glider is turned onto the BASE LEG. The turn which is made to place the glider on to the base leg is called the BASE LEG TURN. By the time the glider starts this turn it will be quite low (typically around 400 feet for a modern glider). It is therefore essential that a safe airspeed is maintained, as there would be insufficient height available for recovery should you allow the airspeed to decay enough for a stall or spin to occur.

THE BASE LEG

The BASE LEG is the leg of the circuit which joins the downwind leg to the approach (Fig 17.9). It is on the base leg that the final adjustments to height and position are made that will place the glider in a good position to start the approach. It is also the last chance to inspect the landing area and to decide on the reference point to be used for your control of the rate of descent on the approach.

The base leg is completed when the glider is turned on to the APPROACH. This turn is called the FINAL TURN. For safety, both the base leg turn and the final turn should be well-banked and well-co-ordinated.

145

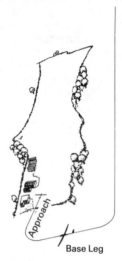

Base Leg

Fig 17.9   Base leg. After the turn onto the base leg, the view of the landing area will improve, giving the opportunity for better inspection and allowing more accurate height judgement.

The APPROACH, being the last leg of the flight, and leading to the landing has been dealt with previously. (See Chapters 12 and 13) Providing that good downwind and base legs have been flown, there is every chance that a good approach and landing will follow. A badly executed circuit will, however, increase your workload in this final stage of the circuit, thus making for a more difficult approach and landing. Indeed, on investigation, many a poor landing can be traced back to a badly flown circuit.

FLYING THE CIRCUIT IN PRACTICE

Given that any wind is light and is blowing straight down the landing run, that there is no conflicting traffic, and that the air that the glider will fly through on the circuit is not rising or descending, then the "ideal" circuit described so far is possible. Powered aircraft fly a similar, if somewhat larger circuit, but unlike gliders, they have control over their height and they can counter the effects of wind more easily. It is more often the case that you will have to modify your circuit, since the air mass in which you are flying, makes it impossible to fly an "ideal" circuit. This is not a problem as long as you anticipate the effects that the air mass may have, and constantly re-assess and make adjustments as necessary.

Now before you decide that maybe power flying would be easier, take heart from the fact that you will not require to learn any new skills to master flying a circuit. (By now you will be capable of flying straight, turning, adjusting airspeed, etc.) Circuit planning is all about JUDGEMENT, and that will be gained quite quickly; firstly by watching your instructor's demonstrations and then by seeing the results of your own attempts and improving upon them. Observing other pilots (of all experience levels) as they fly circuits can also prove useful and sometimes amusing!

In any circuit, providing you are continually monitoring and acting upon four main criteria, you should not find any difficulty in successfully flying the circuit.

These are:

- LOOKOUT
- HEIGHT AND DISTANCE (OR ANGLE) FROM THE LANDING AREA
- LANDING AREA AVAILABILITY
- AIRSPEED

The importance of keeping a good LOOKOUT at all times will have been stressed from the very beginning of your training. While its importance should hardly need to be re-emphasised, it is only mentioned here because the circuit can be a very busy piece of sky and the late sighting of other aircraft can, not only risk a collision, but can also result in the need to alter your circuit pattern, thus increasing your workload at a critical time.

Constant monitoring of HEIGHT against the DISTANCE FROM THE LANDING AREA is essential. Although the circuit may have been joined at a reasonable position and at a suitable height, the rate of descent of the glider will vary depending on conditions. You will regularly need to reappraise the glider's height relative to its position and the distance still to be flown, so as not to run out of height before the landing area is reached.

A well flown circuit will give you the maximum amount of time to assess the state of the landing area. The AVAILABILITY OF THE LANDING AREA can alter quite quickly if another glider lands, or vehicles or aircraft move on to it. If the intended landing area is part of a farmer's field, any unsuitability of the surface or any electric fences may only become obvious as the glider descends in the circuit. Constant inspection of the landing area will disclose such problems as early as is practical, allowing the landing position to be reselected.

Once a safe AIRSPEED has been adopted on the downwind leg, it must be continually monitored and any variation from the chosen airspeed corrected. This becomes of increasing importance as the circuit progresses and the available height for stall or spin recovery reduces.

THE EFFECT OF WIND IN THE CIRCUIT

The downwind leg of the circuit will, strictly speaking, only be a "downwind" leg if the wind is blowing straight towards the landing direction. Despite this fact, the name "downwind leg" is maintained to describe this part of the circuit, irrespective of wind direction. Similarly, the base leg is often referred to as the "crosswind leg", even although there may be no wind, or a tail or headwind on this leg. Accepting these conventions is a minor consideration, compared to the difficulties the wind can create while you are flying a circuit.

Let us assume that the glider is being flown on a RIGHT HAND CIRCUIT; that is, that the base leg turn and final turn will both be turns to the right.

If the wind is blowing from the glider's left on the downwind leg, the glider will tend to drift towards the landing area, resulting in a downwind leg and base leg turn which are too close to the landing area. If this is allowed to happen, the base leg will be shortened or even non-existent and the time available to adjust height on the base leg reduced.

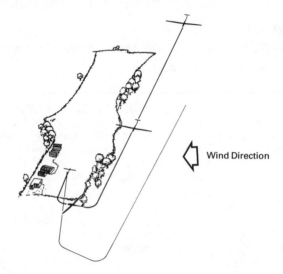

Wind Direction

Fig 17.10   Effect of a wind blowing towards the airfield. A wind blowing in towards the airfield will tend to drift the glider into a position too close to the landing area.

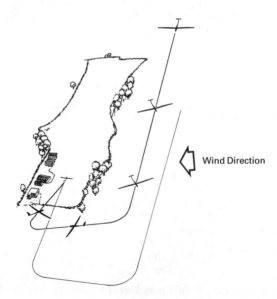

Wind Direction

Fig 17.11   Correcting for drift on the downwind leg. Tracking with the glider's nose pointing slightly away from the airfield will prevent the glider drifting towards the landing area.

To counter this problem, the glider must be flown on a heading which is slightly into wind, so that the desired track is maintained.

The tail wind component during the base leg turn and on the base leg will compound this problem, shortening the time it takes to cover the distance to the final turn. The final turn will also be elongated downwind, and therefore you be will required to anticipate this and begin the turn earlier, otherwise the glider will overshoot the desired approach path.

The stronger the crosswind component from the left, the greater the above problem and the more you will be required to point the glider's nose away from the airfield to maintain track. Indeed, if the crosswind is very strong in this instance, it will be better to start the downwind leg further out from the approach path and landing area (to the glider's left as in Fig 17.12) so as to give a reasonable time on the base leg.

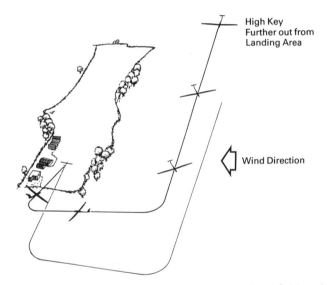

High Key
Further out from
Landing Area

Wind Direction

Fig 17.12   Correcting for a strong crosswind blowing towards the airfield on the downwind leg. With a strong crosswind blowing towards the airfield it may be necessary to deliberately fly the downwind leg further out from the airfield as well as tracking.

If, while flying the same circuit, the wind is blowing in the opposite direction, that is, from the glider's right as it flies the downwind leg, the glider will tend to be blown away from the landing area. Potentially, this is more dangerous as the glider may well be drifted out of gliding range of the landing area. (Fig 17.13)

Again the glider must be flown on a heading which will keep it on the desired track. In this case, if the crosswind is very strong, it will be necessary to fly a downwind leg which is much closer to the approach path and landing area than normal, as it will take longer to cover the distance of the base leg due to the headwind component on that leg. The final turn can be left until later than normal, as the tendency will be to undershoot the approach path on that turn. (Fig 17.14)

149

Fig 17.13   Strong crosswind blowing away from the airfield on the downwind leg. A wind blowing from the airfield side will tend to drift the glider away from landing area.

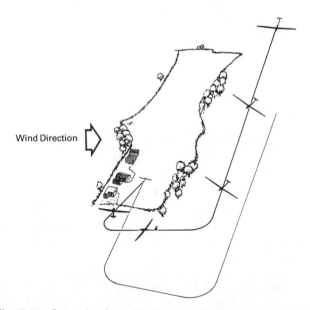

Fig 17.14   Correcting for a wind blowing the glider away from the airfield. To prevent the glider being drifted out of reach of the landing area it will be necessary to track with the glider's nose pointing slightly towards the airfield and possibly also to fly the glider on a closer downwind leg.

Should a moderate or strong wind be blowing diagonally across the circuit, as shown in Fig 17.15, care must be taken not to over-extend the downwind leg, as you will be faced with a headwind component on both the base leg and on the approach.

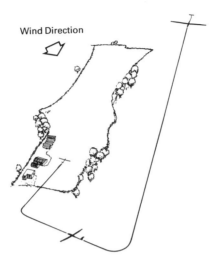

Wind Direction

Fig 17.15   Effect of a strong wind blowing diagonally across the airfield. If a strong wind is blowing diagonally across the airfield, the pilot will have to be careful to prevent the glider being drifted too far away when in the area of the base leg turn.

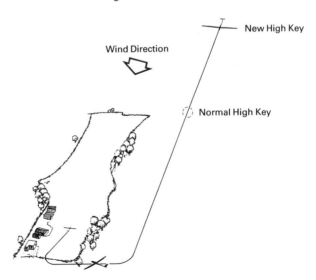

New High Key

Wind Direction

Normal High Key

Fig 17.16   Effect of a strong tail wind on the downwind leg. A strong wind on the downwind leg will create the need for a longer downwind leg and a closer, tracking base leg.

151

In all of these situations the heading of the glider on the approach will have to be such that the glider will track along the desired approach path.

If the landing is to be made into a moderate or strong wind, then the downwind leg, although not being subject to much drift, will be flown with a considerable tail wind component. This will add to the glider's groundspeed and shorten the time available to complete checks and adjust the height to distance-to-fly ratio. To counter this, the circuit can be started further upwind than is usual. Care must be taken not to travel too far downwind while flying the downwind leg. To do so would risk placing the glider in a position from which there would be insufficient height to reach the landing area. The turn onto the base leg will need to be started early, as the effect of the tail wind will be to elongate the turn downwind. There will be a tendency to drift away from the landing area on the base leg, making it necessary to "track" on the base leg to avoid drifting downwind. It is also wise to fly a base leg which is closer to the landing area than that flown on a calm day. (Fig 17.16)

The only potential problems on the approach will be those described in the section on **"The Effect of Wind"**.

THE EFFECT OF RISING OR SINKING AIR IN THE CIRCUIT

Even the perfectly planned circuit, on a day with little wind, can go wrong and need adjustments. If the air through which the glider is flying while flying the circuit is rising or descending, then the glider will gain or lose height and the height against distance to the landing area relationship will be upset. Often these areas of ascending or descending air will be very small and may cancel each other out, in which case little or no modification to your circuit will be necessary. All too often, however, they are of a large enough area and moving at a fast enough rate vertically, that they will require you to adjust your circuit.

Rising air in the circuit can be more of a nuisance than an embarrassment. Assuming that either you have to land immediately, or that you are too low to use any strong updraughts safely, on encountering such updraughts you will have to adjust either the distance to the landing area or the glider's height to keep the distance/height ratio reasonable.

On the downwind leg this can be done simply by moving the downwind leg further away from the landing area until the distance looks about right for the glider's height. Remember though that, "what goes up must come down", and that this also applies to rising air. Be ready to readjust the track back towards the landing area if you fly into a neighbouring downdraught.

If the area of rising air is extensive, then you may find yourself approaching the base leg turn higher than you were when you started the downwind leg! In this case you have two choices. You can either fly back to the starting point of the downwind leg and replan your circuit using some airbrake, or else you can reposition the glider to join a circuit on the other side of the field where there may be less rising air. Both these options are a bit messy but at least you will have hindsight to help your next attempt.

[The author can remember a training flight in Australia where repeatedly, we would join the downwind leg at about 700 feet and be at 3000 feet by the base leg turn. The student meanwhile was complaining bitterly that he wanted to sort out his landings – not go soaring!]

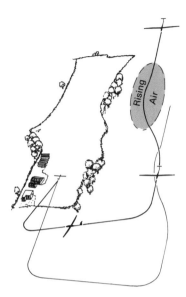

Fig 17.17   Rising air on the downwind leg. Excess height, due to the glider encountering rising air on the downwind leg, can be nullified by moving the downwind leg out slightly.

In such a situation, attempting to lose height by doing one or more 360° turns is usually futile, as not only will the glider probably be drifted further downwind (thus compounding the height/distance-to-fly excess), but the chances are that the glider will also gain height as it carries out the turn in rising air!

Rising air encountered on the base leg can be dealt with by angling the base leg slightly further away from the landing area. However, care must be exercised not to move the base leg too far back, as any downdraughts between the glider and the landing area could result in the glider not being able to reach the landing area. Remember that your aim is to position the glider on an approach path which is well within the range of the airbrakes. A much more sensible approach is to use some airbrake to make the adjustments necessary to the glider's height, but again care must be taken not to dump too much height for fear of creating an undershoot situation.

The use of airbrakes during the base leg and final turn is often wrongly criticised by some "old school" instructors. However, providing that they are used sensibly at these times, they are an excellent aid to circuit flying. It is important that you appreciate that, in a turn, a given amount of airbrake will result in a higher rate of descent than would be the case in straight flight. As always a safe airspeed must be maintained.

Rising air encountered on the approach should not present any problems as most airbrakes are powerful enough to overcome any up-currents encountered. Normal approach control technique should be used.

Flying through sinking air in the circuit can make life somewhat more difficult, unless positive action is taken to keep the landing area within reach.

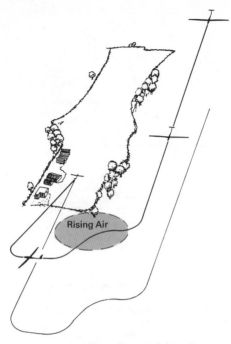

Fig 17.18   Rising air on the base leg. The effect of rising air encountered on the base leg can be nullified either by using the airbrakes or by moving the base leg out slightly.

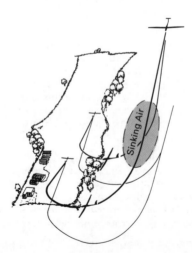

Fig 17.19   Sinking air on the downwind leg. If sinking air is encountered on the downwind leg the glider should be moved closer to the airfield. If the height loss is dramatic it may be necessary to turn in early and land further up the landing area.

If sinking air causes a loss of height on the downwind leg, the downwind leg will have to be moved closer to the landing area so that the height/distance ratio will remain reasonable. If this loss of height is excessive, then the glider may need to be turned onto the base leg or the approach immediately and landed further up the landing area. (Fig 17.19)

Any height loss on the base leg will require a similar action, in order that the landing area be kept within easy gliding range. The important point to remember is that the glider must have completed the final turn by the time its height is equivalent to about twice that of a tall tree.

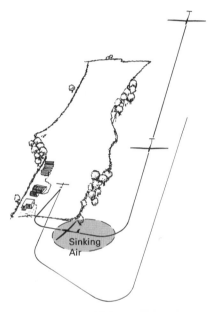

Fig 17.20   Sinking air on the base leg. If sinking air is encountered on the base leg the glider should be moved closer to the airfield or if necessary turned in to land early.

The effects of wind and vertical air currents will combine to give an infinite number of variations to the problems faced when flying a circuit. Providing you constantly monitor the rate of descent, the glider's height in relationship to the distance still to be flown, and act accordingly, then you will not be caught out in the circuit. If adjustments have to be made to the circuit to counter any of these effects, then it is essential that they are made as early as possible rather than delayed until the late part of the circuit, when height and time to manoeuvre may be limited.

FLYING CIRCUITS AT HILL SITES

The circuit technique described above will only be applicable when flying into a landing area in flat terrain. If you are landing back at an airfield which is based at the top of a hill, and there is any wind whatsoever, the circuit you will need to fly will be considerably different from those discussed so far.

155

The main reason for the need for a different technique is the effect of the wind as it blows up and over the hill where the landing area is situated. As it does so it will cause rising air in front of the hill and large, turbulent downdraughts downwind of the edge of the hill.

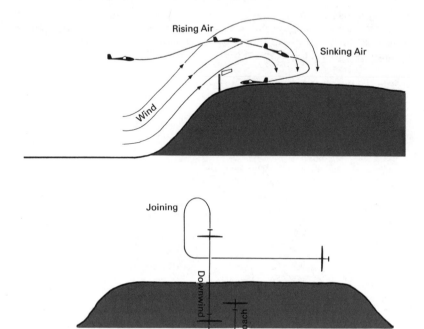

Fig 17.21   Circuits at hilltop sites. Circuits at hilltop sites are often through both rising air and strong sinking air and the circuit pattern must be modified accordingly.

As the glider is flown on the downwind leg, it will initially gain height as it flies through the rising air. The second part of the downwind leg, the base leg and the approach will be flown in air which, apart from being very rough, is descending rapidly. Safety dictates that the glider flies a circuit whose base leg will not go beyond the downwind boundary of the landing area, and that the approach speed (which must allow for a severe wind gradient) is adopted early.

If there are other gliders hill soaring along the face of the hill, then the common technique of joining the circuit is to initially fly out, away from the face of the hill and then do a 180° turn to start the downwind leg. This procedure has the advantage of giving a reasonable length of downwind leg and also allows you to see hill soaring gliders more clearly as you cross their track at right angles. This circuit joining technique is not universal, and there will always be occasions when you are so low that you will have to scamper straight into the circuit.

Using a landing area in the valley near the bottom of a hill also has its problems. If the wind is blowing off the hill, turbulence and sinking air may be severe throughout most of the circuit and the same precautions as when landing on top of a hill must be taken.

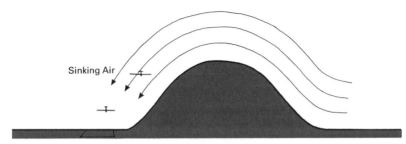

Fig 17.22   Sinking air in the lee of a hill affecting the circuit. A wind blowing off a hill may cause turbulence and sinking air in the circuit of a valley airfield.

If the wind is blowing towards the hill, then you can expect rising air along the face of the hill. If the downwind leg or base leg is flown close to the hillside, then this rising air may lead to an embarrassing excess of height in the circuit. The answer is to fly a circuit on the other side of the landing area if possible, where the air will be a bit less enthusiastic, or to use airbrakes in the circuit as necessary.

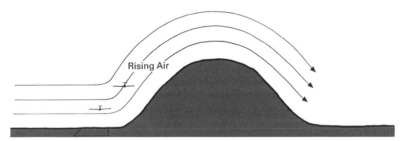

Fig 17.23   Hill lift affecting the circuit. Hill lift may upset the circuit at a valley airfield.

CIRCUITS IN OLDER GLIDERS

Older gliders, particularly of vintage value, tend not to be flown in strong winds unless good hill soaring conditions prevail. However, as their glide angles tend to be poorer than their modern relations, they have to be flown on closer circuits if they are to stay safely within reach of the landing area. In some cases they will have no airbrakes or spoilers, which mean that "S" turning and other means of using up height before landing have to be employed. (Thankfully, the need for "S" turns on the base leg is an unnecessary technique in modern gliders, but do not be taken by surprise if the vintage glider joining the base leg in front of you starts a manoeuvre which by modern standards seems unconventional.)

When you come to master planning and flying the circuit, there is no substitute for repeated practice and successive attempts. By far the best and most cost effective way to achieve this is to launch using a winch or car. Given a launch height of 1000 feet or more, you will have adequate time to plan and fly your circuit (plus a little bit of time to revise or polish up other exercises). Given a good launch rate, you should be able to do three or four launches in succession, allowing you the chance to improve on your previous attempts. Although not nearly as cost effective, if aerotow launching is all that is available, your instructor may be wise to allow you to stop the launch at around 1000 feet, so allowing you to concentrate on your circuit planning and permitting successive launches.

There is also a lot of benefit to be had by flying both left and right hand circuits, local rules permitting, that is.

Two important points to remember when flying a circuit are:

1. The reason we fly a circuit is because it is the most convenient way to set the glider up for an approach and landing. If ever flying a circuit becomes inconvenient due to lack of height, then abandon the circuit, turn in early and land further up the landing area.

2. Gliders can quickly lose height, intentionally or otherwise. They cannot gain height as easily when you need it.

AIR EXERCISE – CIRCUIT PLANNING

STAGE 1

Your instructor will demonstrate how to fly a circuit, explaining the considerations and decisions necessary as the circuit progresses and how to deal with problems such as having too much or too little height.

STAGE 2

You will be allowed to attempt flying the circuit until you have mastered the judgement involved.

STAGE 3

Your instructor will engineer some awkward circuit situations and you will be allowed to practise rectifying these.

CHAPTER 18

LAUNCH FAILURES DURING WIRE LAUNCHES

The frequency of cable breaks during wire launching depends to a great extent on the equipment being used and the surface of the airfield. If the winch has a poor mechanism for leading the cable onto the winch drum, or the surface over which the cable is retrieved is abrasive, then the launch cable will become brittle and worn. In such circumstances cable breaks can be a fairly regular nuisance. Generally, the better the launching equipment and the newer the cable, the fewer the cable breaks which will haunt the launching operation.

No matter how good the launching equipment, there will always be the possibility of the cable breaking during a launch. For this reason, if you are being trained on wire launch, you will be shown how to cope with a cable break, no matter at what point in the launch it occurs. As the glider is designed to fly without power, a cable break or other type of launch failure is not a serious problem providing that some basic procedures are followed. These procedures will be covered in your training.

Whether the launch is a winch, car or reverse pulley launch, the glider will, for the greatest part of the launch, be flying in a very nose-up attitude. As long as the winch or tow car is providing a pull on the glider, and the airspeed is reasonable, the high nose attitude is acceptable as the forward (and upward) movement of the glider means that the angle of attack is well below the stalling angle.

When a cable break or other type of launch failure occurs, the glider's forward speed will reduce and the relative airflow will quickly change from being at a small angle to the wing, to a large angle, unless you prevent this happening. (Fig 18.1)

This change to a large angle of attack, if allowed to occur, would result in the glider stalling, with subsequent loss of height. As there may be insufficient height to recover from a stall, you must prevent its occurrence by lowering the nose of the glider promptly, when the cable breaks. As long as adequate airspeed for the nose-up attitude during the climb has been maintained, the lowering of the nose after a cable break (to an attitude somewhere close to that of an approach attitude) should be achieved easily without any serious loss of airspeed or height.

Bear in mind, however, that the extent to which the nose of the glider need be lowered depends on the height and climb attitude at the moment of the cable break. For instance, if the glider is in the full climb, the change of attitude necessary, will be significant. On the other hand, in the very early stages of the launch, the glider will not be in a steep nose-up attitude, nor will it be at any great height. In this case, to adopt a large nose-down attitude (as opposed to a relatively shallow nose-down attitude) will risk diving the glider onto the ground. So although you should realise that prompt action is necessary to put the glider into an attitude to allow a safe approach to be made, this action must be measured rather than impulsive and you should bear in mind the height of the glider at the instant of the cable break.

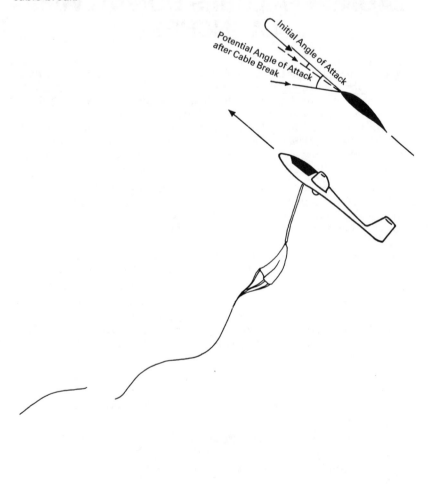

Fig 18.1   Angle of attack change after a cable break. Unless the nose is lowered after a cable break the angle of attack of the wing will increase.

Another problem which can be caused by over-reacting to a cable break and pushing the nose down too rapidly is that this can cause the sensation known as reduced gravity (or reduced "g"). Remember that this sensation is similar to that which you experience if you drive too fast over a humpback bridge and can easily be mistaken for a falling sensation.

The danger is, that if you do move the control column forwards sharply after a cable break, then reduced "g" may be felt and the sensation of falling mistaken for the glider stalling. If you then move the control column further forwards to recover from this wrongly perceived "stall", the reduced "g" sensation will intensify. If all of this occurs close to the ground (and most of a wire launch is close enough to the ground!) there is a very great risk of the glider striking the ground in a steep nose-down attitude.

It is therefore essential that any control movement to pitch the glider's nose down when a cable break occurs, is controlled, and that if a sustained or increasing amount of reduced "g" is experienced, it is realised that the glider is NOT stalled. The reduced "g" will have been caused by over control while pitching the glider's nose downwards. The feeling will cease if you stop pushing forwards on the control column and return it to a sensible position.

After the glider's nose has been returned to a sensible attitude and the glider accelerated to a safe airspeed, you can decide what to do next.

Before you commence any manoeuvres, you must firstly CHECK THE AIRSPEED to confirm that it has reached a safe value and then THINK about what constitutes the safest course of action, requiring the minimum workload and skill.

While you are doing this, you should pull the release knob twice to confirm that there is no part of the cable remaining attached to the glider.

Your options depend on the glider's height, position relative to the airfield, the airfield layout, and the wind. It is impossible to cover every permutation of these ingredients and so here we will attempt to look at general situations. The easiest way to discuss these is by following the launch from beginning to end while considering the possible options, assuming that the cable breaks in a particular height band. **The main aim after any launch failure is to get the glider back on the ground safely with the minimum of pilot workload.**

A cable break during the initial take-off, the transition into the climb or the beginning of the full climb should not require any difficult decision making. After the desired attitude and airspeed have been achieved, you should ask yourself, "CAN I LAND AHEAD?". If so, you should do so. A straight ahead landing will always be the safest option, providing, of course, that there is enough airfield left ahead in which to land. Landing ahead avoids turning while close to the ground and reduces the high workload that such manoeuvring places on the pilot. It is while under such extra pressure that mistakes are made, which may cause the glider to stall or run out of height before the turn is complete. Generally, the stronger the wind, the better the chances of the glider being able to land ahead. This is because the glider's effective approach angle over the ground will be much steeper, and the landing distance required much less.

If the decision has been made to land ahead, it is essential that the airspeed is checked and seen to be at a safe value for the approach BEFORE using any airbrakes, otherwise, if the airspeed is low, the increase in drag may not allow a safe airspeed to be gained. This, combined with the fact that the use of airbrakes will increase the stalling speed, may cause the glider to stall or, at very least, result in a heavy landing when the round out is attempted. Once the airspeed is seen to be adequate, any excess height should be lost quickly by initially applying full airbrake, reducing the airbrake if necessary closer to the ground.

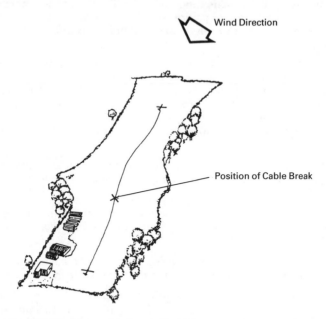

Fig 18.2   Landing ahead after a cable break. Providing enough room exists ahead, a landing straight ahead will be the safest option after a cable break.

As the glider climbs up the launch, there will come a point where, if the cable breaks, it may no longer be feasible to land ahead due to the glider being too high relative to the amount of landing area remaining ahead. It is at this stage where the decisions to be made will be critical.

In the case of an airfield of limited size, the glider's height at the time of the cable break may be too great to allow the glider to land straight ahead. At the same time, its height may be insufficient to allow the glider to fly a shortened circuit or even a 360° turn safely. If this is the case you will have to consider the layout of the airfield in relation to any wind, and manoeuvre the glider accordingly before landing. Fig 18.3 shows some of the possibilities that may exist, assuming a cross runway or wider part of the airfield is available. In the extreme case a neighbouring farmer's field should not be ruled out.

It will save some adrenalin at the time of a cable break if the layout of the airfield and the wind direction is considered before the beginning of the launch, thus giving thought to the choices available before things get busy in the event of a critical height cable break. In general, where there is a crosswind, it will be beneficial to make the first of any turns downwind. This will give the glider more of an into wind approach once the glider is finally lined up for the landing. This manoeuvre should only be done after due consideration of the airfield layout and any obstructions which surround it.

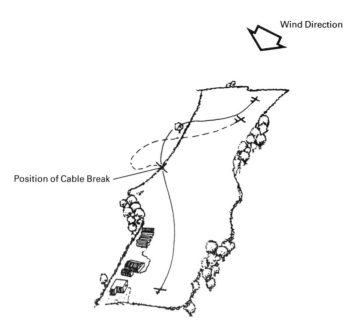

Fig 18.3   "Dog leg" manoeuvre after a cable break. At certain heights a cable break may mean that a "dog-leg" manoeuvre has to be flown.

Notice that Fig 18.3 shows the glider following a "dog-leg" flight path to position the glider so as to have adequate room to land from the height at the end of the manoeuvre. Some of these flight paths resemble an oblique letter "S" and so have gained the name "S" turn, but it should be realised that a true "S" turn is probably inappropriate to a cable break beset with the height versus landing distance problems under discussion. Consider Fig 18.4.

The "S" turn shown involves three separate turns which make up the manoeuvre. The first turn is through 90°, in this case to the left (A to B). The second turn (B to C) is a right hand turn through 180°. The last section of the manoeuvre is another turn to the left through 90° (C to D). If you add up the number of degrees through which the glider will have turned if it completes these turns, the answer is 360°. However, because the whole dilemma hinges on the fact that glider has insufficient height to complete a 360° turn safely, to attempt this manoeuvre would risk the glider coming to a grinding halt before finishing the performance!

So before you embark on an "S" turn, ask yourself, "Will it consist of 360° of turn?" If so, then fly a 360° turn rather than an "S" turn. An "S" turn will not only require a similar number of degrees of turn as a 360° turn, but also a greater number of co-ordinated control inputs and higher workload, with the subsequent risk of losing airspeed, as turn entries, exits or reversals will be required at points A, B, C and D. Another advantage of the 360° turn over the "S" turn is that a 360° turn (once completed) will place the glider in a position with more landing distance available ahead.

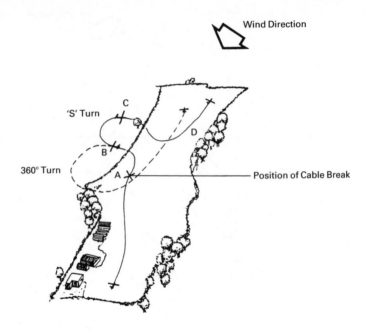

Fig 18.4   360° turn versus "S" turn after a cable break. If an "S" turn will consist of more than 360° degrees of turn, it is safer to fly a 360° turn.

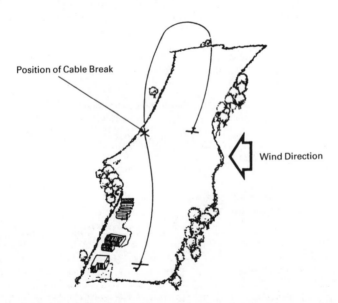

Fig 18.5   Downwind landing after a cable break. In light winds or crosswinds, a "downwind" landing after a cable break may be a possibility.

In light wind or crosswind conditions the option of landing the glider in the opposite direction to the take-off direction should be considered. This will probably necessitate the glider being flown for a short period at a slight angle (say 30° to 45° or so) to the direction of take-off, leaving the glider well positioned for a turn on to its approach with sufficient landing area ahead of it in the new landing direction. It will also avoid the need for last minute manoeuvring very close to the ground.

Once the glider has passed through this critical region, it will be high enough for a shortened circuit to be flown. The extent to which this circuit is extended from a 360° turn (that is, for how long the glider is flown with the wings level on a "downwind" heading) will depend on the glider's height at the time of the cable break. It must be realised though, that the reason for extending the "downwind" leg is to make a greater landing area available after the final turn and **NOT** to increase the convenience of retrieving the glider to the launch point. In any event, the final turn should, wherever possible, be completed by the same height as it would on a normal circuit, even if this results in the glider landing well up the airfield. **Never stretch the circuit.**

Here we have another reason for considered, as opposed to impulsive, use of airbrakes. Having launched past the minimum height where the glider can safely fly a 360° turn, thoughtless use of the airbrakes, immediately after a cable break, would risk descending the glider back into the height band where neither a straight ahead landing nor a 360° turn is possible. Think before grabbing at the airbrake lever, or else you may make life more difficult for yourself.

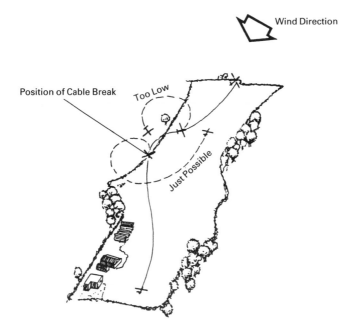

Fig 18.6   Impulsive use of airbrakes after a cable break may result in your losing the option of 360° turn.

165

Whichever type of manoeuvre you decide to fly after a cable break has occurred, all turns involved should be well-banked. Not only will such turns give a faster turn rate but they will also lose less overall height and offer you less chance to co-ordinate badly, thus reducing the risk of stalling or spinning.

If the cable breaks when the glider is near the top of the launch, there may be little need to alter your original plans significantly. In this circumstance you will probably be able to spend a little time searching for rising air and hopefully go soaring. At worst you will be able to fly a circuit and land. Whichever of these two options you end up following, you must remember that you have started with less than the full launch height. As a result, you must reduce your search time for rising air currents or perhaps even limit the size of your circuit, so as to avoid running out of height during the latter part of the circuit. You should aim to join the circuit at a position and height which allows most of the downwind leg, all of the base leg and the final approach to be flown normally.

When operating from a large airfield, the length of the landing area available will make the necessary decisions to be made after a cable break somewhat easier. There is every chance that the awkward phase of the launch will not exist, as by the time the glider is too high to land ahead, it will be more than high enough to fly some form of circuit. Where this overlap of options occurs, you should not allow yourself to be lured into attempting a turn. A straight ahead landing is still the safer option.

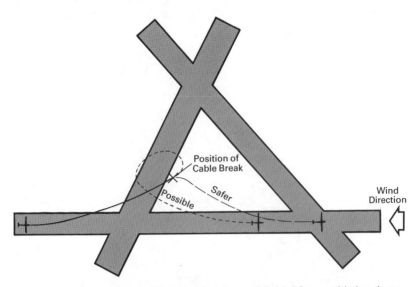

Fig 18.7   Options after a cable break at a large airfield. After a cable break at a large airfield both a landing ahead or a 360° turn may be possible. The land ahead option will always be the safest.

FAILURE OF THE WINCH OR TOW CAR

Mechanical failures of the launch vehicle are not as common as cable breaks, but they do happen. In essence they can present all the same problems as a cable break. However, the main difference is that mechanical failure may not be as sudden or as obvious as a straightforward cable break. The problem is therefore in recognising what may be a gradual loss of power.

The only safeguard is to monitor the airspeed and the rate of climb during the launch. Should you find that the glider has taken a longer than usual time to get airborne or the airspeed is remaining too low to allow you to transition into the full climb, you should immediately check that the airbrakes are closed. If they are closed then there is probably a power problem with the launch vehicle. If a failure occurs further up the launch, the symptom may be a gradual reduction of airspeed requiring you to progressively lower the nose. If this is just an under-estimation by the winch or car driver of the amount of power required for the launch, the airspeed should soon increase again when the launch operator observes that the glider is not climbing well.

The danger of a launch failure is that you will either not notice the decay in airspeed and a stall will result, or as is more likely, you will not take action early enough and find yourself in a difficult position due to the lack of manoeuvring height and landing area still available ahead. The only safe answer is to make a positive decision to abandon the launch while it is still possible to land the glider ahead.

Never travel hopefully up a slow launch. Such an action can easily result in the glider being left in an embarrassing situation requiring more height and skill than you have in store.

To recap on the actions when the launch fails:

- LOWER THE GLIDER'S NOSE TO A REASONABLE ATTITUDE
- CHECK THE AIRSPEED (release the cable when time permits)
- THINK ABOUT WHAT ACTION YOU SHOULD TAKE
- ACT

It is uncommon for the glider to stall as a result of a cable break or launch failure, although if you do not take the appropriate action then this is always a danger. However, most incidents resulting in damaged gliders occur as a result of the action the glider pilot takes or fails to take **after** the initial recovery action is made. The important point here is that before any action is taken, be that opening the airbrakes or commencing a manoeuvre, CHECK THE AIRSPEED AND THINK.

AIR EXERCISE – WIRE LAUNCH FAILURES

Your instructor will demonstrate how to deal with a cable break should one occur or else simulate a cable break by pulling the cable release knob.

Subsequently, you will be given simulated cable breaks to deal with as part of your pre-solo training and during post solo check flights. Failures of the launch vehicle will also be simulated to test your awareness. You will be expected to execute the recovery drill and to choose and follow the safest options to land the glider.

CHAPTER 19

AEROTOW LAUNCH FAILURES AND EMERGENCIES

Launch failures during an aerotow launch are rare, but they do occur. The training you will receive on how to aerotow will make you aware of the possibilities of a launch failure, and show you how to cope with one should it occur.

Launch failures occur for 3 main reasons: the tow-rope breaking, the tow-plane suffering engine failure or the glider pilot having to abandon the launch through being out of position. Whichever of these cause the launch to be prematurely curtailed, the problem with which you are faced is one of deciding what to do next. If the launch has reached circuit height, and the tow-plane pilot has kept the glider within gliding range of the airfield, there is no problem. All you have to do is join a circuit and land. The critical time for the launch to fail is when the glider is low, and the possibility of flying a circuit does not exist.

A launch failure on the ground run should present little problem. The glider can be stopped well before the end of the available runway.

Immediately after the glider (or the tow-plane and glider) has become airborne, the glider should still be able to land ahead on the airfield. If the launch failure is due to a loss of power from the tow-plane's engine, some avoiding action may be necessary if the glider is to avoid running into the tow-plane. A failure at this stage may also require positive, but careful use of the airbrakes if a reasonable landing is to be achieved.

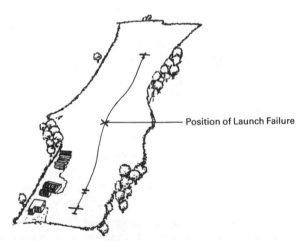
— Position of Launch Failure

Fig 19.1   Aerotow launch failure shortly after take-off. An aerotow launch failure just after getting airborne may mean the glider can still be landed ahead on the airfield.

168

If a launch failure occurs once the glider has reached a position and height where there is no longer a sufficient length of runway available on which to land ahead, the only option available is to select and land in a field beyond the end of the runway. The glider's height may allow for a choice of fields through a relatively wide angle, but time available will demand a quick selection. The wind direction may also be a factor which influences your choice of field. At most airfields, there are usually known, suitable fields which lie within range should the tow-rope break or the tow-plane's engine fail at a critical height. These will normally be pointed out during training and must never be far from your mind as you launch.

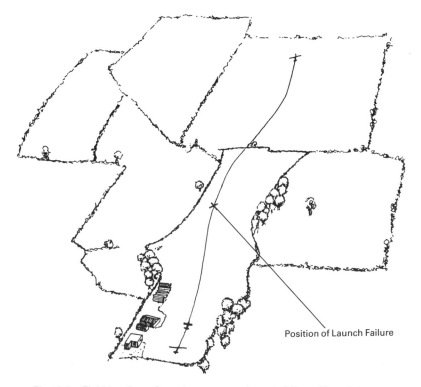

Position of Launch Failure

Fig 19.2   Field landing after a low aerotow launch failure. The glider may have to be landed in a field near the airfield if an aerotow launch failure occurs low down.

After the glider has passed a height of about 300 feet, given a medium or high performance glider and a light wind, the option of turning back towards the airfield and making a downwind landing becomes a distinct possibility. If this option is acted upon, then care must be taken to maintain the airspeed at a reasonable value for the turning manoeuvre and the approach. This option is one that is not available to powered aircraft (and that most definitely includes a self-launching motor glider with retractable engine) whose glide performance in a turn is so poor that the turn would, in all probability, fail to be completed before ground contact occurs.

To help understand why this option is a safe possibility for a glider suffering a launch failure above about 300 feet, we can look at the performance figures for both the climb and the return to the airfield.

Once established in the climb, the tow-plane and glider combination will be flying at approximately 60 knots and will be climbing at around 400 feet per minute. (1 knot is almost exactly equal to 100 feet per minute.) The climb gradient is therefore 60/4 or 15 to 1.

The glide angle of an average training glider is around 28 to 1. If you assume a launch failure at any point during the climb out from the airfield, the glider should be able to glide back to the airfield for a landing in the opposite direction to the take-off run, *providing that the turn back towards the airfield can be made safely without substantial loss of height.*

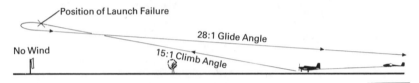

Fig 19.3   Return to airfield after aerotow launch failure. Providing enough height exists to turn safely, a downwind landing soon becomes a possibility after an aerotow launch failure.

As the glider in this example is being towed at 60 knots at the time the launch failure occurs, it should be able to conserve height during the turn and still have an adequate approach speed. Therefore, providing the height is sufficient to complete the turn, the glider should be able to land back on the airfield safely. This is one of the few cases where, providing it has been set to airfield level, the altimeter reading can be used for decision making when low down, since any lag in the instrument will mean that when the launch failure occurs, you will probably be slightly higher than indicated.

The figures given are only approximations for ease of calculation, but tend to be on the pessimistic side, with better glide angles for modern machines, and higher climb rates despite the higher towing speeds of some tow-planes.

In moderate or strong winds it is unwise to attempt a downwind landing. However, the groundspeed on the launch will mean a better angle of climb and give you sufficient landing area ahead for longer, possibly enabling a landing straight ahead on the airfield to be made. For instance, in a 20 knot wind the climb angle will become or 10 to 1.

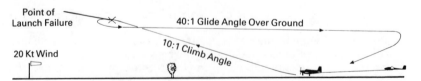

Fig 19.4   Aerotow launch failure in a strong wind. In a strong wind it may be possible to a fly a shortened circuit after an aerotow launch failure even from lower heights.

In this wind, if a turn downwind is made after the launch failure the glider will have an increased glide angle of nearly 40/1 when measured relative to the ground. It may therefore be possible to fly a shortened circuit, although a higher approach speed must be rigorously maintained due to the possible effects of any turbulence and wind gradient.

AIR EXERCISE – AEROTOW LAUNCH FAILURES

At various stages on the early part of the launch you will be asked what action you would take and where you would land the glider if the tow-rope breaks or in the event of the tow-plane giving the "release immediately" signal.

Your instructor will demonstrate the option of returning to the airfield, followed by a downwind landing by simulating a tow-rope break.

If available, a motor glider can be used to simulate aerotow launch failures at various heights and in different positions, allowing you to execute simulated field landings as necessary.

AEROTOW EMERGENCY SIGNALS

Like aerotow launch failures, emergencies during aerotowing are uncommon. As there may not be radio communication between the tow-plane pilot and the glider (and because even when there is, a radio message can be misunderstood) a series of visual emergency signals has been devised. Each of these signals conveys a specific message to the other pilot in the aerotow combination and when received each must trigger the appropriate response. The following emergency signals indicate that either the tow-plane or the glider has a problem.

1. TOW-PLANE ROCKS WINGS – RELEASE IMMEDIATELY

If the tow-plane's wings are seen to rock, you must release the tow-rope immediately, irrespective of the position or height of the glider.

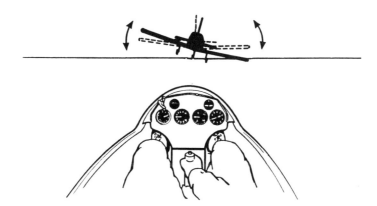

Fig 19.5   "Release immediately" signal. If the tow-plane rocks its wings you must release immediately.

This signal, (appropriately known as the "wave-off" signal) will be obvious, as it involves definite movements of the tow-plane's wings. It is easily distinguishable from any rocking of the tow-plane's wings due to turbulence, by its persistency, coupled with the fact that, in turbulence, the tow-plane's ailerons will be seen to move after, and not before, the wing movement.

The most likely reasons for the tow-plane pilot giving this signal is because the tow-plane is not climbing satisfactorily or has an engine problem. In this event a glider is better equipped to glide than a tow-plane whose engine has failed, and therefore your situation should not delay your releasing the tow-rope. Indeed the tow-plane pilot's situation may be serious enough to cause him to release the tow-rope from the tow-plane, without giving this "wave-off" signal, and so if this signal is seen you can consider that the tow-plane pilot is being nice to you. It would be totally justifiable (and probably safer) for the tow-plane pilot to release the glider without signalling.

Other reasons for this "wave-off" signal being given include:

- if continuing the climb would take the aerotow combination into cloud

- if continuing the climb would take the aerotow combination into controlled airspace

- if the tow-plane pilot is aware of any problem or of a hazardous situation developing which could be averted if the launch is discontinued.

In some circumstances, such as when flying in competitions, the "wave-off" signal is used to indicate that the maximum height permitted on the launch has been reached. The use of this signal for non-emergency purposes should be restricted to pre-briefed situations or training aimed at signal recognition, otherwise the main purpose of the signal can be confused or its urgency devalued. Whatever the perceived reason for the giving of the signal, on seeing it, you must always RELEASE THE TOW-ROPE IMMEDIATELY. It is always wise to then confirm that your airbrakes are closed and locked before manoeuvring.

2. TOW-PLANE WAGGLES RUDDER RAPIDLY – CHECK YOUR AIRBRAKES

If the tow-plane's rudder is being waggled rapidly from side to side, you must CHECK THAT YOUR AIRBRAKES ARE CLOSED AND LOCKED.

Fig 19.6   "Check airbrakes" signal. If the tow-plane's rudder is waggling you should check that your airbrakes are closed.

The reason for the tow-plane pilot giving this signal will be that the rate of climb of the tow-plane is less than is expected, despite all indications that the tow-plane's engine and flap settings are normal. The tow-plane pilot may also have noticed in his mirror that the glider's airbrakes are extended.

Failure to close the airbrakes could result in the launch having to be abandoned, leaving the glider in a poor situation to return to the airfield, with a dangerously high rate of descent and a thoroughly confused pilot.

3. GLIDER FLIES OUT TO THE LEFT AND ROCKS WINGS – GLIDER CANNOT RELEASE

In the unlikely event that you discover that you cannot release the tow-rope from the glider, you should carefully fly out to the left of the normal aerotow position and rock the glider's wings.

Fig 19.7   Glider unable to release tow-rope. If unable to release the tow-rope you should fly out to the left and rock the glider's wings.

This should alert the tow-plane pilot of your problem. While doing so, continue to pull on the cable release knob in the hope that the problem will clear itself. Concentrate on flying the glider so as not to risk losing control of your position while manoeuvring. Care will have to be taken when you rock the glider's wings, so as not to let the glider move back to the right, into or past the normal position behind the tow-plane.

On no account should you attempt to break the tow-rope by "snatching" using the elevator, as this will only cause difficulty for the tow-plane pilot.

Once it appears that the tow-plane pilot understands your problem, you can return to the normal tow position. The tow-plane pilot will take you back towards the airfield, where the rope will be released using the release mechanism on the tail of the tow-plane. You should then fly a circuit with a high base leg and final approach, aiming to land well up the airfield. This high approach and the use of a large amount of airbrake to give a high rate of descent, will reduce the chance of the trailing tow-rope being dragged across any obstructions.

In some countries, glider pilots are taught how to descend and land while still connected to the tow-plane, in case the tow-plane's release also fails to operate. However, to date, the author has never heard (except in bar folklore) of any instances of a malfunction of both the glider and the tow-plane release mechanisms on the same flight. Indeed, the occurrence of any release failure is so rare that the teaching of descending while on aerotow seems pointless, except perhaps as a skill exercise, and only then for use during the cross-country aerotow retrieving of a glider. Even in this situation, if the tow-plane pilot sets up a gentle enough descent, the glider pilot should not be required to alter his aerotowing technique significantly.

(Should the rate of descent be great enough to result in the glider catching up with the tow-plane, opening the airbrakes a small amount should rectify the situation.)

Thanks generally to high maintenance standards, the equipment used, and sensible procedures, emergencies requiring the use of the signals described are uncommon. It is essential, however, that your training includes recognising and acting upon these signals. To this end, your instructor will arrange with the tow-plane pilot for these signals to be demonstrated, in order that you will know what they look like and what to do, in case some day the unusual occurs.

AIR EXERCISE – AEROTOW EMERGENCY SIGNALS

During your training and as part of post-solo check flights, your instructor will arrange with the tow-plane pilot that you be shown or practise the various emergency signals. When receiving such a signal you will be expected to carry out the appropriate drill without delay.

CHAPTER 20

SIDESLIPPING

To increase the glider's rate of descent and thereby reduce its glide angle, we can either decrease the lift produced (as with spoilers) or increase the drag produced (as with airbrakes or tailchutes). Another way of increasing the drag is to fly the glider sideways, so that the fuselage causes the increase in drag. This manoeuvre is called the SIDESLIP. At one time, before airbrakes or other approach control devices were fitted, SIDESLIPPING was the accepted method of increasing the rate of descent on the approach, without gaining excess airspeed. Fortunately, as some form of airbrake is now fitted to most gliders, sideslipping has become more of a useful skill rather than an essential one. It is, however, still a handy skill to possess and one that should be learned if only to improve your handling abilities and maybe someday to get rid of the embarrassment of excess height.

From your earliest attempts at turning the glider, your instructor will have emphasised the need always to use aileron and rudder together and in the same "sense" (that is, when applying left aileron, you should apply left rudder). The only exception to this rule which you will have encountered so far, is when controlling the glider on the ground run during take-off or landing. At these times the movements of the controls will be unco-ordinated.

Sideslipping is another such exception to this rule of co-ordination, in that not only is co-ordinated rudder not applied, rudder is applied in the opposite direction to the aileron. Another exceptional aspect about sideslipping is that, unlike all of the general handling exercises, which are designed to teach you to manoeuvre the glider with the minimum loss of height, sideslipping is a technique employed to lose height.

The reason great emphasis is normally placed on accurate flying, and good co-ordination, is because, in order to keep drag to a minimum, the glider must be flying straight relative to the airflow. If at any time the fuselage meets the airflow at anything other than directly head (or nose) on, there will be an increase in drag. This is due to the larger, less streamlined profile of the side of the glider meeting the relative airflow. (Fig 20.1)

The sideslip is usually used simultaneously with airbrakes to give very high rates of descent.

ENTERING THE SIDESLIP

In order to sideslip the glider, it is necessary to create a force which will pull the glider sideways through the air. To provide this force, we can use our old friend, the lift force produced by the wing. By banking the glider, we can cause the lift force to act at an angle to the vertical, towards the direction of the bank. Resolving the resulting lift force gives us the same two components which we have when turning the glider. These are the vertical component and, the one we need to pull the glider sideways, the horizontal component. (Fig 20.2)

175

Fig 20.1   Sideslipping. A glider flown sideways will offer a larger area to the
airflow resulting in a greater amount of drag.

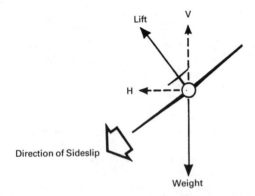

Fig 20.2   Forces in a sideslip. Banking the glider will move it sideways through
the air.

Applying bank in this way will cause the glider to turn, albeit an inaccurate turn. The weathercock stability of the fuselage will cause it to line itself up with the airflow and reduce the drag caused by the initial sideways movement through the air. However, we want this drag, and if the glider is on the approach track when the sideslip is initiated, the last thing we need is for it to begin a turn! Therefore to prevent the glider yawing around into the turn, we apply as much rudder as necessary to prevent the glider turning and to keep it on the desired track. The glider is now in a sideslip.

As when turning, the act of putting on bank will have reduced the vertical component of the lift force. This must be restored if it is to balance the

176

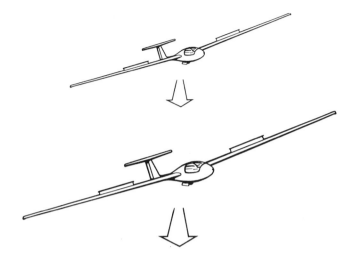

Fig 20.3   The sideslip. Sideslipping can be used to lose excess height.

weight of the glider. To redress this imbalance, the control column will need to be moved backwards, thus increasing the angle of attack of the wing and the vertical component of the lift force. If this is not done, then the nose will drop and the glider will accelerate giving an unwanted increase in airspeed.

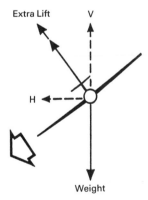

Fig 20.4   Increased lift required in a sideslip. The wing will have to provide extra lift to prevent the nose lowering and the airspeed increasing in the sideslip.

It is the banking of the glider which causes the sideslip and not the application of rudder. If the rudder is applied while the wings are level, increased drag will be produced, but the amount will not be of an extent helpful to the control of an approach. This so-called "wings-level" sideslip has no useful value and at slow airspeeds the entry into it could even result in the glider spinning.

Before entering a sideslip, the desired track of the glider during the sideslip must be selected. As the entry into the sideslip will initially cause a small change in the glider's track, it is necessary to turn the glider slightly off the desired track to counter this slight track change. This turn off track will be away from the wing which is to be lower during the sideslip.

CHANGING THE RATE OF DESCENT

Increasing the angle of bank in a sideslip will increase the rate of descent. This increase in bank will require an increase in the amount of "opposite" rudder in order to prevent the glider from turning. Similarly, to reduce the rate of descent, take off some of the bank, accompanied by the necessary reduction in the amount of rudder to maintain track. Any modification to the angle of bank will also need an elevator input to maintain attitude.

The maximum amount of bank possible will usually be dictated by the effectiveness of the rudder in preventing the glider from turning off the desired track. On many gliders, the rudder is not powerful enough to prevent a turn when very large angles of bank are used. This means that the angle of bank, and the resulting rate of descent, are limited by the tendency to turn, despite full "opposite" rudder being applied.

During the sideslip, the airspeed indicator will probably be giving an obviously erroneous indication of the glider's airspeed. This is due to the airflow passing across rather than directly into the pitot head. The accuracy of other instruments may also be badly affected, depending on the effect that the airflow has on the glider's static vents.

The nose attitude will appear to be higher than usual if large bank angles are being used. This, together with some aerodynamic buffeting and the fact that the airspeed indicator will often be useless, can be somewhat off-putting. However, after some practice at sideslipping, you will get a feel for the correct nose attitude for the angle of bank in use.

The secret of successful airspeed control in the sideslip is to make sure that you have the correct airspeed **before** entering the sideslip, and then prevent any tendency for the glider's nose to lower as the bank is applied. Allowing the nose to drop will result in excessive airspeed which, if the sideslip is being used on the approach, will make the hold-off part of the landing longer and may defeat the advantage of having used a sideslip. Providing a safe entry airspeed is used, and a reasonable amount of bank is applied, there is little chance of the glider stalling during the sideslip, as the elevator will seldom be powerful enough to stall the wing while in the sideslip.

EXITING THE SIDESLIP

On exiting the sideslip, the control column will have to be moved forwards, as once the bank has been removed, the high nose attitude would quickly result in a loss of airspeed and the possibility of stalling the wing.

To exit the sideslip, remove the bank with aileron and centralise the rudder, adjusting the nose attitude with elevator as you do so. As soon as the glider is returned to normal flight, the airspeed indicator will immediately regain its accuracy. As soon as this happens you must **check the airspeed** and adjust it as necessary. Having done this, make any track adjustments necessary using co-ordinated aileron and rudder.

On some gliders, the rudder will suffer from an aerodynamic effect known as "over-balance", which will mean that a considerable force will need to be applied to centralise it. Do not worry if you seem to be encountering some resistance on the rudder, all you have to do is push harder on the pedal and it will respond normally. This force will not be excessive, and is within the power of the weakest legs. This peculiar characteristic, which is only likely when full rudder is being used, is only mentioned here so that if you meet it, you are not taken by surprise.

The sideslip should be exited at a height which gives you plenty of time to carry out a normal landing, and well before there is any danger of the lower wing coming into contact with the ground. Once you are more experienced and providing that you are in current practice at sideslipping, this will be low enough to allow sideslipping to become a useful approach control technique.

USING AIRBRAKES DURING THE SIDESLIP

Normally on a glider fitted with airbrakes (or spoilers), sideslipping would only be used either for practising the manoeuvre for fun, in the rare event that the airbrakes have failed to open, or if a rate of descent greater than that achievable with full airbrake is required.

In the latter situation, you can enter the sideslip either before or after the airbrakes are opened, although normally the sideslip would be entered with the airbrakes fully open. Once the sideslip has been established, the airbrakes can be used to increase or decrease the rate of descent as required. In this way the airbrakes become a useful tool for making "fine" adjustments to what can be a considerable rate of descent. The angle of bank in the sideslip can also be altered as required, giving wider control of the rate of descent.

The rate of descent using sideslip and airbrake together will be very high, therefore it becomes more important to allow plenty of height for recovery from the sideslip, especially if it is intended to keep the airbrakes open for the landing.

As little time exists on the approach for practising sideslips, especially those involving airbrakes, it is essential that the general technique of sideslipping is practised at height before attempting a sideslip on the approach. This is especially so as some gliders display adverse handling characteristics when sideslipping with the airbrakes open, which are not present when sideslipping without airbrakes. When you are learning to sideslip, your instructor will demonstrate any peculiarities which your glider may have. Once you are flying single-seat gliders, you should again explore the handling during the sideslip at height before you attempt to sideslip on an approach.

THE SLIPPING TURN

A very useful variation of the straight sideslip is the SLIPPING TURN. Whereas the straight sideslip is useful at adjusting the glider's height once flying on a straight track (usually the approach), there is often a need to change track while dumping height. Here the slipping turn can prove its worth.

The way to turn while sideslipping is simply to reduce the amount of rudder from that required to keep the glider on a straight track. The rudder can be increased back to its original amount once the new track has been gained.

The slipping turn can also be used while entering into a turn (such as the final turn) by entering a normal turn, but with insufficient rudder (some "opposite" rudder will probably have to be applied later in the entry). Once the glider is on the desired track the slipping turn can either be converted into a straight sideslip by applying the required amount of "opposite" rudder to prevent the glider turning further or the turn exited to resume normal wings-level flight.

Again airbrakes or spoilers can also be used with this manoeuvre and the same considerations apply as when using these devices with the straight sideslip, with special emphasis on being wary of the high rate of descent.

Sideslipping is a relatively advanced exercise and one that is little used normally, thanks to the fact that most gliders are now fitted with excellent airbrakes. It is, however, a useful skill to possess for the day when you need to lose height fast and it is also a very satisfying manoeuvre when performed well. Although when first described, it appears to be an "unco-ordinated" piece of flying, the sideslip flown well, with good airspeed control and co-ordinated airbrake is actually a skilful and enjoyable exercise.

AIR EXERCISE – SIDESLIPPING

The following exercise will be demonstrated by your instructor and you will then be allowed to attempt it. Initial attempts at sideslipping are best carried out at height using a ground feature towards which to track.

STAGE 1

Fly the glider at its approach speed on a high, long approach.

Turn the glider so that it is heading at a slight angle to the approach track required.

Lower the wing which is pointing more towards the landing area but prevent the glider turning by applying sufficient opposite rudder.

Prevent the nose from lowering with elevator.

Increase or decrease the rate of descent in the sideslip as required by increasing or decreasing the angle of bank, (with a corresponding change in the amount of rudder to prevent the glider turning).

Return to normal flight by levelling the wings and realigning the glider with the landing track, lowering the nose to the required attitude as you do so.

Check the airspeed.

STAGE 2

Fly the glider at its approach speed on a high, long approach.

Open full airbrake and use the sideslip to increase the rate of descent.

Increase or decrease the rate of descent by adjusting the amount of airbrake.

Return to normal flight, remembering to lower the nose to the required attitude as you do so.

Check the airspeed and adjust the airbrake setting as required.

STAGE 3

Fly the glider at its approach speed on a high, long approach.

Set up a sideslip (preferably without airbrakes, to give more time).

Experiment with the amount of rudder to adjust the glider's track during the sideslip.

Return to normal flight early enough to allow you to realign the glider with the desired track.

Check the airspeed.

CHAPTER 21

THE USE OF FLAPS

The use of flaps tends to be treated as an advanced exercise. This is not because flaps are difficult to use, but simply because very few training gliders and single-seat gliders available to early solo pilots are fitted with flaps. There are however, a few notable exceptions and as progress can often be made quickly to private ownership of a glider which is fitted with flaps, this section is included to give you some idea of how to operate flaps efficiently and safely.

WHY FLAPS ARE FITTED

To understand why designers think it is worthwhile fitting flaps, let us look at the shape of various wings. If we look at the wing section of a typical vintage glider, we would see a highly-cambered, convex upper surface and a lower surface which is concave.

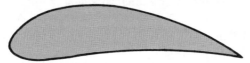

Fig 21.1   Early wing section. Early wings had a large amount of camber.

With this large degree of camber, this wing section will produce a large amount of lift, but due to its thickness and large surface area, will also produce (by modern glider standards) a lot of profile drag. As profile drag increases with airspeed, the drag penalties of this wing section are enormous at higher airspeeds. This means that this wing section will only be efficient over a small range of airspeeds and will be best at lower airspeeds.

A section through a modern wing section, will show a much thinner wing with much less camber on the upper surface and a virtually flat lower surface. (In fact, on a modern glider the lower surface of the wing will probably have a very complicated profile, but unless you examined it very closely, it would appear relatively flat.)

This wing section will produce less lift at low airspeed because of its lack of camber, but will also produce less drag due to its thin profile and lower wing area. As the airspeed is increased the drag produced will increase at a lesser rate than it would with a thicker wing.

Fig 21.2   Modern wing section. The modern wing section is much thinner and less cambered.

Both of these wing sections have their merits. The early (thicker and more cambered) wing will enable its glider to fly slower, resulting in the glider having a smaller turn radius, a lower stalling speed and as a result a lower landing speed. The modern wing will give less drag over a greater airspeed range, a better glide angle throughout this range and better handling.

Both wing sections have their opposite disadvantages, but it is the advantages that the designer wishes to combine and this is where flaps come in useful. By lowering or raising the flap the pilot can change the wing section at will, thus selecting the best wing section for the phase of flight.

Fig 21.3 Flaps combine the advantages of both the highly cambered and the less cambered wing sections.

In addition to these advantages, sensible use of flaps will keep the wing operating near its optimum angle of attack and will also result in the fuselage meeting the airflow at the angle which causes least drag.

Fuselage Centreline

Relative Airflow

Fig 21.4 Fuselage alignment with flaps. Flaps help keep the fuselage at an optimum angle to the airflow.

TYPES OF FLAP

Flaps fitted to gliders are usually of a plain, hinged type, designed to change the camber of the wing.

A few gliders have been designed with flaps of a type which, as well as altering the wing's camber, also allow the wing's area to be increased or decreased. This type of flap is not common on gliders, as the mechanisms required to operate such flaps can be complicated and it is difficult to produce a flap-to-wing joint which will fit well and thus create little drag. Indeed, unless this flap-to-wing joint is a good fit, the resulting drag may well cancel any advantages gained from having flaps fitted.

Extension

Fig 21.5 Area-changing flaps. Some flaps can be used to increase the wing area for slow speed flight.

The plain hinged flap commonly found on gliders will allow the trailing edge of the wing to be lowered through, typically, two angles (or STAGES). The first of these stages is around 8° for flight at slow airspeeds and the second stage is around 30° for the approach and landing.

Fig 21.6   Positive flap. There are usually 2 positive (down) flap settings. (+8° and +30°)

Often, on high performance gliders, the flaps can also be raised through two stages above the neutral (or 0°) flap position to reduce the camber of the wing. These flap settings are used for flight at high airspeeds.

Fig 21.7   Negative flap. There are normally 2 negative (up) flap settings. (-4° and -7°)

The flaps may be linked to the ailerons, so that as flap is raised or lowered, both ailerons rise or lower in unison, thus making sure that as much of the wing as possible has the best camber for the phase of flight. However, as the flaps are lowered, aileron drag will increase and the ailerons will lose some of their effectiveness. For this reason, the flap/aileron interlink is usually designed in such a way that the ailerons lower to a lesser extent than the flaps. When full down flap is selected for landing, the ailerons will become independent of the flap movement, thus ensuring no further degradation of the glider's lateral control at this critical stage of the flight.

A further refinement of this flap/aileron interlink is to have the flaps connected to the ailerons in such a way that when aileron is used, the whole of the trailing edge of the wing acts as an aileron (e.g. Pik 20 and LS 6 single-seat gliders). This system should, in theory, give as good a roll rate as conventional ailerons with less angular deflection of the control surface and less drag.

On a few gliders, the flaps are the only means of controlling the rate of descent on the approach. On these gliders, the flaps can be lowered to much greater angles, giving large amounts of drag and high rates of descent.

FLAP CONTROLS AND THEIR CALIBRATION

The flaps are normally controlled by a single lever in the cockpit which is moved aft to lower the flaps and forwards to raise them. On the Pik 20B, on which it is normal to use large amounts of flap to control the glider's rate of descent on the approach, a rotating handle is employed to adjust the flaps. On the Kestrel 19, in order to select landing flap, a separate control lever is used from that which selects performance flap. This system prevents the interlinked ailerons from lowering when landing flap is used. With these exceptions, the simple, one-lever control has become standard, making flap operation less complicated and easy to use.

The flap lever on modern gliders will operate through a small range of movement, and will be calibrated so that the pilot can see how much flap is selected. This is normally done by having the flap lever spring loaded, so that it will rest in one of several detents against which will be inscribed the corresponding amount of flap. This calibration may be in the number of degrees of flap selected (for example, +30°, +8°, 0°, -4° or -7°) or simply the stage of the flap (Land, +1, 0, -1, -2).

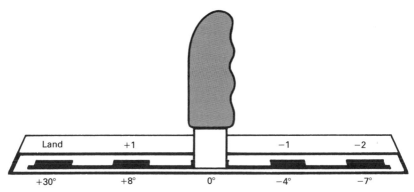

Fig 21.8   Flap control. The flap lever is either calibrated in degrees (°) or in stages of flap.

There may be a safety guard fitted to prevent the flap lever being moved once the airbrakes are opened, such as on the Mosquito, on which, if the airbrakes are not locked shut, a metal bar prevents the flaps being moved. This system reduces the chance of cockpit confusion leading to the raising of flap instead of the closing of the airbrakes.

USE OF FLAPS ON TAKE-OFF

For take-off the flaps should be set to give the wing enough camber to produce the maximum amount of lift, as early as possible, without creating too much drag. There will be a flap setting for take-off which will typically be with the flaps lowered by about 8°. This setting may well be the same as that used for low speed flight.

Some manufacturers may recommend that zero flap is used for take-off. This may be to ensure adequate aileron control during the ground run. On many gliders, it may be necessary, when aerotowing, to begin the ground run with the flaps in a negative (upward) setting, such as -7°. This will raise the ailerons and give the maximum aileron control at low airspeeds. This may be necessary in light crosswind conditions in order to prevent a wing dropping during the early part of the ground run. As soon as good aileron and directional control is gained, the flaps can then be lowered to the recommended take-off setting. Should this technique be used, it is essential that,

a) your hand is kept on the cable release knob and NOT on the flap lever, until definite aileron and directional control is gained. (No amount of fiddling with the flaps will prevent the glider swinging on take-off, so there is little point in holding the flap lever at this early stage!)

and

b) when you decide to change the flap setting, you should positively identify the flap lever before operating it.

Changing the flap at this stage may cause the glider to become airborne suddenly. Be ready for this and avoid climbing too high above the ground in case you cause problems for the tow-plane pilot.

Generally, if you can avoid having to make flap changes during the take-off run, you are best to do so. Any headwind present may remove the need for this technique, which can be a distraction at a time when even the most experienced pilot needs to concentrate on the aerotow. Starting the launch with a negative flap setting should not be necessary on a wire launch, as the initial acceleration will be much greater, giving aileron control almost immediately.

One advantage of having flap lowered during an aerotow is that the glider will fly more nose down than it would in zero flap. This will give you a better view of the tow-plane.

The use of any of these techniques will depend on the manufacturer's advice given in the glider's operating manual. If this is not available, then seek the advice of an instructor who has experience of the particular glider to be flown.

USE OF FLAPS IN FLIGHT

Flaps which can be used in flight to improve the glider's overall performance are appropriately known as PERFORMANCE FLAPS.

The large airspeed ranges used by modern gliders, especially when racing on cross-country flights, will mean that if flaps are fitted, they should be adjusted as the airspeed is changed. This will keep the glider's wing flying at the optimum angle of attack and give it the best amount of camber for the phase of flight at any one time.

Essentially, this means that when the glider is circling in, or flying slowly through an area of rising air, the flaps should be lowered slightly (usually to a setting of +8°). To lower them beyond this amount will probably incur such a large drag penalty as to cancel out the benefit of any extra lift gained. (There may be exceptional cases where the area of rising air is so small or turbulent that a greater degree of flap may be beneficial. This is especially so if this further lowering of flap results in no further loss of aileron effectiveness. This will depend greatly on the particular glider and its flap/aileron linkage.)

Zero flap (0°) is the flap setting with which the glider will achieve its best glide angle. Typically this setting would be used over a range of airspeeds on either side of the airspeed which will give the best glide angle.

Once the glider accelerates to fly at airspeeds of 60 knots and over, then a thinner, less cambered wing is an advantage. Not only will a thinner wing create less drag but there will be no need for a large amount of camber, as the increased airflow over the wing will produce more lift, making up for any lift lost due to the decrease in camber. If the glider is fitted with performance flaps which can be raised above the zero flap position, then the pilot can create the less cambered wing required by selecting the flaps to an upward (negative flap) position.

Normally there will be two negative flap positions, these are -4° and -7° of flap.

The first stage of negative flap (-4°) should be used at airspeeds of between about 60 to 75 knots. Once the glider is flying faster than 75 knots, then the second stage of negative flap (-7°) should be selected.

The airspeeds given are only approximations to give you some idea of the use of performance flaps. If using these flaps sounds complicated, do not worry, as there is usually a considerable overlap of the airspeed ranges suitable for each flap setting. The table below shows the manufacturer's recommended flap settings and the corresponding airspeed bands for a typical high performance glider.

FLAP SETTING	OPTIMUM RANGE (Knots)
+8°	up to 52
0°	49 to 67
−4°	54 – 86
−7°	67 and above

It is important to appreciate that, when using performance flaps, flying at an airspeed above the airspeed range for the flap setting selected, will create excess drag and reduce the glider's performance. On the other hand, trying to circle in rising air with a zero or negative flap setting will require extra airspeed due to the wing having less camber and will result in larger radius turns. This could mean the difference between gaining or losing height, depending on the rate of ascent and the size of the area of rising air.

In order to get the best performance from a flapped glider, you should keep your hand on the flap lever when in flight, easing the flaps up or down as the airspeed is increased or decreased through the various airspeed ranges. Try and avoid jerky flap movements and unnecessary changes of flap.

USE OF FLAPS DURING THE APPROACH

The final turn on to the approach will normally be made with the flaps set to the first stage of positive flap (+8°). Although this flap setting will spoil the glider's handling slightly, it will also reduce the stalling speed and give a more nose-down attitude on the approach.

If the glider is fitted with airbrakes (and thankfully most are) the flaps can be selected to their LAND setting (+30°) once you are sure that the glider is well within range of the landing area, with no danger of undershooting. The rate of descent can then be controlled with the airbrakes, without the need to re-adjust the flaps. Indeed, once the flaps have been set to LAND, they should not be raised, as this will cause a reduction in the lift produced by the wing, an *increase* in the stalling speed, and a loss of height at a time when this could result in an undershoot.

Unlike when you select the take-off or positive performance flap settings (+8°), selecting LAND flap lowers the flap beyond the angle at which a useful amount of extra lift is produced (after about 10° down) to a setting where there is a large increase in the drag produced. This will reduce the glide angle while still allowing a low touchdown airspeed, and make it easier to judge and execute the landing.

If airbrakes are not fitted, then the flaps may be the only approach control device available. If this is the case, then a different approach technique will be necessary if safe approaches are to be made. Gliders which are designed to use flaps alone will usually have flaps which extend downwards through much larger angles (80° to 90°).

Again, when using these flaps, it is essential, before lowering landing flap, that you are sure you can safely reach the landing area. Once you are safely within range of the landing area, you can increase the amount of flap to adjust the touchdown position as desired. Once you begin the round out, leave the flaps at a constant setting and concentrate on landing the glider. Do not attempt to reduce the flap on the final part of the approach because as well as the initial loss of height, the airspeed may increase due to the reduction in drag from what was a large degree of flap. This could make control of the landing more difficult.

If the flap mechanism permits, selecting negative flap on the ground run, may give better aileron control and help prevent a wing dropping before the glider has stopped. This selection will only be possible if the flap operating mechanism allows swift flap adjustments. If for any reason this will prove a distraction, do not use this technique, but instead, give your full concentration to controlling the glider during the ground run.

LIMITING FLAP SPEEDS

The lowering of flap causes a change in the position of the centre of pressure and in the amount of lift (and drag) produced by the wing. This results in twisting loads being exerted on the wing. Since all of these forces increase as the airspeed increases, it is common to limit the maximum airspeed for flight with the flaps lowered.

The airspeed limitations will vary depending on the degree of flap being used, and it is essential that flap is not lowered if the airspeed exceeds this limiting value.

Some modern gliders have very generous flap limiting airspeeds. For instance, on the Janus C, two-seat glider, you can use any flap setting except landing flap, up to the maximum permitted airspeed for the glider (known as Vne) which, in this instance, is 135 knots. The landing flap has a maximum airspeed limit of 76 knots. The Slingsby Kestrel on the other hand has a more complicated flap system than most, with a larger range of maximum flap airspeed limits to remember. To illustrate this point, these limits are shown below.

FLAP SETTING	MAXIMUM AIRSPEED (Knots)
−2	135
−1	100
0	100
+1	70
+2	65
LANDING FLAP (with cruise flap at +2)	65
½ LANDING FLAP (with cruise flap at +2)	65

TRAILING EDGE AIRBRAKES

Instead of being fitted with conventional airbrakes, which appear as vertical paddles on the top, or on the top and bottom of the wing, some gliders are fitted with airbrakes which, like flaps, are situated along the trailing edge of the wing. This type of airbrake may or may not be linked to a performance flap system.

THE SIMPLE TRAILING EDGE AIRBRAKE

In its simplest form, the trailing edge airbrake is a hinged surface designed to rotate so as to project into the airflow above and below the wing. The amount to which it is rotated, dictates the amount of drag which will be produced and the rate of descent achieved.

Such drag-producing devices, fitted so far back on the wing, should not significantly affect the glider's stalling speed. However, these airbrakes tend to be very powerful and care must be exercised in case the airspeed reduces as they are opened. Whether or not there is some extra lift

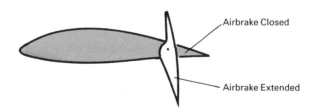

Airbrake Closed

Airbrake Extended

Fig 21.9   Trailing edge airbrakes. With simple trailing edge airbrakes the whole surface rotates when airbrake is used.

produced as this type of trailing edge airbrake is opened, depends very much on their design, but generally this is unnoticeable and more than cancelled out by the large increase in drag produced.

FLAP/AIRBRAKE SYSTEMS

A more complex system of trailing edge airbrake is the flap/airbrake system (known as FLAP BRAKES). With this system, the glider possesses conventional performance flaps which will have a setting for approach and landing. In addition to, and linked to this flap, will be a trailing edge airbrake. When the airbrake lever is operated, a portion of the upper surface of the wing, just in front of the flaps, rotates upwards to cause extra drag.

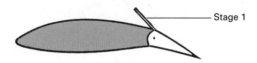

Stage 1

Fig 21.10   Flap brakes – stage 1 movement. Operating the first stage of flap brake raises a section of airbrake at the trailing edge of the wing.

Once this airbrake section has reached a certain extension, further aft movement of the airbrake lever will, as well as extending the airbrake section further, lower the flaps to a large angle (around 80°) to increase the drag and rate of descent dramatically.

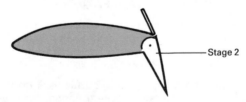

Stage 2

Fig 21.11   Flap brakes – stage 2 movement. When full flap brake is used the first stage of the flap brake opens further, pushing the flaps down to a large angle.

These flap brakes are among the most effective airbrakes to be found on gliders and approaches can often be made in such gliders, using only the first stage of flap brake, leaving the second stage to reduce the float during the hold off.

With this type of airbrake, there may again be a momentary increase in lift as the flap section is lowered, but this should not create any difficulties, as the total drag produced is impressive. Due to this ability to increase the drag dramatically, adequate airspeed on the approach must be adopted and carefully maintained.

Both types of trailing edge airbrake tend not to show the "suck-open" effect of the paddle type of airbrake, but it remains a good habit to keep your hand on the airbrake lever once the airbrakes have been opened.

The characteristic of reducing lift when flap is raised at slow airspeeds, is still something you should be aware of if you find yourself undershooting the landing area when using this type of airbrake. Due to the effectiveness of trailing edge airbrakes, approaching slightly higher than necessary should not be a problem as excess height can readily be lost. However, causing the glider to be low on approach, as a result of premature use of large amounts of airbrake may leave you in a predicament (or the field before the landing area).

All in all, trailing edge airbrakes are excellent devices for controlling the rate of descent on the approach, and often will be powerful enough to have an airspeed limiting role. They are easy to use, and with a little practice, can give a pilot confidence when the need to land in a restricted landing area arises.

USEFUL HINTS WHEN FLYING FLAPPED GLIDERS

Apart from the airspeed limits which apply to flight in particular flap settings and the dangers involved if the flaps are raised on the approach (resulting in loss of height), there are a few other precautions which are worth taking when flying a flapped glider.

Firstly, the cockpit of a flapped glider will have at least one more control lever than an unflapped machine. While on the face of it, the addition of one lever should not increase the workload significantly, the result in the small cockpit area of most gliders will be a certain clutter of controls. The flap lever will almost certainly be close to the airbrake lever, and although these will be different colours, on some gliders they are of the same shape and size. When the designer decides to make the undercarriage lever a similar size and shape, and situates it close to the other two controls, then all the ingredients are present for the wrong control to be operated. This is especially so when the workload is high, such as on take-off and on the approach. To reduce the chances of this happening, especially in a glider in which you have little or no experience, take time to familiarise yourself with the control layout. This is best done by sitting in the glider and identifying the position and feel of various control levers. Do this while the glider is away from the bustle of the launch point. When in flight, identify each control lever visually before operating it, checking visually that the setting selected is that which is required.

A useful *aide-memoire*, that will be of assistance in making sure that you are not flying in a wrong flap setting relative to the glider's airspeed, will be to note an airspeed in the middle of each of the flap airspeed ranges and display it on a card on the instrument panel with its corresponding flap setting. The best place for this card is close to the airspeed indicator. As you change airspeed away from one datum airspeed towards another, you can change to the next flap as the airspeed passes the halfway point between the two airspeeds.

Better still is to construct a ring which fits around the airspeed indicator. This ring can be colour-coded and marked to show the airspeeds at which the flap setting should be changed. If this ring is properly calibrated (from the glider's handling notes) then the airspeed indicator needle will indicate the required flap setting. This ring can also be marked with the various maximum airspeeds, if the airspeed indicator does not already show these.

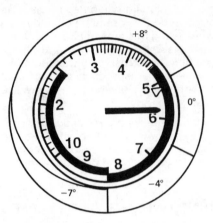

Fig 21.12   Air speed indicator calibrated with flap speeds. Calibrating the airspeed indicator with flap speeds saves having to remember the various speed ranges.

SECTION 2

TECHNICAL SECTION

CHAPTER 22

GLIDER DESIGN

A common question from anyone contemplating a first flight in a glider is, "Is it safe?" The inquiry may be a general one regarding the concept of flight without an engine, or it may be directed at the controllability or structural integrity of the glider about to be flown.

Engineless flight has been around for a long time, and apart from the ability to take-off or gain height on demand, a glider is designed with the same basic controls and the same aerodynamic principles in mind as any powered aeroplane, be that a light single-engine aeroplane or a jumbo jet.

As for the structure of the glider about to be flown, all gliders have to meet stringent design criteria, normally set by recognised international authorities. These will ensure that the glider is strong enough to withstand both the aerodynamic loads of flight and the loads placed upon it during take-off and landing. All of these criteria assume flight in adverse conditions, and safety factors are applied. Annual (and indeed daily) inspections are carried out to ensure no deterioration of the structure as a whole. (Certificate of Airworthiness and Daily Inspections).

The general handling and control of the glider is also an essential element where safety is concerned. If a glider were to be very difficult to fly, then the pilot's workload would be intolerably high and safety would suffer. The designer, therefore, tries to produce a glider which has good handling and is easy to fly. Although the designer's ultimate target may be to design a glider with world-beating performance, the aerodynamically perfect machine will not be much good if it cannot be flown at a chosen airspeed or if the wing stalls every time the pilot sneezes.

With the handling characteristics in mind, every new type of glider receives a series of test flights, both by the manufacturer's test pilots and by pilots appointed by the national authority of any country in which the glider will be flown. These test flights will explore all of the glider's flying characteristics, throughout the full range of allowed centre of gravity positions, thus exploring how the glider will behave for the lightest or heaviest of pilots. If any shortcomings are found, the glider will not be allowed to be sold or imported until modifications are carried out.

The handling and strength of gliders has improved immensely since gliding became popular in the 1920s. Whether a glider is constructed of wood and fabric, metal or glass fibre, you can rest assured that it has been declared safe by a group of competent test pilots.

DESIGN FEATURES

Apart from the wing (which is essential to produce an upward force to counter the glider's weight) and the fuselage (which accommodates the pilot) almost all of the design features of a glider are either to provide the pilot with reasonable handling characteristics or the maximum performance possible. Often there will be conflict between these two aims and the end result will be a compromise between handling and performance.

CHAPTER 23

DESIGN FEATURES WHICH PROVIDE GOOD HANDLING

STABILITY

A certain degree of STABILITY is necessary if the glider is to be easy to fly. STABILITY can be defined as the tendency of the glider to return to its original condition of flight after being upset by a gust or other disturbance. A common analogy for the various degrees of stability is to consider a ball sitting on a curved bowl. If the bowl is placed concave side up, and the ball is lying inside of the bowl, then this situation is one of stability. That is, if the ball is displaced from the central position, it will tend to roll back to its original position, albeit after a series of decreasing oscillations to either side.

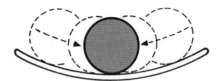

Fig 23.1   Stability. A ball inside a bowl would return to its original position if disturbed.

On the other hand if the bowl were inverted (convex side up) and the ball placed on top of it, any disturbance would result in the ball accelerating away from its original position. This would therefore be an UNSTABLE situation.

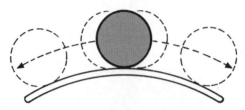

Fig 23.2   Instability. A ball on top of an inverted bowl would, if disturbed, accelerate away from its original position.

If the glider is UNSTABLE, you would find that you would constantly have to make control inputs to keep it flying at a constant attitude and in the desired direction. Clearly this would make the task of flying difficult and very tiring. If the glider is too STABLE, then large control deflections, and

196

possibly large forces, would be necessary to manoeuvre the glider, again adding to your workload. A compromise is required, and as a result, gliders are designed with a reasonable degree of stability but without so much stability that manoeuvring is difficult.

During early training you will probably find that the controls seem light and sensitive and that the glider has a mind of its own. However, if you were to release the controls of your training glider for a few seconds, (assuming that the glider is trimmed and is somewhere near a normal attitude) then you will find that the glider settles down in a reasonable attitude, after a few oscillations. The moral of this exercise is clear, "Relax! The glider is better designed to fly than you; so let it."

DIRECTIONAL STABILITY

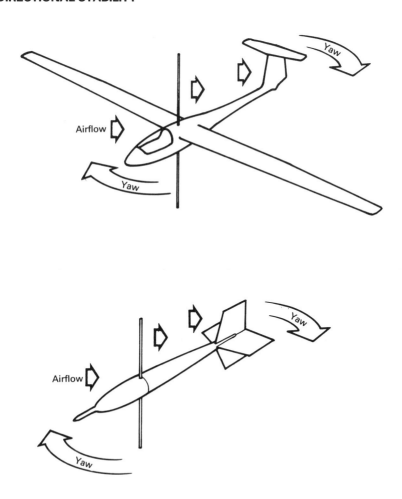

Fig 23.3   Directional stability. A glider is shaped similar to a dart. The fin gives it directional stability.

197

Probably the easiest type of stability to understand is DIRECTIONAL STABILITY. In many ways the glider is not unlike a dart, with its centre of gravity quite well forward and a vane-like structure (the fin and tailplane) trailing at the end of a long lever (the fuselage) similar to the fins or feathers on a dart. If the dart was to begin to fly sideways, the air would exert a force on its feathers causing it to line up with the airflow. Thus the feathers give the dart directional stability. (Fig 23.3)

Similarly, if the glider was to meet the airflow anyway other than head-on, a force would be created which would act on the large fin and rudder area, causing the glider to line itself up with the direction of the airflow. Thus the fin, and to some extent the rear fuselage, give the glider directional stability. The size of the fin and rudder, and the length of the rear fuselage will dictate how directionally stable the glider is.

Additionally, although only found on older wooden gliders, a fuselage with flat vertical sides will increase the directional stability. On some gliders, (e.g. the Bocian two-seater) where the fin area has proved lacking, the overall side area of the rear fuselage has been increased by adding an insert called a DORSAL STRAKE, between the rear fuselage and the fin, to give greater directional stability.

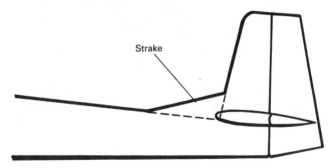

Strake

Fig 23.4   Dorsal strake. A dorsal strake may be incorporated to increase directional stability.

LATERAL STABILITY

If either wing is lowered, the glider will tend to turn towards that wing. Should this occur as a result of a gust or the presence of rising air under one wing, the glider will change heading and the pilot will be forced to return the glider to the desired heading by using aileron and rudder. The need for these continual corrections would be a nuisance, and to prevent this, gliders are designed with features which tend to level the wings automatically after such unintentional excursions from wings-level flight. The glider is therefore said to possess some LATERAL STABILITY.

The most effective design feature employed on gliders to give lateral stability is called DIHEDRAL. This involves setting the wings at an angle to the horizontal, when viewed from in front, so that the wing tips are higher than the wing roots. This angle is called the DIHEDRAL ANGLE.

If a wing lowers without the necessary input of rudder (as might happen in a gust) the glider will begin to slip sideways through the air, towards the lower wing (just as in a sideslip). The designer, by use of dihedral, uses this fact to raise the wing until the wings are again level and the sideslipping ends. Here is how it works.

Dihedral Angle

Fig 23.5   Lateral stability – dihedral. Dihedral is employed to give lateral stability.

If a glider which has dihedral starts to slip towards the lower wing, the airflow will meet the lower wing at a higher angle of attack than it will meet the higher wing. This will cause more lift to be produced by the lower wing than the higher wing. This imbalance of lift will cause the wings to level, removing the slip. Once all the slip has been removed the balance of lift between the wings will be restored, and the dihedral will have done its work.

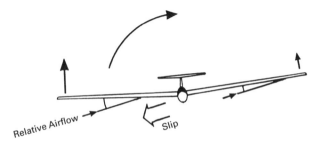

Relative Airflow   Slip

Fig 23.6   How dihedral works. The differential lift created due to dihedral raises the lower wing.

High-speed aircraft usually have wings which are swept back towards the wing tips to increase their high-speed performance. Sweeping the wings back in this way has the effect of giving an aircraft lateral stability. This SWEEPBACK is seldom employed on gliders, being more beneficial on high-speed aircraft. However, many two-seat gliders display SWEEP FORWARD which is laterally destabilising, and as the aerodynamics of the two features are linked, a brief description of how they work is in order.

In normal, wings-level flight, both wings will meet the airflow head-on producing an equal amount of lift from each wing. (Fig 23.7)

If the wing has sweepback, any tendency of the glider to slip towards the lower wing will cause that wing to encounter the airflow more at right angles causing it to produce more lift. The higher wing will meet the airflow at a reduced angle thus producing less lift. The imbalance in the lift produced at each wing will tend to level the wings. Just as with dihedral, this effect is only present when sideslipping. (Fig 23.8)

For the same reasons, sweeping the wings forward has the opposite effect, that is to reduce lateral stability. The reasons a glider designer might have to employ sweep forward will be discussed shortly, but if you look around

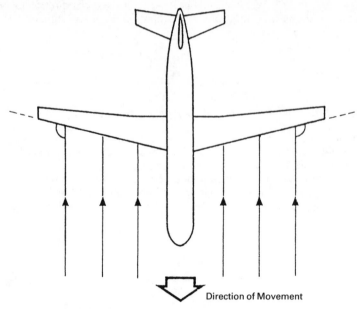

Fig 23.7   Sweepback. When the airflow meets both wings head-on, an equal amount of lift is generated at each wing.

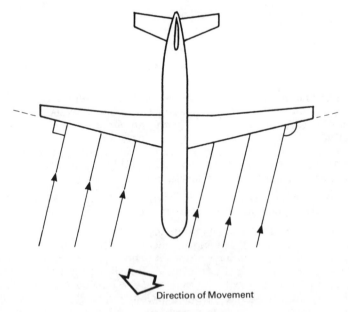

Fig 23.8   How sweepback works. If an aircraft with sweepback sideslips, the lower wing will meet the airflow more at right angles than the other and produce more lift, raising that wing.

any gliding club, you will notice that the gliders which display sweep forward usually have lots of dihedral (e.g. Bocian and ASK 13 two-seat gliders). This is the designer weighing a de-stabilising feature, the sweep forward, against a stabilising one, dihedral.

Incidentally, the opposite of dihedral, the sweeping downwards of the wing, is called ANHEDRAL. The Harrier Jump-jet is a classic example of an aircraft designed with anhedral. Next time you see a photograph of a Harrier, see if you can work out the countering feature in its wing design.

Another design feature which will make the glider more reluctant to roll in the first place, is the size of the glider's wings. If one wing is raised, whether as a result of a gust or as a result of aileron application, there will be a resistance to the downward movement of the other wing as it meets the airflow at an increased angle of attack, resulting in more lift being produced at that wing. This resistance to any rolling motion will only be present while the wing is going down and it will not level the wings. The larger the glider's wingspan, the more pronounced will be this effect.

As this feature does not return the glider to wings-level flight, strictly speaking it does not increase the glider's lateral stability.

LONGITUDINAL STABILITY

The last type of stability to be considered is LONGITUDINAL STABILITY. This is stability in a nose up/nose down sense, often called PITCH STABILITY.

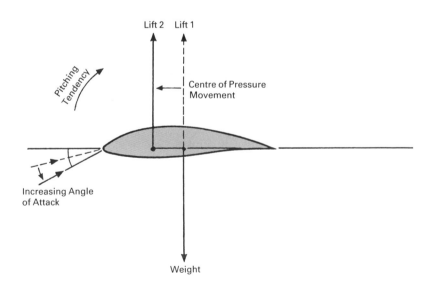

Fig 23.9   Longitudinal instability of the wing. If the angle of attack increases the centre of pressure will move forward, further increasing the angle of attack.

The conventional wing on its own is unstable. This is due to the fact that, although the position of the centre of gravity is fixed during flight, the centre of pressure moves. As the angle of attack of the wing increases, the centre of pressure moves forwards, tending to tip the wing leading edge upwards around the centre of gravity. This in turn increases the angle of attack further, aggravating the situation, and so on. (Fig 23.9)

To counter this instability, the designer needs to employ another, smaller aerofoil positioned forward or behind the wing. On gliders this aerofoil is placed at the rear of the fuselage and is known as the TAILPLANE or, if you prefer an appropriate American expression, the STABILISER. Some aircraft have this stabiliser at the front of the aircraft and then the design is known as a CANARD, but this style has not caught on in glider design and need not be considered here.

Now that our glider has been fitted with a tailplane, let us look at how this creates longitudinal stability. If the glider encounters a gust which increases the angle of attack of the wing, the same gust will also increase the angle of attack of the tailplane. Although the tailplane has a much smaller area, its distance from the glider's centre of gravity means that although it produces a relatively small force, this force acts at the end of a long lever (the distance from the tailplane to the glider's centre of gravity) and this MOMENT (force x distance) can counter the de-stabilising moment occurring at the wing.

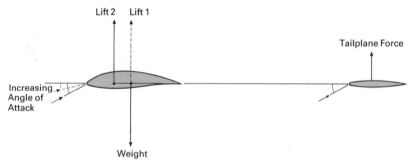

Lift 2   Lift 1

Tailplane Force

Increasing Angle of Attack

Weight

Fig 23.10   The tailplane gives the glider longitudinal stability.

The size of the tailplane and elevator, and the length of the rear fuselage are critical in achieving longitudinal stability. Designers aim to keep both of these to a minimum, but if the tailplane is too small for the length of fuselage, or the fuselage too short for the size of tailplane, then stability will suffer.

The longitudinal stability of a glider can be affected even after the glider has been constructed with an adequate size of tailplane and a suitably long fuselage. Remember that the centre of gravity of the glider is the point about which the moments produced by the wing and the tailplane act. The designer has based his calculations on a specific range of positions of the centre of gravity. The pilot's weight will have a large bearing on the position of the glider's centre of gravity. The lighter the pilot, the further aft will be the centre of gravity, and the greater the moment arm from the centre of pressure, resulting in the glider being less stable.

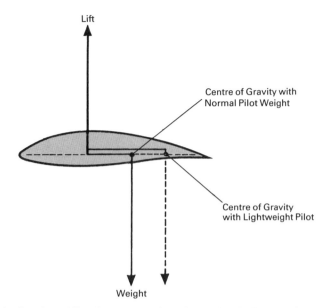

Fig 23.11   Longitudinal instability due to an underweight pilot. A pilot who is too light will move the centre of gravity aft and tend to make the glider unstable.

To avoid the glider having too little stability for safety, the designer will specify a minimum weight for the pilot. The glider should not be flown by a pilot who is less than this weight (including parachute) as it will result in the glider being unstable, more difficult to control and probably dangerous to fly. In the event that you are close to this MINIMUM COCKPIT LOADING limit, you should only fly the glider if you have installed enough ballast in the glider in order to place the cockpit loading well within the permitted weight range. This ballast, which normally comes in the form of pre-shaped lead weights, must be secured to the strengthened fittings usually provided on the cockpit floor.

In tandem, two-seat gliders, a large range of cockpit loads is required, in order that the glider can be flown dual or solo. In order to achieve this, the wings of these gliders will often display sweep forward. By using such a wing shape, the designer can seat the rear pilot close to the centre of gravity, without the glider's wing getting in the way. This means that the glider can be flown solo from the front seat, with little or no extra ballast. In addition, there are the advantages of better visibility and easy access for the rear seat pilot.

While stability is essential, the need to provide it causes performance penalties. Providing a large enough tailplane and fin, and a long enough fuselage will contribute to the surface area of the glider, and this leads to more skin friction, which will contribute to the profile drag produced. Having wings that are anything but horizontal (as with dihedral) will mean that the lift they produce will be at an angle to the vertical and more lift will have to be produced to provide a large enough vertical component to counter the glider's weight. This may result in an increased amount of induced drag. (Fig 23.12)

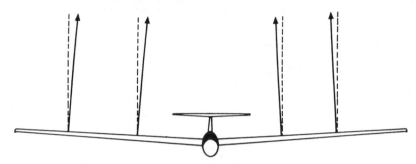

Fig 23.12   Angled lift from dihedral. Lift produced by a wing with a large amount of dihedral will act at an angle to the vertical.

DESIGN FEATURES WHICH REDUCE CONTROL FORCES

The in-built stability of a glider, while essential, does cause the designer other problems. The more stable the glider is, the more powerful the controls will have to be to overcome the glider's desire to keep flying straight when the pilot wants it to manoeuvre. This may require it to have larger control surfaces than a similar, less stable glider, and as mentioned previously, any increase in surface area will add to the amount of drag which the glider produces.

If the forces required on the control column are found to be excessive, then the designer may fit devices which will reduce these forces. These modifications may take the form of a HORN BALANCE or a GEARED TAB on the control surface.

HORN BALANCES

A HORN BALANCE is an extension to the control surface forward of the hinge line, upon which the airflow acts to assist the deflection of the surface in the direction required for the manoeuvre. This device usually only appears on the rudder of a glider and is more common on older gliders.

GEARED TABS

GEARED TABS (sometimes referred to as SERVO or BALANCE TABS) are small aerodynamic surfaces which are fitted to the trailing edge of control surfaces; mainly ailerons. On gliders, they are activated by a small pushrod which moves the tab in the opposite direction to the desired deflection of the main control surface. The tab in this position creates a force which assists the control column input to move the control surface. Geared tabs are rare on gliders, and can only be found on a few older types. The only notable British example was the Slingsby Skylark 3F.

Both these devices will incur drag penalties which is the main reason why their incorporation in modern glider designs is uncommon.

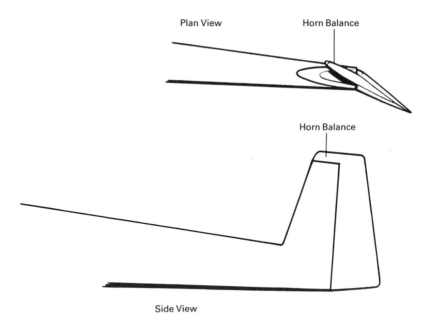

Fig 23.13   Horn balance. A horn balance reduces the force required by the pilot to move the control surface.

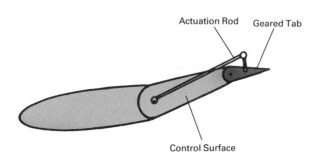

Fig 23.14   Geared tab. A geared tab assists the movement of the primary control surface.

DESIGN FEATURES WHICH MAKE TURNING EASIER

The need to use rudder to overcome aileron drag whenever aileron is applied is a constant source of workload to any student glider pilot. The designer can reduce the amount of rudder necessary by incorporating either FRISE or DIFFERENTIAL AILERONS, both of which are designed to reduce the amount of adverse yaw produced when the ailerons are moved.

FRISE AILERONS

With Frise ailerons, the hinge point of each aileron is positioned such that when up aileron is applied, some of the forward edge of the aileron protrudes downwards into the airflow, causing increased drag on this, the down-going wing. The aim is to balance or counter some of the aileron drag produced by the down movement of the other aileron and prevent, or reduce, any adverse yaw. They may also provide some horn balance effect.

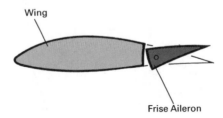

Wing

Frise Aileron

Fig 23.15   Frise ailerons are designed to counter aileron drag.

Unfortunately, Frise ailerons actually contribute to the glider's drag while attempting to combat adverse yaw. This makes them less popular than another commonly used system, known as Differential ailerons.

DIFFERENTIAL AILERONS

As it is the increase in the difference in the relative air pressure above and below the wing, caused by deflecting an aileron downwards, which causes aileron drag, one simple answer would be to not lower an aileron at all when applying bank, but rely totally on the reduction of lift created at the down-going wing, by raising its aileron. While this system would reduce the adverse yaw, it would probably give such a poor rate of roll as to make aileron drag seem a small price to pay by comparison. The solution is a compromise which involves designing the ailerons so that the down-going aileron moves through a smaller angle from its neutral position than the up-going aileron. Hence the name Differential ailerons.

Fig 23.16   Differential ailerons. Differential ailerons reduce the effect of aileron drag by reducing the amount by which the down-going aileron lowers.

Both Frise and Differential ailerons may be incorporated on some gliders and motor gliders. The Scheibe Falke and Super Falke motor gliders are excellent examples of this.

Despite an essential preoccupation with drag prevention, the designer may decide that, in certain circumstances, the need to turn the glider quickly exceeds the need to keep drag to a minimum. For this reason, the

NIMBUS 3 glider, some models of which have a wingspan measuring 25.5 metres, has a peculiar aileron system to help turn the glider. With this system, if full aileron is applied, the outer part of the up-going aileron (on the down-going wing) projects vertically upwards like a spoiler, reducing the lift and increasing the drag at that wing tip. This helps combat the effect of adverse yaw which can be considerable on gliders which have very large wingspans.

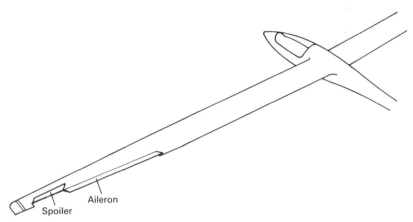

Fig 23.17   Nimbus 3 aileron/spoiler system. The Nimbus 3 aileron system utilises a spoiler to counter adverse yaw.

GIVING THE CONTROLS "FEEL"

Although we think of moving the control column in a particular direction to achieve a manoeuvre, this movement may be quite small. In actual fact, we tend to fly more by subconsciously monitoring the force required on the control column, rather than by the amount of movement required. If no force were required on the controls, that is, if they do not provide any "feel", then the glider would be very difficult to fly, as judging the amount of control applied would become guess-work.

Fortunately, the design of the ailerons and rudder cause the airflow to tend to return the control surface to the neutral position, and therefore a force is normally required to keep the control surface deflected. However, the elevator, unlike the ailerons and rudder, is rarely in its neutral position when in flight and does require special consideration.

For any one nose attitude, assuming that the glider is in steady (unaccelerated) flight, the elevator will have a given position; that is, providing the centre of gravity (pilot weight and ballast) remains constant. With a conventional tailplane/elevator this will often involve the elevator being deflected upwards or downwards. To keep the elevator in this position will require a force to be applied on the control column. To avoid the need for the pilot to constantly apply such a force, the trimmer is used to provide a substitute force. As far as any applied force is concerned, once the glider is trimmed correctly, the position of the elevator at that time can be regarded as the "new" neutral position, and a progressively increasing force will be required to move the elevator from that position. In this way the trimmed elevator now matches the other control surfaces in that it will tend to return to its trimmed position if no force is applied to the control column.

However, should the elevator be very powerful or of a design which provides the pilot with very little "feel" (such as with an ALL-MOVING TAILPLANE, where the whole tailplane is designed to act as the pitch controlling surface with no separate elevator), then it is necessary to incorporate a device in the system which will produce reasonable control forces. There are two such devices used to increase the elevator/all-moving tailplane control force. These are either springs in the elevator control circuit or an aerodynamic tab fitted to the trailing edge of the elevator, called an ANTI-BALANCE TAB.

SPRINGS IN THE ELEVATOR CIRCUIT

In the section on trimming, the idea of putting a spring in the elevator control system was mentioned when the spring trimmer was discussed. In that instance, the purpose of the spring was to remove any control force. When the glider is correctly trimmed, the moment produced by the spring exactly balances the aerodynamic moment tending to move the elevator. If any fore or aft movement of the control column is made when the glider is correctly trimmed, the spring will resist this movement, creating a control force. Often there will be more than one spring in the system. Springs can therefore be used to provide trimming and "artificial feel" and have the advantage that no extra drag is created as they are fitted within the glider's fuselage.

One disadvantage in using springs to give control "feel" is that the control force required to move the elevator, being artificially and not aerodynamically created will not be proportional to the glider's airspeed. If the pilot is not careful, it is possible to make too large a control movement and over-stress the glider at higher airspeeds if a spring device is all that is fitted. However, many types of glider are fitted with such devices, and the safety record of such gliders has shown that initial concern about their handling was generally ill-founded.

ANTI-BALANCE TABS

Just as it is possible to fit a small aerodynamic control surface to the trailing edge of the elevator to "trim off" the control force and make control less fatiguing (a trim tab), so it is possible to fit a similar tab which will do the opposite, that is, create a control force. To do this, all we have to do is have the tab move in the same direction as the control surface, in other words behave in the opposite way to a trim tab. Such a tab is called an ANTI-BALANCE TAB.

The advantage of an anti-balance tab over a spring device is that, since the force created by it is an aerodynamic one, this force will increase in magnitude as the glider's airspeed increases, thus giving the pilot more "feel" for the control input required. The disadvantage is that, being an aerodynamic addition, some extra drag will be created.

As with the spring trimmer system, the anti-balance tab is often combined with the trimming system, especially where an all-moving tailplane is fitted (such as on the BG 135 glider). In this situation the same tab is used, and the act of trimming the glider merely aligns the anti-balance tab with the centre-line of the control surface, removing any control column force. This also has the advantage of reducing the drag, providing the glider is flown correctly trimmed.

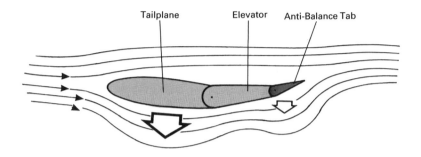

Fig 23.18   Anti-balance tab. An anti-balance tab produces a force which gives the primary control "feel".

MASS BALANCING OF CONTROLS

While we are discussing aspects of the controls, it is worth mentioning another design feature which tends to go unnoticed although it is of vital importance, that is, MASS BALANCING.

If a control surface is hinged at such a point that its CENTRE OF MASS is behind the hinge point, then a phenomenon, known as CONTROL FLUTTER can occur. This phenomenon occurs because the control surface, having mass, also has inertia. As a result, if the glider encounters a sudden updraught, the control surface (e.g. an aileron) will lag behind the main surface due to inertia. The downward deflection of the aileron in this way will result in it momentarily supplementing the effect of the gust. (Fig 23.19a)

As the upward movement of the wing ceases, the aileron's inertia will cause it to overshoot the neutral position, causing it to deflect upwards and in turn force the wing back down. Again the aileron will be left behind and the cycle will repeat itself automatically. (Fig 23.19b)

The fact that the control surfaces are often hinged close to their leading edge means that most of their natural mass tends to be well behind the hinge point. To prevent flutter occurring, the mass of the control surface has to be balanced about the hinge point and this is usually done by mounting a lead weight on an arm in front of the hinge (or occasionally situating the hinge slightly further aft). This weight, if used, is called a MASS BALANCE. On some older gliders mass balances can be seen mounted in front of an all-moving tailplane (e.g. Cobra, BG 135) or the rudder (e.g. Silene), although on modern gliders they tend to be situated along the leading edge of the control surface and therefore concealed within the glider's structure to reduce drag. (Fig 23.20)

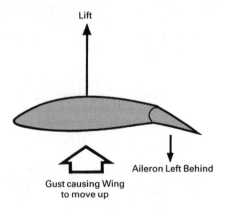

Fig 23.19a   Control flutter. If an unbalanced aileron encounters an upward gust, the wing will be moved upwards leaving the aileron behind and creating more lift.

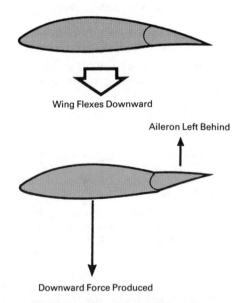

Fig 23.19b   The wing's flexibility will result in it eventually flexing downwards, causing the aileron to deflect upwards, creating a downward force, and so on.

Control flutter is related to airspeed and the high airspeeds of modern gliders with their long flexible wings add to the possibility of flutter occurring. Excessive play in control hinges and couplings, and loose mass balance weights could also help precipitate its occurrence, leading to potentially disastrous structural problems.

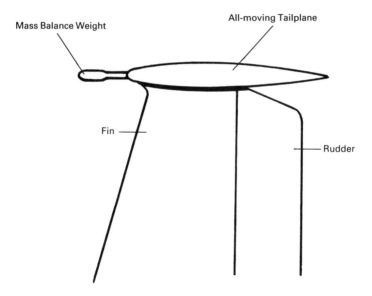

Fig 23.20   Mass balancing. Mass balancing of a control surface prevents flutter.

WASHOUT

The dangers associated with the wing tip stalling before the rest of the wing have already been discussed in the stalling and spinning sections. To make a glider safer in this respect, the wing can be designed to reduce the risk of the wing tip reaching the stalling angle before the main part of the wing. This is especially necessary if the wing is highly tapered towards the wing tip. This is done by designing the wing with a "twist", so that the wing section at the wing tip will meet the relative airflow at a lesser angle of attack than the wing root. This design feature is known as WASHOUT. As the angle of attack of the wing is increased, the wing near the fuselage will stall first, reducing the possibility of the wing tip stalling and a spin developing before recovery action can be taken.

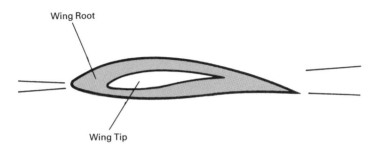

Fig 23.21   Washout. The wing can be designed so that the wing root has a higher angle of attack than the wing tip, thus reducing the chance of an inadvertent spin.

211

Although washout has a considerable safety advantage, it has serious performance disadvantages when the glider is flown at higher airspeeds. The fact that the wing section at the wing tip will be at a lower angle of attack than the rest of the wing means that this part of the wing will be producing less lift. At high airspeeds the outer wing may even be producing a downward force, depending on the amount of washout incorporated.

This different angle of attack of the wing tip from the rest of the wing will also mean that the centre of pressure will be further aft on the outer wing, causing twisting loads to be set up. To allow for these, the wing will have to be strengthened, adding to the weight of the glider and possibly limiting the wingspan.

CHAPTER 24

DESIGN FEATURES AIMED AT GIVING BETTER PERFORMANCE

Before we discuss the design features which are aimed at adding to the efficiency of a glider, let us look again at how the performance of a modern glider is defined, and the basic physical elements which can influence it.

These days it is not sufficient for a glider to be able to fly at a low airspeed in the updraught created by the wind blowing against a hillside. Gliders are often flown on cross-country tasks for hundreds of kilometres and at airspeeds which vary from slow climbing flight to fast glides between areas of rising air. In fact, as you will later learn, in order to lose the minimum of height while crossing an area of sinking air, a glider must be flown at a higher airspeed in order to spend as little time as possible in the descending air mass.

The glider must therefore not only have an adequate airspeed range, but also be designed to lose as little height as possible at whatever airspeed it is flying.

THE POLAR CURVE

To measure this performance criterion, we can observe the rate of descent at various points throughout the glider's airspeed range. When we do this and plot the results on a graph, we get a curve called a POLAR CURVE.

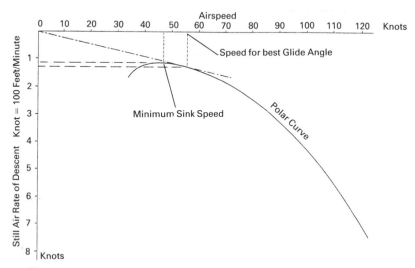

Fig 24.1 *The polar curve. A polar curve shows the rate of sink that can be expected at any given airspeed and therefore is a measure of a glider's performance.*

213

The polar curve of any glider will only be a theoretical guide to the glider's performance as it will not allow for the movements of the air mass in which the glider is flying. That is, it assumes that the glider is flying in still air. The polar curve will however give a reasonable idea of the glider's performance when compared with the polar curve of another type of glider. When making such comparisons, one important point should be borne in mind. With the exception of a series of performance tests carried out in the USA and Germany, most polar curves are supplied by the glider's manufacturer. Some polar curves will therefore tend to be optimistic as regards the glider's performance and should only be used as a rough guide. An inspection of the polar curve of a typical glider shown at Fig 24.1 will highlight some basic points.

1. Note that as the airspeed increases, so too does the rate of descent. The flatter the curve as the airspeed increases, the better the performance of the glider.

2. The airspeed at which the rate of descent is least (known as the MINIMUM SINK SPEED) appears opposite the highest point of the curve.

3. The airspeed at which the best glide angle is achieved (best lift/drag ratio in still air) is opposite the point where the tangent from the graph's origin touches the polar curve.

4. Note that at the lower airspeeds the curve is very flat, showing that there is a reasonable airspeed range over which the glider is very efficient and will not lose excessive height.

5. The glide angle (lift/drag ratio) at any airspeed can be calculated simply by dividing the airspeed by the corresponding rate of descent.

6. If the airspeed is decreased below the minimum sink speed, the rate of descent increases. This increase is gradual at first and then rapid as the glider approaches the stall.

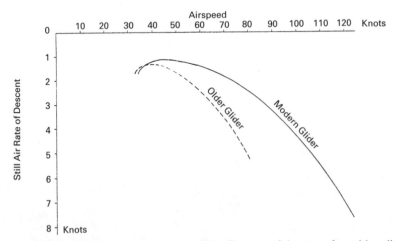

Fig 24.2   The polar curve of an older glider. The rate of descent of an older glider will increase more rapidly as airspeed is increased compared to that of a modern glider.

Fig 24.2 shows the polar curve of an older glider compared with that of a modern glider. Notice how the range of airspeeds at which the older glider can fly without incurring a large rate of descent is much smaller than that of its modern rival. The airspeeds at which the minimum sink rate and best glide angle occur are greater on the modern glider.

The important point to remember when considering the polar curve of a glider, and its performance in general, is that the glide angle at any airspeed depends on the amount of lift and drag being produced at that airspeed. The designer will therefore attempt to design a glider which will give the maximum ratio of lift to drag across as large an airspeed range as possible. This aim lies behind all of the features on a glider which are intended to increase its performance.

THE DESIGN OF THE WING

In the section describing the use of flaps, it was mentioned that the shape of the wing section influences the amount of lift and drag produced. To recap, the greater amount of camber on the wing, the more lift and the more drag the wing will produce. Camber-changing flaps will allow the best wing section to be selected for a particular phase of flight, thus giving the best lift-to-drag ratio for any given airspeed.

The wing area will also influence the amount of lift and drag produced. If the wing area is increased, lift will increase, however the larger wing area will cause an increase in the amount of skin friction. This will add to the total profile drag, which will increase as the airspeed is increased. If flaps which change the wing area are fitted (e.g. SB 11 and SIGMA experimental gliders) the wing area can be increased for slow flight when skin friction will be lower, and reduced to give less drag at higher airspeeds. The camber of the wing is also increased when these flaps are extended.

The planform of the wing will also affect the total amount of drag produced. In this case, the particular type of drag which can be a nuisance is induced drag. With a short stubby wing, the air will move easily around the wing tips, from below the wing to above the wing, where the air pressure is lower. This will cause the air to swirl, creating wing tip vortices and will waste energy by imparting it to the air.

If the wing were infinitely long, these vortices could not form and the induced drag would not be a problem. However, producing a very long wing presents many control and structural difficulties, and so the designer

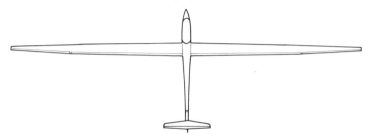

Fig 24.3   The modern glider. The long, thin wings of a modern glider produce the minimum amount of drag.

has to compromise. The answer is to have as long a wing as is practical. The result of all of these considerations is that high performance gliders have long, thin wings which are not very wide. (Fig 24.3)

As the chord of a wing usually gets smaller towards the wing tip, it is common to take the average value for the chord called the MEAN CHORD.

As the wing area equals the span multiplied by the mean chord, two gliders with the same wing area can have different wingspans if their mean chords are different.

formula: WING AREA = SPAN × MEAN CHORD

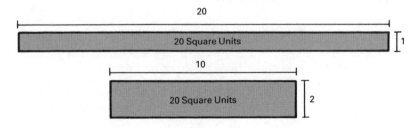

Fig 24.4   Aspect ratio. These 2 rectangles have the same area although their lengths differ.

The glider with the larger wingspan of the two will need to have a smaller chord if the wing area is to remain the same as that of the other glider. A more useful value than the wing area, when referring to the wing's shape is the ASPECT RATIO which is the span divided by the mean chord.

formula: ASPECT RATIO = SPAN/MEAN CHORD

OR

formula :   ASPECT RATIO = SPAN^2/AREA

Gliders tend to have high aspect ratios, which satisfy their low drag requirements, mainly by reducing the induced drag produced at low airspeeds. Aspect ratios in the region of 25 to 1 or greater are not uncommon.

TAPERED WINGS

One way to reduce the amount of induced drag created is to reduce the amount of lift produced at the wing tips. This is the reason for tapering the wing to a small chord as it approaches the wing tip. With less area and less pressure differential at the wing tip, less lift and subsequently less induced drag will result. The ideal lift distribution over the wing would therefore look similar to that shown in Fig 24.5.

In practice, the fuselage distorts this ideal distribution slightly, as shown in Fig 24.6.

Tapering the wings can lead to some less desirable handling characteristics, the worst of which is the tendency of the wing tip to stall before the rest of the wing, potentially leading to a spin.

Ideal Lift Distribution

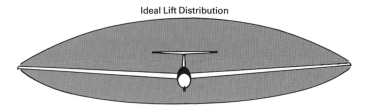

Fig 24.5   Ideal lift distribution. The ideal lift distribution would be elliptical.

Actual Lift Distribution

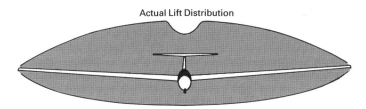

Fig 24.6   Actual lift distribution. The actual lift distribution is likely to be slightly distorted by the fuselage.

WINGLETS AND WING FENCES

Another design feature, which is incorporated to make the air "think" that the wingspan is greater than it really is, and thus reduce the induced drag created at the wing tips, is the use of some form of barrier, such as a FENCE or a WINGLET.

Anything that physically stops the air from flowing around the wing tip will reduce the effect of induced drag. On many gliders, this may simply be a slight change in the shape of the wing tip, perhaps by curving the wing tip, or part of the wing tip, upwards or downwards. Such shaping of the wing tip may only involve the last two or three inches of the wing, but, if correctly fashioned, this may be enough to reduce the amount of induced drag and add to the glider's performance.

A less subtle way to achieve the same effect is to fit a vertical end plate on to the wing tip. In this case the end plate is a form of WING FENCE. (Fig 24.7)

Both of these designs may also provide some much needed protection for the wing tip when it comes into contact with the ground after landing, and it is not uncommon for such a fence to be fitted with a metal rubbing strip.

A much more impressive-looking structure, designed to reduce the effect of induced drag, is the WINGLET (sometimes known for some reason as a WING SAIL). WINGLETS are vertical aerofoil structures which are fitted to the wing tips. Usually they project upwards only. The height of the winglets fitted to a particular glider will depend on the glider and may be as much as a ½ metre from top to bottom.

The use of winglets as a way to counter induced drag, as opposed to a longer wing, came to prominence as a result of competition rules, where in certain classes of competition, competing gliders are restricted to those having a maximum wingspan of 15 metres. Vertical structures, such as winglets, do not increase the glider's wingspan which is measured horizontally.

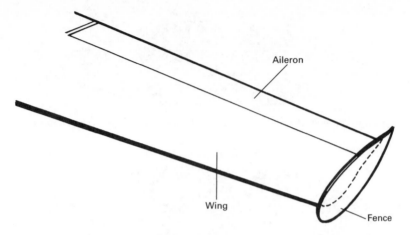

Fig 24.7   Wing fence. Wing fences may help prevent the outward flow of air which leads to induced drag.

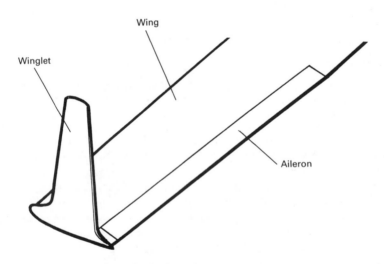

Fig 24.8   Winglet. Winglets are designed to reduce the effect of induced drag.

When the first winglets appeared on gliders, there was a feeling that the benefits gained, due to the reduction of induced drag, during the slow airspeeds used when circling, were cancelled by the increase in profile drag created by the winglets' structure at higher cruising airspeeds. As a result of this and the high cost of these appendages, winglets went out of fashion somewhat after their initial introduction. However, as improvements have been made in their design, there has been some resurgence of gliders fitted with winglets. It is also believed that winglets can improve a glider's handling at slower airspeeds.

CHANGING PLANFORM AND WING SECTION

The necessary obsession to reduce the amount of induced drag does not stop at producing ever longer wings, wing tapering or adding bits to the wing tip. Later research introduced completely new wing planforms for gliders which have improved performance considerably, especially for the smaller span gliders previously mentioned. In particular, glider manufacturer Schemp Hirth braved a design change with their Discus 15 metre glider which gave a new performance target for other manufacturers. According to one theory, by sweeping back the outer portion of the wing, the designer has effectively confused the airflow which creates induced drag by creating a slight outward airflow along the upper surface of the wing and thereby disrupted the formation of wing tip vortices.

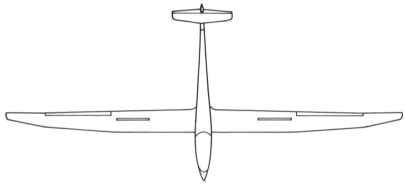

Fig 24.9   Sweeping the wing tips backwards. Sweeping the wing tips backwards is aimed at reducing induced drag.

THE NEED FOR SMOOTH SURFACES AND A LAMINAR AIRFLOW

The layer of air very close to the wing's surface is known as the BOUNDARY LAYER. The airflow in the lower part of the boundary layer will be slowed down by friction as it passes over the wing's surface. The further away from the wing's surface, the less effect friction will have on the airflow until eventually, it will be flowing at the same speed as the general airflow past the wing. In general, the boundary layer will be a fraction of a millimetre in depth near the leading edge of the wing and will get deeper as the air flows towards the wing's trailing edge.

Where the layers of air are flowing smoothly past each other as distance from the wing is increased, the boundary layer is said to be LAMINAR. However, even with the smoothest of surfaces, there will come a point when the boundary layer becomes TURBULENT. The point at which this happens is called the TRANSITION POINT. (Fig 24.10)

As long as the boundary layer remains laminar, the minimum amount of drag will be produced. When the boundary layer becomes turbulent, the amount of drag caused by skin friction will increase and the glider's performance will suffer. There is therefore a need to ensure that not only the wing surfaces, but all of the surfaces of the glider are smooth to reduce skin friction and help keep the boundary layer laminar for as long as possible.

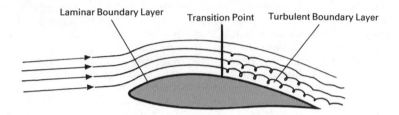

Fig 24.10   Laminar boundary layer. For the minimum of drag, the boundary layer is kept laminar.

With modern materials, such as glass fibre, the surfaces of a glider can be profiled to a much higher degree of accuracy than previously possible with wood or metal. These materials also allow more advanced wing sections to be produced and much effort goes into the surface finish to keep drag to a minimum. Any imperfections, such as undulations on the surface, or contamination, such as dirt or even flies, will reduce the glider's performance. The handling and glide angle of many gliders are badly affected if the wings become wet with rain. As the stalling speed will also be increased due to the rain contaminated wings, you should never launch with wet wings, and if approaching to land while the wings are wet, give yourself up to 10 knots of extra airspeed.

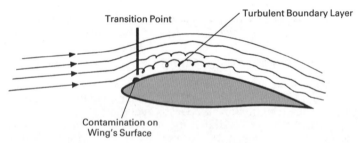

Fig 24.11   Contaminated wings. Even small irregularities on the surface of the glider will disrupt the laminar airflow.

On many modern wing sections, the profile of the wing section itself causes the airflow to separate from the wing's surface, causing increased drag. (Fig 24.12a) At the point where this separation occurs, a region of "stagnant" air, called a LAMINAR SEPARATION BUBBLE, forms.

Surprisingly enough, the way to avoid this drag, is to stir up the air just in front of where this laminar separation bubble would form. Deliberately turbulating the airflow in this way has the effect of preventing the formation of the laminar separation bubble and stopping the airflow detaching from the wing's surface. (Fig 24.12b) Whilst making the airflow turbulent in this way will create some additional drag, the amount of drag created by doing so will be much less than the amount which would exist if the airflow were allowed to separate from the wing's surface.

(a)

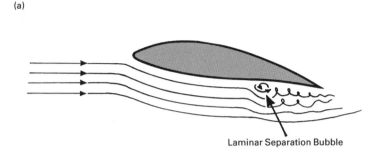

Laminar Separation Bubble

(b)

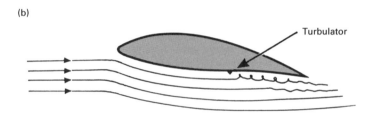

Turbulator

Fig 24.12   Turbulators. Deliberately turbulating the airflow prevents the airflow separating from the wing and results in a reduction in the total drag produced.

A device used to excite the air in this way is called a TURBULATOR and on gliders it is common to use a thin strip of sticky tape with small bumps along its length or "zig-zag tape" as a turbulator.

Another, more expensive way of achieving the same objective is used on the DG 300 glider. In this instance, high pressure air is scooped in through a pitot tube under the wing and vented through a row of tiny holes underneath the wing. Again, the turbulent air this creates prevents the laminar separation bubble forming.

THE NEED FOR A WELL-SEALED GLIDER

As you have probably gathered by now, keeping the amount of drag to a minimum can be a major headache to the glider designer. Part of the problem is that drag comes in many forms and can be caused in many ways. As well as the forms of drag which have already been discussed, there is another unavoidable type which is called INTERFERENCE DRAG.

Where two surfaces join, such as the wing to the fuselage or the tailplane to the fin, the airflow will become confused and disrupted where the flows conflict. The drag produced as a result is called INTERFERENCE DRAG.

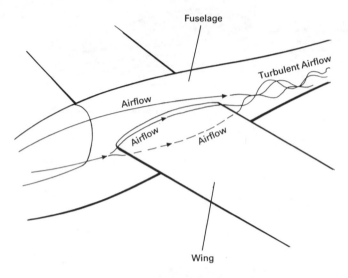

Fig 24.13   Interference drag occurs at places where two airflows conflict such as where surfaces join.

The designer will attempt to minimise this drag by carefully designing the region where the surfaces join so that the minimum disruption of the airflow occurs. This is usually achieved by using FAIRINGS and generally curving the surfaces so that they fit together well, with no discontinuity.

Any air which leaks through the wing/fuselage joint will upset the smooth flow of air at the wing root, causing extra drag and reducing the amount of lift produced. As this is a critical part of the wing as far as performance is concerned, every effort must be made to minimise this leakage of air from the higher pressure air under the wing to the lower pressure air above the wing. For this reason it is common to seal the wing/fuselage joint with plastic sealing tape. Although this technique is seen regularly on glass fibre gliders, it is beneficial on all but the oldest gliders. Similarly, the tailplane/fin joint should also be sealed as well as is possible.

Another, less obvious, source of interference drag is the air which is introduced to the cockpit as ventilation for the pilot. Even when the ventilator scoops and windows are closed, the air in the cockpit will be at a higher pressure than the air on the outside of the glider, especially that above the wing. The result will be that air from the cockpit will try to escape through every available gap, causing the laminar airflow to become disrupted where this occurs.

Various steps can be taken to prevent this unwanted effect. Probably the most effective of these is to make sure that cockpit air is vented at a point where it does little harm, for example, from the tail area.

A good-fitting, well-sealed canopy will reduce the amount of air escaping from the canopy/cockpit joint and the potential adverse affect when the airflow reaches the wing root. On the PIK 20 gliders, the canopy can be sealed pneumatically to ensure a good seal.

A further disruptive effect of this escaping air occurs when it flows out through the fuselage via the apertures for the control push rods, along the inside of the wing and exits via the airbrake slots. By exiting in this way into the low pressure air above the wing, the escaping air disrupts the all important laminar flow above the wing, thus reducing lift as well as causing extra drag.

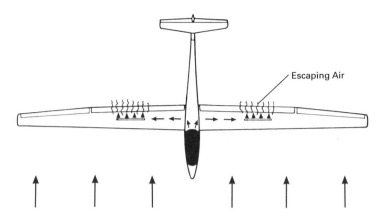

Fig 24.14   Sealing of joints. Drag will be caused where air escapes and disrupts the laminar airflow.

In order to combat this problem, most manufacturers of high performance gliders seal the control push rods at the point where they enter the wing.

SEALING OF CONTROL HINGE GAPS

While on the subject of the air's desire to take the easy route from an area of high pressure to one of low pressure, it is worth mentioning some other gaps which should always be sealed. These are the gaps which exist along the hinge line of a control surface, such as an elevator, rudder, aileron or even a trimmer tab. Normally the manufacturer will use a strip of flexible sealing tape to seal these gaps in such a way that will not restrict the range of movement of the particular control surface. If this tape is torn or missing, some air will flow freely through the gap instead of supplying the desired force on the glider. The drag penalty will be high and the effectiveness of the particular control may be badly impaired.

TAILPLANE DESIGN

The style of the tailplane has been the one striking variable throughout the years of glider design. Many designers have preferred the conventional cruciform tailplane, either fitted low on the fuselage or slightly higher up on the bottom half of the fin.

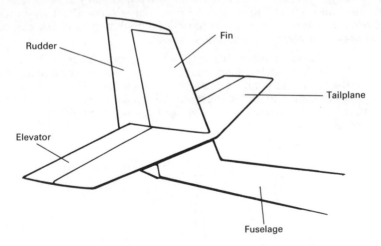

Fig 24.15   Cruciform tail.

Others have seen advantages in having the tailplane mounted at the top of the fin, forming a "T" tail.

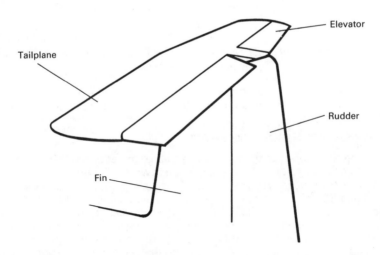

Fig 24.16   "T" tail.

A few decided that the best design for their glider was the "V" tail.

Whichever of these designs were in fashion at the time the drawing board was set up, you can rest assured that the designer had only one thought in mind when choosing the tail configuration, and that was, "Since I have got to have one, which one will give me the least drag and weight and still do the job?"

Tailplanes

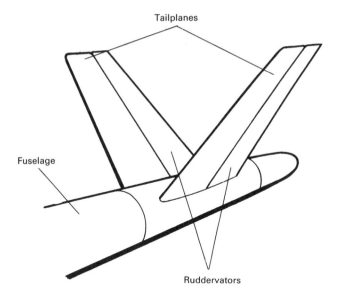

Fuselage

Ruddervators

Fig 24.17   "V" tail.

Let us look at some of the reasons for and against the various tailplane configurations.

As far as the glider's overall performance is concerned, having to have a tail at all is a nuisance. So much so that a few gliders have appeared over the years without any tails. The tailplane itself is a very inefficient aerofoil. Its low aspect ratio means that whenever it is doing any work, it will be producing induced drag as well as its share of profile drag. As it may well be required to produce a force even when the glider is not manoeuvring, any design features which will reduce the tailplane's drag contribution are welcome. It is for these reasons that designers have been willing to give the various tail designs a try.

The conventional low set tailplane can do the work of controlling pitch and giving the glider stability quite adequately. In the area where it is fitted to the fin, there will be a certain amount of interference drag, as there are four "corners" around which the airflow can conflict. Another disadvantage of this low set tailplane is that it will always be in danger of being damaged should the glider inadvertently be landed in a field of long grass or crop.

The "T" tail on the other hand will be well above the dragging effect of long crops. It will also benefit from only introducing two "corners" to contribute to the interference drag problem. The tailplane's upper surface will be unbroken by the fin and indeed, will provide an endplate to the fin. This may help reduce induced drag produced at the top of the fin when the rudder is deflected. The big disadvantage of having the tailplane fitted on top of the fin is that there will be increased stresses imposed upon the fin by the weight of the tailplane during the ground run on take-off or after landing, and the tailplane loads imposed upon it when sideslipping or when rudder is applied. This will mean that the fin will have to be of a more solid construction than those on other types of tail. This will mean extra weight.

The "V" tail at first glance, has the advantage of having one less control surface and therefore less surface area to create skin friction. In fact, since it has to do the same amount of work as any other type of tail, it tends to have the same overall surface area. Depending on the design of the tailplane to fuselage fitting, there may be slightly less interference drag created. The "V" tail will almost certainly always produce more induced drag than the other types of tail. Some gliders with "V" tails suffer from lack of ground control as a result of the designer's desire to keep control surface size to a minimum.

With a "V" tail, the same control surface is used as an elevator and a rudder. This surface, which is similar to any other hinged control surface, is sometimes called a RUDDERVATOR. When the control column is moved forwards, both ruddervators move downwards. The reverse occurs when the control column is moved backwards. Both ruddervators move to the right when right rudder is applied, and to the left for left rudder. When elevator and rudder are required at the same time, the ruddervators move by the appropriate amount in the necessary direction.

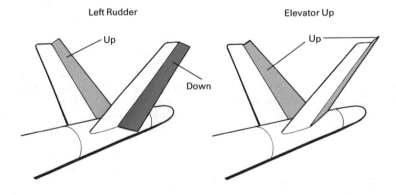

Fig 24.18   Control surface movement on a "V" tail. The control of a "V" tail relies on a mixing device to give the desired effect.

All of this requires some form of control mixing device. This is usually a mechanical gadget and having such a device can add to the weight of the glider. This extra weight is especially annoying if any part of the control mixer system is situated in the tail of the glider where it can make the tail very heavy to ground handle. The "V" tail will be less prone to crop damage than the conventional tail, but as the control linkages can be complicated, any straining of the tailplane fittings, whatever the cause, can be serious and expensive to put right.

The conventional tail and the "T" tail seem to vie for popularity, although the "T" tail seems the more popular at present. The "V" tail on the other hand, seems to have had its day, but in the quest for efficiency, who knows what might be seen on tomorrow's glider?

ALL-MOVING TAILPLANES

Irrespective of which of the three types of tail designs is fitted to a glider, the fixed tailplane with hinged elevator surface (or surfaces on a "V" tail) may be replaced by a one piece, uninterrupted control surface, known as an ALL-MOVING TAILPLANE (e.g. ASK 6E, STANDARD CIRRUS and BG 135 gliders).

With an all-moving tailplane, the front of the tailplane will angle downwards when the control column is moved backwards, giving a downwards force at the tail which results in the nose of the glider being raised. Moving the control column forwards raises the front end of the tailplane giving the opposite effect.

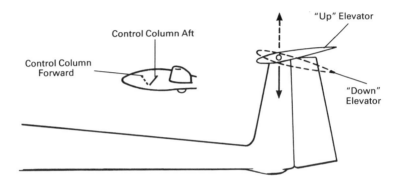

Fig 24.19   With an all-moving tailplane the whole tailplane acts as the control surface.

The idea is that an all-moving tailplane will produce less drag than a conventional tailplane and elevator combination, as there is no discontinuity of its surface. In certain circumstances, there may be a need for anti-balance tabs or mass balances to be fitted and this will to some extent reduce the advantages of using this type of tailplane.

FUSELAGE DESIGN

The fuselage of a glider does not normally contribute to the amount of lift produced by the glider. Therefore the designer's aim must be to produce a fuselage which causes the least drag and the least disruption of the lift produced by the wing.

With this in mind, the surface area of the fuselage will be kept to a minimum, so as to reduce the amount of skin friction. The fuselage surface will also be smooth and will be profiled in such a way as to avoid blunt edges or discontinuities which may disrupt the laminar airflow.

For the same reasons, the cross-section of the fuselage at the cockpit will normally only be wide enough to accommodate the pilot, and the rear fuselage will be tapered. The size of the fin and rudder will be as small as is possible but without being so small as to compromise stability and control.

Unfortunately, the fuselage must be festooned with various appendages, which although detrimental to the glider's performance, are essential for its operation. These include wheels and skids upon which to land, radio aerials and sensing probes for instruments. The answer to reducing the considerable drag which these fittings produce, is either to STREAMLINE them or to hide them inside the fuselage when they are not being used.

STREAMLINING is the shaping of an object to make it less disruptive to the airflow, and as a result reducing the amount of turbulence it leaves behind it. The more turbulence the object produces, then the more drag it will create. An object with a flat or circular cross-section will create more drag than one that has been streamlined by giving it a "tail".

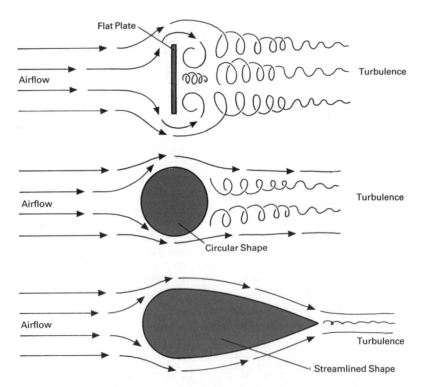

Fig 24.20   Streamlining. A streamlined shape will produce less drag than a flat or circular shape of the same size.

The main wheel of a glider can be streamlined by use of a fairing fitted around the wheel well (ASK 21, ASK 23, SPORTS VEGA and later GROB two-seat gliders). The same applies to tail and nose wheels. Tail skids can be shaped so as to reduce their influence on the airflow.

Instrument sensing probes can be streamlined, but generally they can be designed and positioned in such a way so that they do not offer a large area to the airflow and thus contribute little to the total drag. Aerials, unlike sensing probes, can be hidden inside the fuselage or fin of most gliders, but become a problem if the glider is constructed of metal, or possibly of carbon fibre. A metal fuselage will not only hide the aerial from the airflow, but also screen it from incoming radio waves and disrupt outgoing transmissions. There is no easy answer to this problem, and because of the frequencies used by glider radios, the aerial will have to stick up vertically by about 2 feet (60 centimetres) into the airflow. Despite the thinness of the aerial, it will still create a significant amount of drag and reduce performance at higher airspeeds.

A RETRACTABLE UNDERCARRIAGE would appear to be the answer to the drag caused by the main wheel. In fact, at least one glider has appeared with a tail wheel which also retracts. Retracting the wheel will reduce the drag produced, particularly at higher airspeeds. If however, your glider does not have a retractable wheel, you may find that at lower airspeeds, the performance penalty is not that great, providing its main wheel is fitted into the fuselage so that it does not protrude into the airflow more than is necessary.

Whether the main wheel is retractable or not, it is important that the wheel well into which it fits is sealed off from the rest of the inside of the fuselage. Failure to ensure this will not only result in mud or water getting into the rear fuselage, but will also result in unwanted airflow in or out of the fuselage from the wheel area, with a subsequent increase in drag. Sealing this area will also make for a quieter cockpit.

WATER BALLAST

Strange as it may seem, in some ways the performance of a glider can be increased by making it heavier. The way in which this is done is by filling specially designed tanks in the wings with WATER BALLAST.

If a glider is made heavier, the wing will have to produce more lift to counter this increased weight. The way that this is achieved is by flying at a higher airspeed. In certain conditions, such as when the track required is into a headwind, or fast glides are required between areas of rising air, it can be advantageous to have water ballast on board.

To gain a wider understanding of what happens to the glider's performance when water ballast is carried, look at the polar curves shown at Fig 24.21. The solid line is for a glider without water ballast. The broken line shows the polar curve for the same glider, but this time with water ballast being carried.

1. Note how the whole curve is moved towards the right and downwards when water ballast is carried, that is, towards the high airspeed 'range. Therefore the airspeed for minimum sink and that for best glide angle are higher when water ballast is carried.

2. Note also that with the higher airspeeds comes a higher descent rate. Water ballast does not improve the overall glide angle achieved.

3. The advantage of carrying water ballast on a glider is that the airspeed for any given glide angle is increased.

The higher descent rate in still air when water ballast is carried means that the rate at which the glider will climb in rising air will be diminished, relative to the same glider without water ballast on board. For this reason, it is only worth carrying water ballast when the average rate of climb of the glider in rising air exceeds 3 knots (approximately 300 feet per minute).

Once the average rate of climb falls below this value, or a decision is made to land, the water ballast can be jettisoned through drain holes on the underside of the wings or fuselage. As "dumping" what may be up to 60 gallons (600 lbs.) of water ballast may take 5 minutes or more, the decision to get rid of the ballast should be made early. It is usually possible to close the drain valves again in flight, and so partial ballast dumping is possible, enabling the pilot to "fine tune" the glider to the prevailing weather conditions.

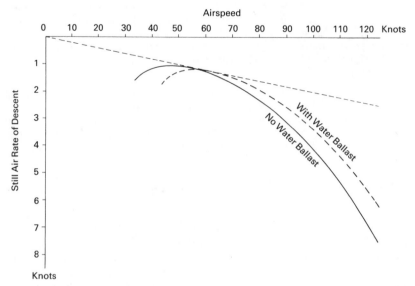

Fig 24.21   Water ballast. Comparison of the polar curves of the same glider with and without water ballast shows that the speed at which any one glide angle is achieved is increased when water ballast is carried.

TAIL BALLAST

Some high performance gliders are fitted with a small water ballast tank in the fin. This ability to carry TAIL BALLAST, although aimed at improving the glider's performance, does not do so for the same reasons as when large amounts of water ballast is carried in wing tanks.

If the glider is flown with its centre of gravity in any position other than one "ideal" position, the elevator will constantly be required to be deflected to produce a balancing force. This will incur an induced drag penalty from the tailplane. If the glider can be set up so that its centre of gravity is in this "ideal" position, despite the effect of a heavy pilot or a large amount of water ballast in the wings, then this drag force will be avoided. A tail ballast tank in the fin allows the glider's initial trim to be adjusted to accommodate this aim. This tail ballast can be jettisoned at the same time as the water ballast. However, in order to avoid being left with a tail heavy and potentially unstable glider, the tail ballast tank will normally drain at a quicker rate than the main ballast tanks.

SECTION 3

BASIC SOARING

CHAPTER 25

SOARING

No book on gliding would be anywhere near complete if it did not at least introduce every glider pilot's aspiration, SOARING. Soaring is the skill of keeping the glider airborne using only the rising air currents which occur in the atmosphere. Once the basic elements of soaring are mastered, these can be improved and used for altitude, cross-country and competition flying. In fact, soaring is such a large subject and covers so many aspects, theories and techniques that to cover it satisfactorily would require a manual of similar size to this one. This final section is intended as an introduction to the art of soaring and is aimed at giving you enough knowledge to enable you to improve your skills and become accomplished at this challenging and satisfying aerial sport.

During your basic training, you will probably have encountered up-currents, and by the time you have gone solo, you may have had some success in using some of these to gain height. From this beginning you can develop your skills and after your first solo flight you can further explore the vagaries of the atmosphere to extend your flight times and knowledge.

By continually experimenting with techniques and enquiring about the nature of the air in which the glider is flying, you will develop your soaring ability, making available all aspects of the sport and increasing its challenge and enjoyment.

THE PRINCIPLE OF SOARING

A glider will always be descending relative to the air in which it is flying. Although reducing airspeed may momentarily reverse this trend, the fact is that height will be lost unless the glider encounters an area of air that is rising faster than the glider is descending.

At first this may seem to contradict what has already been said regarding the balance of forces existing in unaccelerated flight. However, the point to remember is that the balance of lift and weight only means that the glider will not *accelerate* downwards. It will continue to descend at a steady rate if the air is still.

To maintain height the glider must be flown in air which is rising at a rate equal to its still air rate of descent. For instance, if the glider is flying in still air at a steady airspeed and is descending at 1 knot (100 feet per minute), then it will have to encounter an area of air which is ascending at a rate of 1 knot just to arrest its descent. This would be similar to your walking down an ascending escalator at the same rate as it ascends. (Fig 25.1)

To gain height the air mass in which the glider is flying will need to be ascending at a rate greater than the glider's rate of descent in still air, that is, in this example, greater than 1 knot. (Now the escalator has increased its ascent rate.) (Fig 25.2)

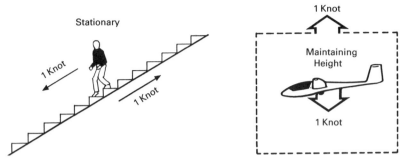

Fig 25.1   Rising air arresting the glider's descent. A glider will constantly
descend unless it is flown in air which is rising at a rate equal to its still
air descent rate. This is similar to walking down an escalator at the same rate
as it ascends.

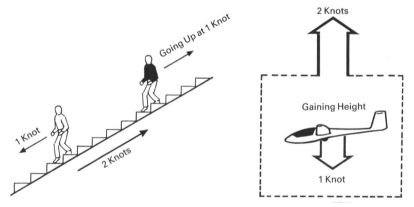

Fig 25.2   Rising air causing the glider to gain height. Air rising at a rate greater
than the glider's still air descent rate will result in an increase in the glider's
height. This is similar to walking down an escalator which is ascending faster
than your walking speed.

Your aim as a glider pilot is to find and exploit such areas of rising air. The
first task, finding a suitable updraught can be challenging enough,
depending on the nature of the up-current. Successfully using it is the
second task which will require many of the handling skills which you have
gained during your basic training.

Often when discussing such rising air currents, glider pilots refer to these
simply as LIFT. In order to avoid confusion with the aerodynamic force
called "lift" which has featured in previous chapters, any reference to "lift"
during this section on basic soaring can be taken as meaning an area of
rising air. The expression commonly used to describe descending air, and
used throughout the text, is SINK.

The following chapters describe the main mechanisms which cause the air
to rise and how you can use the resulting rising air. They are known by
their respective names of HILL LIFT, THERMALS and WAVE LIFT.

CHAPTER 26

HILL LIFT

WHAT CAUSES HILL LIFT

When the wind meets any form of barrier, such as a hill or mountain, it has either to go around it or over it. If the obstruction is a long hill (or a line of hills), then most of the air mass will be deflected upwards and will pass over the top of the hill. This upward deflection of the air will provide a large area of rising air in which it is possible to soar a glider for as long as the wind continues to blow against the hillside. Such HILL LIFT may take the glider to altitudes of 1000 feet or more above the top of the hill being soared.

After the air flows over the crest of the hill, it will start to descend and become turbulent. This can produce heavy sink and can be a danger to a glider which is allowed to drift downwind of the area of hill lift. This downdraught is often known as CURL OVER or the CLUTCHING HAND which, in strong wind conditions, accurately describes the disastrous effect which it can have on any glider caught in it. Depending on the shape of the hill and the wind conditions, the transition from hill lift into the curl over area may be quite sudden.

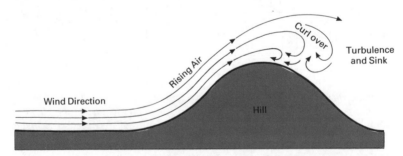

Fig 26.1   Hill lift. As the wind blows against a hillside the air is forced upwards. As the air flows over the crest, it becomes turbulent and can cause severe downdraughts.

The rate of climb and the height which a glider can achieve in hill lift depends on many factors.

WIND STRENGTH AND DIRECTION

Generally the stronger wind, the stronger the hill lift and the higher a glider will be able to climb in front of any particular hill. The direction of the wind is critical, as apart from requiring the wind to be blowing against the hillside, a wind blowing at right angles to the face of the hill will give better lift. If the angle between the wind direction and the hillside is less than 90° the amount of hill lift will also reduce. This is due to the fact that the air mass will be deflected along the face of the hill as well as over it. In the extreme case of the wind meeting the face of the hill at a shallow angle, then little or no hill lift may be produced.

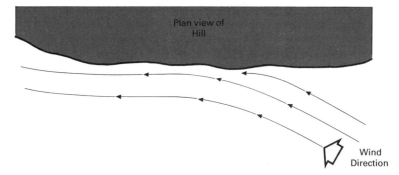

Fig 26.2   A wind at an angle to the hill. A wind blowing at an angle to a ridge is unlikely to produce as much lift as one blowing perpendicular to it.

Fortunately, the sides of hills and mountains are seldom straight and as a result there are often spurs and outcrops on the face of a hill or mountain, and these may provide a surface perpendicular to the wind to give usable hill lift.

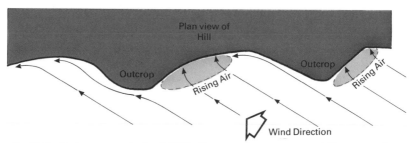

Fig 26.3   Outcrops producing hill lift. Spurs and outcrops on a hill may produce better lift than the main hill face if the wind is at an angle to the main face.

HILL SIZE AND SLOPE

First impressions might suggest that the bigger the hill, the better the lift. The size of the hill will influence the potential height that can be gained in hill lift. One would quite rightly expect that a glider using the lift produced from a mountain which is 3000 feet in height would gain more height than one soaring a hill slope 400 feet high. However, more important than the size of the hill is the shape of the face of the hill against which the wind is blowing.

The ideal hillside is one that is steep enough to deflect the air smoothly upwards, but not so steep that the deflected air becomes turbulent. As long as the airflow against and over the hill is laminar, the air will continue to accelerate as it ascends, thereby giving a hill soaring glider a better rate of climb.

If the hillside is too steep, as in a cliff face or a vertical ridge, the angle through which the air mass will need to be deflected is large and the result is that the air will become turbulent, causing eddies and downdraughts as well as hill lift. These effects may well be so pronounced as to make what hill lift exists difficult to use safely and give only marginal gains of height.

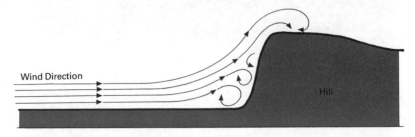

Fig 26.4   Sink near a steep hill face. If the face of the hill is steep then the wind may cause eddies and downdraughts to form instead of usable lift.

SURFACE OF THE HILLSIDE

Just as the surface of the glider's wing needs to be smooth in order to achieve a laminar airflow over it, for optimum results, the surface of the hillside also needs to be of a nature which will present little drag to the airflow if this is to be kept laminar. Rough terrain on the lower slopes, trees or rocky outcrops on the hillside will all disrupt the air mass as it progresses up the slope, leading to turbulence and reducing the hill lift.

UPWIND TERRAIN

The terrain upwind of the intended soaring slope can also have a dramatic influence on whether or not the hillside will produce any hill lift. If there are other hills or mountains immediately upwind of the hillside, these can disrupt the airflow and shield the hillside from the wind. In addition, such hills may make the air very turbulent, degrading soaring conditions and making flying on the ridge quite unpleasant.

Hills or mountains further upwind, as well as having the above effects, may cause large downdraughts on their lee side. If these downdraughts happen to descend in the area of the intended soaring slope, they can often be powerful enough to cancel out the hill lift and even cause large amounts of sink where you might expect to find lift.

Where a club operates within reach of a hill, mountain or ridge, local knowledge will be of benefit in anticipating what conditions are to be found when embarking on a hill soaring flight. When approaching a slope with the intention of soaring along it, some consideration of the above points may avoid the disappointment of not finding lift, or prepare you for what might be a rough ride. In this respect a cautious approach is a safer approach and if your suspicions are ill-founded then the better the surprise as your glider soars up the hillside.

STABILITY OF THE AIR MASS

If the air mass is very cold and stable, there will be a tendency, despite the general wind direction being towards the hill or ridge, for the wind to attempt to flow around the ridge, if at all possible. This may result in the wind being deflected along the face of the hill or ridge, instead of over it. This effect may be pronounced on cold winter mornings, but may well change as the day progresses and the valley air warms up, resulting in usable hill lift. (For a more thorough description of atmospheric stability, refer to Chapter 28.)

ANABATIC LIFT

In addition to, and sometimes instead of, the hill lift created by the effect of the general wind, the glider may be able to soar on a local wind, known as an ANABATIC WIND. ANABATIC LIFT is caused by the fact that warm air, being less dense and therefore lighter than cold air, will rise, just as a hot air balloon rises. When the sun heats the surface of a hillside, the air close to the hillside will also be heated. Being lighter, this air will start to move up the hillside, creating what is called an ANABATIC FLOW or ANABATIC WIND. This flow can be strong enough to enable a glider to gain height. The strength of the lift will depend greatly on the amount of heating, which in turn will depend on the size and surface of the slope and its orientation relative to the sun.

Even when soaring in pure, wind-driven hill lift, the effect of any anabatic wind should not be disregarded. Often this will manifest itself by the best "hill lift" being at the sunny end of a curved ridge!

CHAPTER 27

HILL SOARING

Using hill lift to maintain or gain height is called HILL SOARING and was the first type of soaring to be achieved. These days, hill soaring is used as a means of local soaring or when no other types of lift are available. Even while cross-country flying, the possession of hill soaring skills can be useful if a long line of hills lies roughly on the glider's track. The hill lift from such a ridge can be used to increase the glider's average cross-country speed and the utilisation of such a ridge has contributed to the success of non-stop glider flights over record distances in excess of 1000 miles.

GENERAL TECHNIQUE

Given that a hill, ridge or mountain is producing hill lift, all that you need do is fly the glider on the windward side of the hill and in a position relative to the hill where the best lift is to be found. This will depend on the wind strength and the glider's height relative to the top of the hill.

In very light winds the glider may well have to be flown very close to the hillside, in order to make the best use of the hill lift. In stronger winds, it may be possible to climb while flying the glider at a more comfortable distance away from the hillside. In any event, the glider will still be relatively close to the hillside, (never usually more than a few wingspans away) and with the ground this close, a safe margin of airspeed is essential.

As height is gained, the area of best lift will be found further out from the hill's face. The glider should therefore be flown progressively further out from the hill as it gets higher. (Fig 27.1)

With this increase in the distance from the hill, the glider's airspeed can be reduced to an airspeed which will better suit its climbing characteristics. However, as a general rule, when the glider is within approximately 500 feet of the hill, or if conditions are turbulent, then the airspeeds used when hill soaring should be similar to that used on approach.

By maintaining a safe airspeed, the glider's controls will be more responsive and the danger of stalling or spinning while close to the hill will be reduced. This extra airspeed will also give the glider some reserve of energy if a sudden downdraught is encountered.

Once established in the hill lift, it is necessary to track along the windward face of the hill to stay in the best lift. Depending on the wind strength, this may involve flying the glider with its nose pointing out from the hillside to avoid being drifted towards it or, if the glider is above the hill, behind the face of the hill. (Fig 27.2)

The degree to which it will be necessary to track in this way will depend on the wind strength. In very strong winds, it may be possible to remain in the hill lift with the glider pointing directly into wind and more or less stationary relative to the hill.

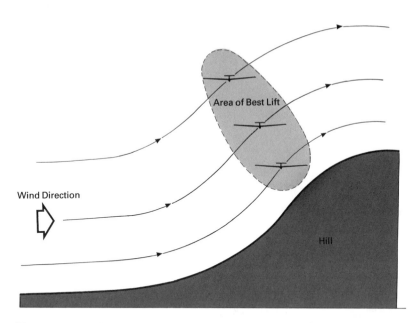

Fig 27.1   Area of best hill lift. The best area of hill lift will be further out from the
hill's face as height is gained.

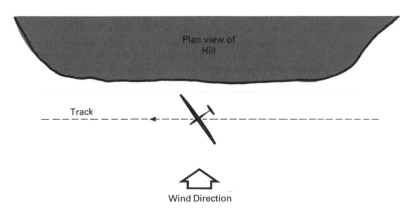

Fig 27.2   Tracking in the hill lift. It may be necessary to "track" the glider along
the hill's face to prevent the wind drifting the glider towards the hill.

As the effect of the wind will be to drift the glider towards or behind the
hill, the turn made at the end of each beat along the hill should be made
away from the hill. Such turns can be put to good advantage by making
them in an area of good lift, thus increasing the time spent in such an area,
rather than waiting until the glider moves out of the lift at the end of the
ridge before turning. The timing of such turns must take other hill-soaring
traffic into account.

239

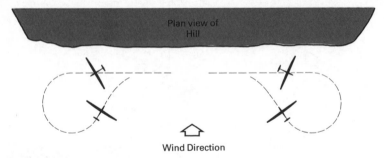

Fig 27.3   Turning at the end of each beat in the hill lift. The glider is turned away from the hill at the end of each beat.

APPROACHING THE HILL

The initial approach to the hill should be carried out with caution and with some extra airspeed in hand. As well as allowing for any turbulence close to the hill, it will also allow for the fact that the glider is entering a vertically moving air mass which, at the moment of entering it, may cause an increase in the glider's angle of attack. This is more likely if the rising air forms a narrow band with a sudden interface with the general air mass.

Despite the fact that the wind appears to be blowing in a favourable direction for the production of hill lift, you can never be sure that lift is present, unless other gliders are hill soaring at a similar height. It is therefore important to set yourself a minimum height and a position at which to abandon your attempts to hill soar if lift is not encountered. Normally this will be determined by the height needed to return to the gliding site or a suitable field in which to land.

If approaching the hill head-on, the turn along the hill's face should be started early, in order to avoid flying into the hill due to the tail wind and the elongated turn this will cause. The stronger the wind, the earlier this turn must be initiated. A safer tactic is to plan your entry into the hill lift from a more oblique angle, thus giving more time to turn and also to assess the conditions near the hill.

LANDING OUT NEAR A HILL

Should an attempt to hill soar fail, or the hill lift become unusable, it may be necessary to land. If the hill on which you are flying is not within range of an airfield, a landing will have to be made in a field.

There are many factors to be taken into account when considering the suitability of a field for a landing, but apart from the field's size and surface, slope will usually be a major problem when the field is near a hill. For the reasons described earlier, a landing into wind is normally preferred to a downwind landing. This will mean that, on the face of it, the ideal landing direction will be away from the hill. However, as the terrain at the base of a hill will often slope downwards for a long way out from the hill, there is every chance that many fields will be unsuitable due to a down slope in the direction of an into-wind landing. ON NO ACCOUNT SHOULD YOU ATTEMPT A DOWNHILL LANDING, as even a slight down slope will make it difficult to place the glider on the ground. Even if this is accomplished, the ground run will be lengthened and it will be difficult to stop the glider before the boundary fence is reached.

The answer is to select a field well away from the hill and to abandon any attempt to hill soar early enough to ensure that you can reach this field and still be able to fly a circuit.

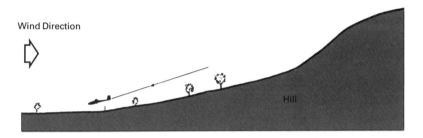

Fig 27.4   Field landing near a hill. Should a field landing be necessary, watch out for slope in the fields anywhere near the hill.

If this is not possible and a sloping field is all that is available, then an uphill, downwind landing is safer than attempting to land into wind and down hill. In moderate or strong winds, the only safe solution is not to get yourself into such a predicament.

AIRMANSHIP AND RULES WHILE HILL SOARING

As always, the need to maintain a good look out is essential. When a hill which is producing lift is within range of a gliding site, there is every chance that gliders will congregate in the area in front of the hill. This increase in traffic density increases the risk of a mid-air collision. Not only will gliders be coming from a head-on direction, but gliders will also be joining the hill lift from other directions.

As the maximum height possible in the hill lift is achieved, your glider and the others will all find themselves more or less at the same height. Safety is dependent on everyone searching the sky for other gliders.

Despite keeping a vigilant lookout, other factors increase the risks.

Flying into a low or setting sun will make oncoming gliders difficult to see. Hazy conditions or a dirty canopy (or both) aggravate this situation. Never fly with a dirty canopy; your life could depend on its clarity!

In winter, when a low sun-angle is common, misting of the canopy can also occur. Watch out for these situations and if you are concerned about your chances of seeing other traffic, move away from the hill lift, or plan your beats along the hill so that when you are in the thick of the traffic you are travelling down-sun. Never assume that the other pilots will see you.

In order to reduce the risk of a collision when hill soaring, the following rules apply regarding your behaviour with respect to other gliders.

241

- When two aircraft are approaching head-on at a similar altitude while hill soaring, the glider with the hill on its left shall alter course to the right. (This is common sense as the other glider is in a poor position to obey the normal convention as the hill or the curl over area is on its right.)

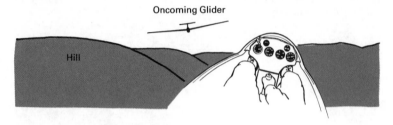

Fig 27.5   Approaching another glider head-on while hill soaring. When two gliders are approaching head-on, the one with the hill on its left shall alter course to the right.

- In the United Kingdom and in the U.S.A., when overtaking another glider while hill soaring you should overtake between the other glider and the hill. (In practice there is often not enough space between the hill and the other glider for this manoeuvre, in which case it is better to end your beat of the hill early, turning outwards and then back along the ridge.) In other countries hill soaring gliders overtake on the side away from the hill.

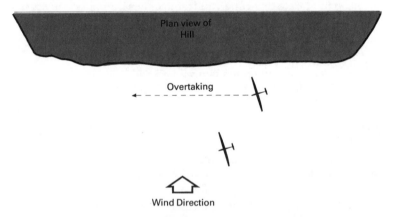

Fig 27.6   Overtaking while hill soaring. When overtaking another glider (in the UK and USA) overtake between the other glider and the hill.

DANGERS WHEN HILL SOARING

CURL OVER

The curl over zone downwind of the hill lift can cause a straying glider to descend rapidly, perhaps even forcing it onto the hilltop. Care must be taken to keep the glider out of this zone and to avoid being drifted back over the edge of the hill, where much turbulence and sink may be encountered.

OROGRAPHIC CLOUD

The air rising up the face of a hillside will cool as it rises. As air cools it is no longer capable of holding as much water as a vapour. If the air is very moist, the cooling effect of its ascent will result in cloud forming close to the hillside. This OROGRAPHIC CLOUD can form quickly, especially if an area of moist air arrives, often shrouding the hill in fog. If this occurs while a glider is hill soaring, then there is a great danger of the glider suddenly finding itself in cloud in close proximity to the hill.

It is difficult to predict this event and the only safeguard is always to know which heading to adopt in order to fly directly away from the hill. Turning onto such a heading will result in the glider quickly arriving in clear air as soon as the glider exits the area of lift, and therefore the orographic cloud.

CHAPTER 28

THERMALS

Hill soaring is good fun, but unless some other form of lift is found, the glider is restricted to staying within gliding range of a soarable slope. Cross-country soaring, as we know it today, really took off when a different form of lift was discovered and used, the THERMAL. This form of lift, which is dependent on the effect of the sun's heating and not on the wind, frees the glider pilot from hills and makes soaring possible over many types of terrain.

HOW THERMALS FORM

The sun emits large amounts of energy, some of which reaches the earth. Some of this energy is scattered and filtered by the atmosphere, but much of it reaches the earth's surface and causes it to warm up. The energy which passes through the atmosphere does not heat the air directly, as it is in the form of short wavelength radiation which is not absorbed by the air. However, when it reaches the earth's surface, this energy is absorbed by the land and seas, and surface heating occurs. In a sense the atmosphere acts like the glass of a greenhouse, in that the glass itself does not get warm, but the non-transparent contents of a greenhouse do.

When the earth's surface heats up, it re-emits some of this energy as longer wavelength radiation and much of this is absorbed by the atmosphere. The result of all of this is that the air close to the surface is heated due to its contact with the warm ground, and not directly by the sun.

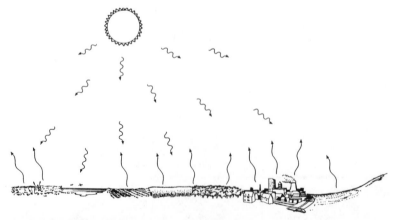

Fig 28.1   Solar heating and the environmental lapse rate. The sun heats the surface of the ground without significantly heating the atmosphere. The warm ground then heats the air close to the ground. Therefore the temperature of the atmosphere generally reduces as altitude increases.

Therefore air temperature decreases as altitude is increased. With minor local variations, this general rule holds good for altitudes up to around 36,000 feet. The rate at which the temperature decreases with altitude on any one day is known as the ENVIRONMENTAL LAPSE RATE (ELR).

Different surfaces will heat up at different rates, as will the air coming into contact with them. This differential heating will mean that adjacent areas of air may vary in temperature by several degrees.

As the temperature of a parcel of air increases, it becomes lighter and will want to rise. If the temperature difference between this parcel of air and its surroundings is great enough, then the parcel of air will break away from the surface and rise, much as a hot air balloon rises. As this air ascends it will cool at a rate of 3° per 1000 feet. This figure is known as the DRY ADIABATIC LAPSE RATE (DALR).

If the DALR is greater than the ELR, then the parcel of air will eventually reach a height at which its temperature is the same as its surroundings. In theory, when the parcel of air reaches this height it will stop ascending. (In practice, as the thermal may contain as much as 50,000 tons of air rising at possibly 1000 feet per minute, its momentum will carry it some height above this temperature equilibrium level.)

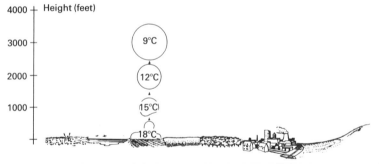

Fig 28.2   Dry adiabatic lapse rate. As a parcel of air rises it cools at the dry adiabatic lapse rate.

Up to this height this air mass is said to be UNSTABLE. Above this height STABILITY is said to exist. This rising parcel of air is what is known as a THERMAL. Thermals vary in size and rate of ascent, but they are often plentiful, large enough and strong enough to allow long, cross-country flights to be carried out with the glider achieving high rates of climb.

When the parcel of air contains a reasonable amount of water vapour, then the above characteristics change somewhat, often to the advantage of the glider pilot searching for a thermal.

The amount of water vapour that any parcel of air can contain is dependent on its temperature. The higher the temperature, the more water that can be contained as a vapour. Because its temperature decreases as it ascends, the air becomes more saturated, until eventually the parcel of air can no longer contain its water content as vapour. At this temperature, known as the DEW POINT, the water vapour will condense out into water droplets and form cloud.

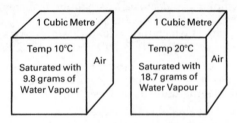

Fig 28.3   Relative humidity. The amount of water vapour that a parcel of air can hold decreases as its temperature is reduced.

If a parcel of air is still rising when it reaches this temperature, a cloud, known as a CUMULUS CLOUD, will form. These clouds are often called "fair weather clouds" and are recognisable by their "cauliflower-like" appearance.

The height at which these clouds form is known as the CONDENSATION LEVEL. These cumulus clouds mark the position where there is, or perhaps has been, a thermal.

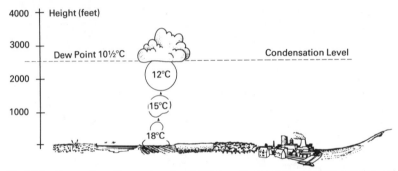

Fig 28.4   Formation of cumulus cloud. When a thermal reaches the condensation level a cumulus cloud will form.

Once the cloud forms, the DALR changes to the SATURATED ADIABATIC LAPSE RATE (SALR) which is only around 1.5° per 1000 feet. This is because the condensing out of the water vapour into cloud releases heat (known as the LATENT HEAT OF CONDENSATION) into our parcel of air, giving it an added boost. The air within the cloud will therefore be capable of ascending faster, and possibly further, than it would have done if it had been too dry for cloud to form.

If the air continues to rise within the cloud, the small cumulus cloud can build into a huge, towering CUMULONIMBUS cloud, which could result in heavy rain, hail, thunder and lightning.

All of this can be summarised as follows:

• Air that is warmer than its surroundings will want to rise.

• As air rises it cools.

• This air will stop rising when (or shortly after) it cools to the same temperature as the surrounding air.

- If the air is moist enough, cloud will form when it rises to its condensation level.

Fig 28.5   Cumulonimbus cloud. If the air within the cumulus cloud continues rising then a large cloud called a cumulonimbus may form.

The fact that on any given day, cumulus clouds may not form, does not mean that there are no thermals. It may be that the air is too dry for cloud to form. Remember that the cumulus cloud, if present, is a product of the thermal, and not vice versa! These "dry thermals" are known as BLUE THERMALS and the days when they occur are called BLUE DAYS.

THE SOURCE OF A THERMAL

Normally, for a thermal to form, the air must be heated as a result of its contact with the ground. It therefore follows that the warmer the ground, the warmer and more buoyant the air will become. Another criterion is the length of time that the air which is being heated is in contact with the "hot spot" on the ground. For instance, in strong winds, a parcel of air may only be over the area of warm ground for a short time before it is blown past it.

Fortunately, the surface of the earth varies immensely, and not only will some surfaces heat up more than others, but some areas will trap air for considerable periods of time, allowing it to increase in temperature.

For instance, take a wheat field just before harvest. The crop is dry, and the land probably well-drained and so very little of the sun's heat will be wasted in evaporating moisture. Not only is the surface suitable for heating, but the crop will trap a lot of air close to the ground, so that the heat can be conducted to the trapped air for longer.

Concrete areas such as towns, have the same characteristics and will often contribute by producing their own heat sources, such as factories, car emissions and heating systems in buildings.

Every surface has its characteristics as a thermal source, ranging from excellent to poor. Among those which are good sources are towns, airfields, power stations and dry fields (some with crops and others of earth or stubble surfaces). A list of poor thermal sources would include marshy areas, lakes or generally areas which have a large water content.

THE FORMATION AND STRUCTURE OF A THERMAL

To talk about a typical thermal is difficult, as any meteorological phenomenon is blessed with the ability to be infinitely variable in its structure, shape and size. The best that can be achieved here is to describe an idealised thermal, which will give a general picture of what a thermal would look like, if only the air of which it is composed were not invisible.

The beginning of our ideal thermal can be regarded as a volume of air next to a part of the ground which is hotter than the neighbouring surfaces.

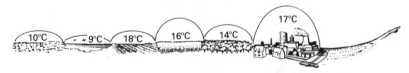

Fig 28.6   Thermal sources. A thermal starts as a volume of air being heated by an adjacent "hot spot" on the ground.

As the surface heats this local air mass, the air will become increasingly buoyant until, either due to some independent disturbance (known as a TRIGGER) or its own degree of buoyancy, it overcomes its tendency to adhere to the ground and breaks away.

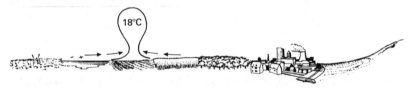

Fig 28.7   Birth of a thermal. Eventually the air will break away from the ground and rise.

As this thermal "bubble" rises, it will be ascending to levels where the atmospheric pressure upon it is less. It will therefore expand as it rises. It will also encounter some drag from the air through which it is passing. This drag will affect the outer areas of the thermal. There will also be some degree of mixing with and entrainment of the air through which it is passing. The result of these latter events is that the outer air of the thermal bubble will be descending relative to the centre of the thermal bubble (the CORE). The accepted shape of a thermal is therefore one of a three-dimensional vortex ring, with air rising up the centre and spilling downwards on the periphery. (Fig 28.8)

This shape will assume some horizontal movement of the air at the top and bottom of the thermal bubble, with an inflow at the bottom and an outflow at the top.

Two important points should be realised from this model of a thermal.

1. Despite the fact that the air on the outside is descending relative to the core, the whole bubble is rising relative to the ground.

2. From the above, it can be visualised that in the core of the thermal the air will be ascending faster than the thermal bubble as a whole.

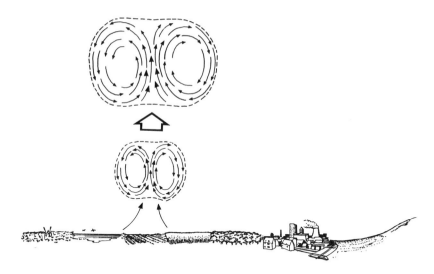

Fig 28.8   Thermal bubble. As it ascends the thermal will acquire a vortex motion with its core rising faster than its outer edges.

Whether all thermals take the form of a bubble being released in this way, or whether some are continuous streams of rising air forming a column, has been a point of debate for many years. If conditions are favourable, a good thermal source will fire off regular thermals, and if these are frequent enough, then the result may well give the impression of one continuous column of lift as each bubble released follows behind its predecessor.

However, all too often, it is possible to find oneself searching unsuccessfully for lift under other climbing gliders. This would suggest that the thermal bubble has ascended past your level. In other words "you have missed the bubble". Once the warm air close to the ground has ascended, it will take time for the warm ground to heat the air that has replaced it. How long this takes, will depend on the prevailing conditions. If you are lucky, the next thermal bubble may be on its way up. If you are unlucky, you may watch from the field below, while your colleagues climb in this later thermal bubble. Who knows, your landing may even have disturbed the air enough to trigger this new thermal! (Fig 28.9)

In certain conditions, the wind and the circulation caused by rising thermals, will result in a phenomenon known as THERMAL STREETING. This is most obvious in moderate to strong winds when cumulus clouds form long lines in the sky, called CLOUD STREETS. Under such streets can be found long lines of lift, while under the clear areas between them you can expect to find large amounts of descending air. Fig 28.10 shows the circulation which causes such conditions.

Note however, that such a circulation is not restricted to days when cumulus clouds are present to show the streets. Blue thermal streets are also common and the lack of cloud in these situations can add to the challenge of thermal finding.

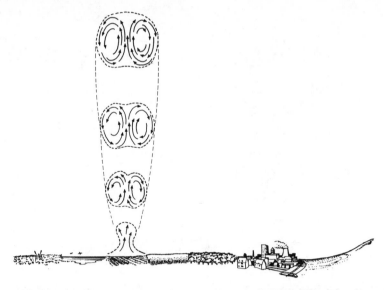

Fig 28.9   Thermal column. Often a thermal source will set off regular thermal
bubbles giving the impression of a continuous column of lift.

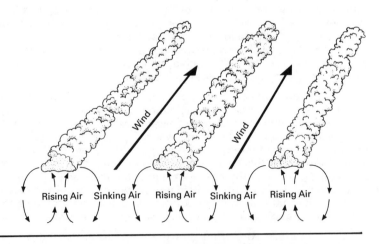

Fig 28.10   Cloud streets. In windy conditions cloud streets will often form
indicating the presence of long lines of lift.

CHAPTER 29

THERMAL SOARING

FINDING A THERMAL

Finding a thermal is the first task that you will face when you embark on a thermal soaring flight. How difficult or easy this is will depend very much on the local weather conditions on the day. It will also depend on how you read the signs which give clues to a thermal's presence and on the way in which you search for a thermal.

SKY READING

If cumulus clouds are present, you will probably find a thermal beneath or close below such a cloud. You might wrongly assume that directly under every cumulus cloud will be a thermal. Remember, however, that the cloud is the end product of a thermal, and that the thermal which produced the cloud may have stopped feeding the cloud some time ago. If this is the case, the cloud may well be decaying, and under such a cloud the air may be descending rather than rising. A cumulus cloud therefore has various stages in its life depending on the degree of activity of the thermal or thermals supplying it; there may be more than one thermal per cloud.

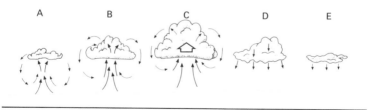

Fig 29.1   Life of a cumulus cloud. A cumulus cloud starts as a thin wisp, and builds into a well-defined cloud before collapsing and dissipating.

At first, as the thermal reaches the condensation level, the cumulus will appear as a small wisp of cloud (Fig 29.1a). As more moisture condenses out, the cloud will build into a more recognisable cumulus cloud, with a firm base and well-defined sides (Fig 29.1b and c). If the thermal feeding the cloud ceases, then the cloud will start to decay. It will lose its well-defined appearance and start to break up and subside (Fig 29.1d and e).

By watching the cumulus clouds as they develop and decay, and by trying to judge which are the active clouds, you will stand a better chance of finding a thermal. A building, well-defined cloud will usually be an indication of where a thermal will be found. On the other hand, decaying, ragged-edged clouds should be avoided.

Often, especially when the glider is at a much lower level than the cloud, the thermal will not be found directly under the cloud. Instead it may be displaced to one side. As the thermal ascends, it will be passing through different air masses which will be subject to differing wind strengths and directions. It will also be subject to wind shears caused by neighbouring vertical air movements. All of this may have a tilting effect on the thermal's path. As a result, at lower levels the thermal may be found some distance upwind from its cumulus cloud and the thermal source may be a considerable distance upwind if the wind is strong. Once this angular relationship is established on a particular day, it will probably remain the same for several hours or maybe even the whole of the day, unless wind or soaring conditions change. As a general rule, if lift cannot be found directly beneath a cloud, try searching upwind of the cloud. The stronger the wind and the lower the glider, the further upwind you should search for the thermal. You will also increase your chances of finding the thermal faster if you plan your flight path so that you approach the area where you expect to find the thermal by flying directly into or downwind.

15 Knots

10 Knots

5 Knots

Fig 29.2   Sloping thermal ascent. If any wind is present a thermal may follow a sloping path.

GROUND READING

On blue days, when no cumulus clouds are present to aid your search for a thermal, or when you are too far vertically from cloud base for the clouds to assist in accurately pin-pointing a thermal, you will have to use other clues to find lift. In the absence of any other visual clues, identifying a likely thermal source and flying in the air above or near it may be your only hope of finding lift.

Remember that the effectiveness of a surface as a thermal source will depend on how quickly and how much it warms up and heats the air immediately above it. The longer the air lies close to this warm surface, the greater the temperature of the air and the more buoyant it will become.

When looking for a suitable thermal source, you should bear in mind both of these essential ingredients. First try to imagine which parts of the earth below will be the warmest to touch. Concrete areas as found in towns, on motorways or hard-surfaced runways of both active and disused airfields will become too hot to touch if exposed to direct sunlight. Dry earth fields will have similar characteristics. Some ripe crops have good attributes as thermal sources. (Try walking through a golden wheat field on a hot day and you will feel that the temperature is higher among the stalks than outside of the crop.)

Areas containing large amounts of water, such as marshes, lakes or deciduous forests should be avoided as they generally prove to be poor thermal sources.

The effectiveness of the thermal source will depend greatly on the sun's rays striking it. Any cloud shadows passing over or sitting upon an area will reduce or even cancel its thermal producing qualities.

On the other hand, if the surface is angled in such a way as to receive the sun's rays at a more direct angle, then the surface will be a much more efficient source. Hillsides and mountain slopes facing the sun will provide such sources and will also have the benefit of being well-drained.

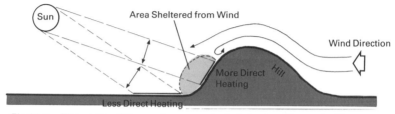

Fig 29.3 The angle of the sun's rays and wind shadow thermals. The more directly the sun's rays strike the ground, the greater the surface heating. Areas sheltered from the wind by a hill will allow air to remain in contact with the warm ground for longer, increasing the chances of a good thermal forming.

Apart from crops and towns, the downwind sides of hills offer some shelter from any wind present, and allow areas of stagnant air to remain close to the thermal source long enough for them to form a good thermal.

TRIGGERS

Once you have identified a probable thermal source, there is one more ingredient which will add to the chances of your finding an active thermal in that vicinity. A thermal bubble still attached firmly to the ground is of no value to you when you are getting low and need lift quickly. What you require is something to trigger the thermal so that it breaks away from its source and begins rising. If you can identify a good thermal source which is accompanied by a suitable trigger feature, then your chances of finding a thermal will be increased considerably.

The best of such visible triggers are man-made. Anything which disturbs the air can kick off a thermal. Cars, trains, launching cables and tow-planes, even combine harvesters and tractors can all stir up the air enough to start a thermal on its way. All you need to find a thermal is a sharp eye, some imagination and a little bit of luck.

OTHER VISUAL CLUES

SOARING BIRDS

Even the youngest of soaring birds has a greater instinct for finding and using lift than the most experienced glider pilot. Vultures and eagles are classic examples of experts at thermal soaring. Other more common species such as buzzards, hawks and gulls can also teach us a thing or two about thermalling, and indeed soaring in general. Therefore when birds are seen circling or flying without flapping their wings for any length of time, this can be taken as an indication of the presence of lift. Indeed, not only an indication that lift is present, but usually where the best lift is to be found. Providing you have sufficient height margin to safely reach the bird's thermal, on joining it you will usually be rewarded with a good rate of climb. Conversely, a soaring bird will not hesitate to join your thermal if it thinks that you have found better lift than it. This can be taken as the ultimate compliment.

If the air is suddenly full of swifts darting around your glider as they chase insects, you can also be assured that locally, lift is plentiful, although this sight more commonly occurs near cloud base.

OTHER GLIDERS

Sometimes, just as helpful, although often less reliable than thermalling birds, are circling gliders. Unlike birds, gliders circle for reasons other than to maintain or gain height (for instance when practising turns, for training purposes, or even to lose height before landing). Add to this the fact that some pilots have slightly more soaring ability than an ostrich, and you will understand why risking a long glide with little height margin to join a circling glider can be unwise.

If on the other hand, a glider or a gaggle of gliders is seen to be gaining height, then the risk of not finding lift is reduced, but never eliminated. Thermalling gliders flown by known, competent pilots, whose thermal can be joined at the same height or higher, will offer the best chance of contacting a usable thermal.

Where competition gliders are found thermalling in a gaggle, you will usually be able to assume that they are in the best lift available, although the density of traffic in such gaggles may cause concern to the less experienced pilot, to the extent that you may prefer to find your own less crowded thermal.

SMOKE AND FIRES

The presence of smoke can be an indication of anything from weak or unusable lift, to a strong, rapidly ascending thermal, depending on the source of the smoke.

Large fires, such as when straw is burnt (often called stubble fires) can cause large, dark columns of smoke, which often indicate the presence of phenomenal updraughts. These can give rapid rates of climb, depending on the ferocity of the fire below. The lift is often very turbulent and accompanied by neighbouring heavy sink. As visibility can be poor in such thermals, cloud flying techniques may have to be used.

Depending on the care taken in burning the source field, little or no usable lift may be found and so care should be taken not to arrive too low at the smoke. In the United Kingdom straw burning is subject to restrictions and will soon be illegal and thus a valuable extension to the British soaring season will be lost.

Small fires, such as bonfires, may or may not generate enough heat on their own to produce a usable thermal, but their effect on the local air may be enough to trigger the thermal for which you are looking.

Many power stations are recognised thermal sources, producing much steam from cooling towers and often smoke from the main chimney. Whether the lift associated with these stations comes from the towers and chimneys, or the complex in general, is debatable. One thing is for sure, when these sources are producing smoke and thermals you can rely on a smelly ascent in the choking smoke which often marks the lift.

When smoke is not a part of a usable thermal, its behaviour is often a good indicator of where a thermal can be found. If a thermal starts to ascend close to some smoke, the entrainment of the neighbouring air often changes the angle of ascent of the smoke. Observation of any column of smoke, from whatever source, may therefore reveal the presence of a nearby thermal.

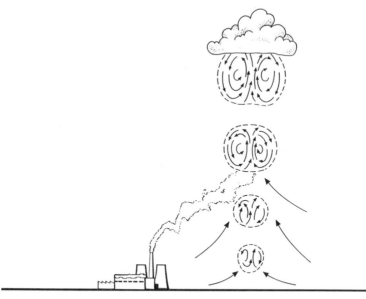

Fig 29.4 Thermals indicated by smoke. Deflected smoke can often indicate air being entrained into a thermal.

As the thermal breaks away from the surface, there will be an inflow of air into the place from where it came. This local wind will cause a disturbance which may be visible as a dust or straw-devil, or even as a rippling in an area of crop. Watching for and acting upon relatively subtle signs can result in your placing the glider right in the path of a rising thermal.

SEARCH PATTERNS

Whether you are using visual clues or attempting to locate a thermal source by deduction, it is important that you plan your search methodically.

The advantage of approaching a cumulus cloud or a thermal source into wind or downwind, has already been mentioned, but there are many other ways of increasing your success rate when thermal hunting.

Thermals are anti-social. They do not want gliders taking a free ride. If a glider's wing tip encounters the rising air of a thermal, the lift will tend to tip the glider away from the thermal. This tipping action may be very gentle, almost imperceptible, but can still be enough to alter the glider's course away from the thermal. If the glider is allowed to wander in this way, it will follow a flight path which will take it between most of the thermals in the sky.

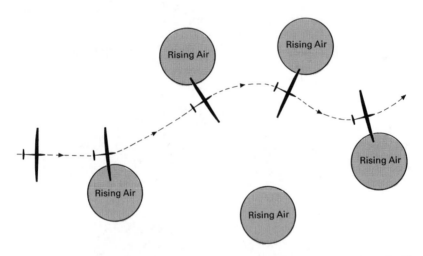

Fig 29.5   Heading deviations due to thermals. Thermals are anti-social and will tend to tip the glider, turning it away from the thermal.

The answer is to select a track, and a visual feature at which to aim, (usually a cloud or a suspected thermal source) and then fly directly towards it. If the nose of the glider moves off this track, it will probably be due to such a thermal disturbance. Small, unintentional changes of track should be resisted. If the tipping sensation is pronounced, turning towards the rising wing may reveal a usable thermal.

The height available for thermal searching will usually be the determining factor in how far you can search before returning to the airfield or a preselected field. In order to use this height to best advantage, you should plan your search, so that if lift is not found on your outbound track, you can return to base without retracing your exact track. Even a return track displaced by a short distance from the outbound route will take the glider through different air and double the chance of finding lift.

When thermal streeting is seen to be present from the alignment of clouds or is suspected on a blue day, then the search pattern should be oriented relative to the wind.

When cloud streeting exists, flying into wind under the clouds should reveal many thermals. When approaching a cloud street, do so at 90° to the street in order to spend as little time as possible in the sinking air between the streets.

When no clouds are present to show where the streets are, heading directly into or downwind from a source will again give a better chance of encountering a thermal. If nothing but sink is encountered, you are probably in a SINK STREET. In this event, altering course by 30° to 45° for a short period may well place you in lift. On encountering lift, you should return the glider to a heading which is directly into or downwind to follow the lift street.

Whatever search pattern you adopt, fly it at a sensible airspeed. This will mean that in air that is giving little sink, the airspeed used will be close to the airspeed which gives the best glide angle. In air which is sinking at a faster rate, higher airspeeds should be used. This will ensure that you are not wasting height by flying unnecessarily fast and also that the glider does not spend too long in descending air.

Once you have made some progress at basic soaring, you will be shown how to modify the above rule to get the best performance from your glider in all air masses, be they rising or descending.

CENTRING IN THERMALS

Having found a thermal, your next task is to position the glider in that part of the thermal which is ascending at the greatest rate, that is, the core. The act of manoeuvring the glider into the thermal's core is known as CENTRING and due to the thermal's changing shape as it ascends, centring may be a continuous task throughout the whole climb.

If you ask ten top glider pilots how they go about centring in a thermal, you will probably get ten different answers. Most of them may use more than one technique, varying which is used depending on the size, roughness and strength of the thermal. Centring technique is therefore a highly personal skill. It will depend on the rate of roll of the glider being flown, the sensitivity of the instruments and, probably most of all, on how sensitive the pilot is to the gusts and lulls which accompany most thermals.

For these reasons, it would be wrong to say that there is one correct or infallible method of centring in a thermal. Many books and instructors will show you various methods of centring in thermals. You should try them all and then use the one or more methods which suit you. The following method is one which many pilots use in a number of variations, and is one that can be developed as experience is gained, so that quicker centring can be achieved.

If the glider flies into air which is rising at a faster rate than that which it was in previously, there will be a momentary change in the angle of attack of the wing, and a resulting change in the forces it produces. The noticeable effect will be a slight surge in the airspeed and a physical push on the "seat of the pants" of the pilot.

257

How pronounced these sensations are, will depend on the sharpness of the transition between the air in which the glider was flying and the rising air it is entering. This in turn will be relative to the strength of lift being entered.

What all this means is that if a surge is encountered, the glider is flying into air which is rising faster than the air which it was in. On feeling this surge, you should momentarily reduce the angle of bank of the wings, to move the glider towards the lift. This reduction of the bank angle should only be for a very short period of time; perhaps 2 – 3 seconds. The wings should then be returned to the original degree of bank. This manoeuvring is continued as each gust is felt, until the glider is circling within the core of the thermal.

Let us look at the technique diagrammatically in order to visualise what we are trying to achieve. For simplicity, we will use a cross-section through our idealised thermal and assume that in its core the glider will climb at 4 knots (400 ft/min) reducing as we go further out from the core until eventually it will descend at 6 knots in the sink on the periphery of the thermal.

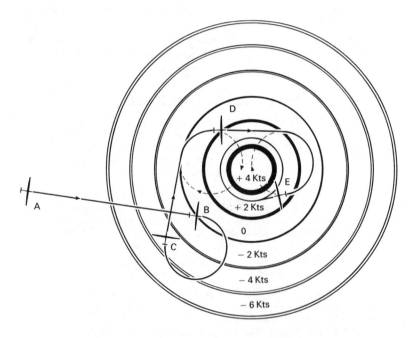

Fig 29.6   Thermal centring. Reducing the bank angle each time a gust is experienced will move the glider towards the thermal's centre.

At A the glider is cruising in sink. Due to the descending air around the thermal, it is common to experience an increase in the rate of descent as a thermal is approached. In this instance, you need to have the courage to press on, height permitting, or else you will spend your life turning away from thermals.

At B the rate of descent will have reduced and the air will probably be somewhat more "lively". There may be a slight or even a pronounced tipping effect away from the thermal as the left wing is raised. If this is felt, you should turn towards the rising wing, in this case, to the left.

Let us assume that you do not, and take the worst case of turning the wrong way; that is, to the right. In this situation, continue the turn.

In the vicinity of C, you will be moving from air which is descending at 4 knots to air which is descending at 2 knots. As you fly into this better air, you will feel a slight surge or gust. When you sense this, reduce the bank angle or even level the wings completely. This will move your circle towards the better air. After a second or two, re-establish the original amount of bank.

A similar sensation requiring the same manoeuvre will occur at D, this time as you move into rising air.

Note that although the human body is very sensitive to the changing rates of ascent or descent of the air, it is not very well calibrated. As a result, flying into air that is descending less will give the same sensations as flying from air that is descending, into air that is rising. Therefore the glider's variometer must be used to confirm that the glider is indeed being manoeuvred into rising air each time a gust is felt (E). Using this technique the glider will eventually be placed in a circle in the core of the thermal.

As the glider climbs in the thermal, any gusts experienced should be acted upon in the same way, thus continually re-centring the glider in the thermal's core.

The intensity of the gusts will depend on the rate at which the glider is moving into faster rising air. If you miss a gust, or are not sure, note the direction in which you were heading when you thought you felt it, and continue the turn, anticipating the onset of the gust and your action the next time the glider nears that position.

The duration of levelling of the wings (or reduction of bank) depends on the strength of the gust felt. If you are positive about where the lift is, act positively. If in doubt, act cautiously. The longer you delay re-establishing the turn, the further the turn will be moved in the direction of straightening. Moving the turn when you are uncertain of exactly where the better lift is, is a quick way to lose a thermal.

If you do lose the lift after having been established in a thermal, reduce the bank slightly. This will result in a larger radius of turn and more air being covered. Providing you have not been over-dramatic with your previous manoeuvres, you should re-encounter the lift. You can then begin careful re-centring.

Successful centring requires constant mental mapping of the air, noting where the surges and gusts occur and comparing these with the readings on the variometer. Unfortunately, even the fastest reading variometer has lag, and therefore will show what the air was doing a few seconds before. Fortunately, the sensations the human body receives are instantaneous and with a bit of practice you will learn to use all of these inputs to centre quickly in the best lift.

COMMON FAULTS WHILE THERMALLING

Thermals vary in size and strength. Every glider has its own performance characteristics once it is established in a turn. It is therefore necessary to match these two variables to get the optimum rate of climb. Failure to do so, along with other faults, will degrade your rates of climb or even lose you the thermal altogether.

INSUFFICIENT ANGLE OF BANK

The first criterion is to place the glider in a turn, the whole of which lies within the best area of lift. The greater the angle of bank used, the smaller the radius of the glider's turn. Therefore by using a reasonable angle of bank, you stand a better chance of keeping the glider in the area of best lift.

If you are taking more than 20 seconds to turn through 360°, then the chances are that your rate of turn and the glider's turning circle is too large, with the result that part of the time the glider will be turning in air that is ascending at a lesser rate or even in air that is sinking.

TOO MUCH BANK

Conversely, too much bank will, while keeping the glider in a smaller turn, have a performance penalty due to what is known as the glider's TURNING POLAR.

Due to the extra work required from the wing while turning, as the bank angle is increased, so too is the glider's still air descent rate. The following table shows the minimum rate of descent in still air of a typical medium performance glider when different bank angles are used.

BANK ANGLE	MINIMUM RATE OF DESCENT IN STILL AIR (Knots)
0°	1.38
30°	1.71
45°	2.36
60°	3.94
70°	6.89

If the thermal is weak and too much bank is used, then it is possible to cancel out any rate of climb which could be achieved due to the increased rate of descent incurred as a result of too much bank.

The optimum angle of bank will depend on the size, strength and degree of roughness of the thermal. In a strong, narrow thermal, angles of bank in the region of 45° or more may be appropriate, whereas in a large, weak thermal, a smaller amount of bank will often give better results. Around 30° of bank is usually a good starting angle until you have assessed conditions.

UNNECESSARY VARIATION OF THE BANK ANGLE

Changing the angle of bank for even a short period of time will move the circle that the glider describes. The gusts associated with some thermals will, unless countered, cause the bank angle to change. Add to this any unnecessary variation of the amount of bank by the pilot and it can be very easy to lose track of where the lift is in relation to the glider. To avoid losing the best lift, or perhaps even the whole thermal, only make considered control inputs and avoid unnecessary changes in the amount of bank.

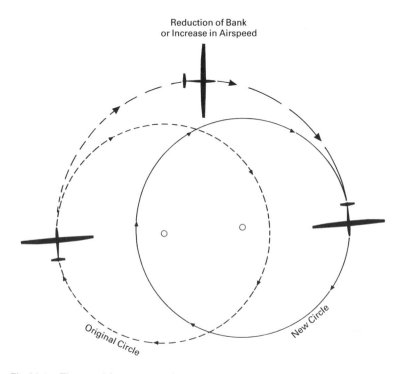

Fig 29.7 The need for accurate flying when thermalling. Any reduction in bank angle or increase in airspeed will increase the glider's turning circle.

UNINTENTIONAL AIRSPEED CHANGES

Just as altering the angle of bank will result in a different radius of turn, so too will changing the airspeed. Flying the glider faster will result in a larger radius of turn for the same angle of bank than would a slower airspeed. This means that if the airspeed is allowed to increase unintentionally, the glider's turn will be elongated. Once the airspeed is returned to its original value, the glider will return to its original radius of turn, but the centre of the turn will have moved. Therefore poor airspeed control can result in the glider leaving the thermal, and possibly cause the pilot to lose track of where lift is to be found. To avoid this occurrence, regularly monitor attitude and airspeed.

LOOKOUT SUFFERING DUE TO OBSESSION WITH THE VARIOMETER

Climbing quickly to the top of a thermal would be a total waste of time, if it is followed by a slow descent by parachute (or an even faster descent without one)!

Mid-air collision is one of the greatest risks in gliding. Gliders will tend to congregate in thermals and due to centring manoeuvres, differing airspeeds, turn rates and climb performance there will always be the risk of collision. Despite rules which are designed to reduce this risk, the only answer is to maintain a good lookout.

Looking out, using a regular scan, will also help the accuracy of your flying and, as a result, your climb rate. A good scan will not only take in the sky and other gliders, but also the nose attitude and wing tip, which in turn, indicate the consistency of the airspeed and angle of bank. The variometer and ASI can be included in the scan, although airflow noise and an audio system fitted to the variometer can be used to free some of your attention from these internal "distractions".

AIRMANSHIP AND RULES WHEN THERMAL SOARING

- When joining another glider in a thermal, you are required to circle in the same direction as the glider already in the thermal.

- The first glider established in a thermal dictates the direction of turn.

- When joining a thermal you should enter the thermal in such a way that your entering will not necessitate the need for other pilots already in the thermal to alter their turns to avoid you.

- Never fly for any length of time in another glider's blind spot. (Typically, this will be close behind and/or below the other glider.)

- Should you lose sight of another glider known to be in the thermal, avoid sudden changes of track. If you suspect that this other glider is too close, you should consider leaving the thermal.

- On leaving a thermal, do so in such a way that reduces the risk of straightening up in front of another glider.

- Do not fly in the company of other gliders near the base of cloud, where the visibility, by definition, will be poor.

CHAPTER 30

MOUNTAIN LEE WAVES

Hill lift is not the only type of lift which is produced as a result of the wind blowing against and over a ridge of hills or mountains. If the atmospheric conditions are right, other areas of lift are created in the lee of the high ground. This lift is part of a large scale deflection of the air mass which creates a phenomenon known as MOUNTAIN LEE WAVES or, as the high ground may be no higher than a line of hills, simply LEE WAVES.

THE FORMATION AND CHARACTERISTICS OF LEE WAVES

Next time you are standing by a shallow stream, take a look at the way a completely submerged rock causes a series of waves to form in the water flowing over it. Although the water might be flowing quite fast, the waves will remain more or less in the same position, that is they are STANDING WAVES.

If you imagine that the water were the earth's lower atmosphere and that the rock were a hill or mountain, then you might be able to visualise a similar effect which exists in the air.

As the wind blows against an obstruction such as a line of hills, initially the air will be deflected upwards. (We have already seen this effect giving hill lift.) Depending on various factors, one of which is the shape of the hill, the air will flow over the hill and down the hill's downwind or lee side. If the state of stability of the atmosphere is favourable, the air will "rebound" upwards to form the front of a standing wave. This initial wave is called the PRIMARY WAVE. The air will rise until it reaches the crest of this wave and then descend again. This wave effect often continues with decreasing intensity through many cycles and for many miles downwind of the original line of hills. If atmospheric conditions are favourable, the effect may also be magnified vertically, creating waves, the top of which may reach altitudes of 50,000 feet or more. The expression used to describe the vertical depth of a wave is known as the wave amplitude. This is taken as half of the vertical distance between the crest and the trough of a wave.

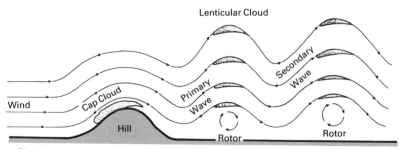

Fig 30.1   Mountain lee waves. When the wind blows over a range of hills or mountains it often forms a series of waves downwind of the high ground.

263

This wave effect can be very powerful with the air rising and descending at thousands of feet per minute when strong winds blow across large mountain ranges. In fact, the effect can be so great that warnings of the presence of "mountain lee waves" are frequently issued to airline crews. As far as glider pilots are concerned, the stronger the updraughts the better, but then glider pilots, unlike airline pilots, are not too worried about maintaining level flight. Unfortunately, the downdraughts are every bit as strong and as plentiful as the updraughts.

CONDITIONS WHICH FAVOUR THE FORMATION OF LEE WAVES

The formation of lee waves needs more than just a line of hills or mountains and some wind. The wind must be of a reasonable strength (usually 15 knots or more) for good waves to be produced. It must also be blowing at, or close to, right angles to the line of hills.

The atmosphere must contain the right mixture of stable and unstable air if the lee wave is to rebound and set up a wave system. This combination of air mass stability can be regarded as a sandwich of air masses with a layer of unstable air from the ground to around 4000 to 5000 feet, with a stable layer above this height, and a further unstable layer above.

FEATURES ASSOCIATED WITH LEE WAVES

Apart from the large areas of rising and sinking air, there are several other features which are associated with lee waves.

LAMINAR AIRFLOW

For reasonable lee waves to exist, the air must adopt a smooth or laminar airflow. At lower levels the air may suffer from mixing due to turbulence or thermals, but once clear of such disturbances the airflow will be smooth and laminar.

FOEHN GAP AND LEE DOWNDRAUGHT

As the wind flows down the lee side of the hill or mountain, the descending air will often be drier and as it descends it will be heated. As a result, any cloud may be evaporated back into water vapour, leaving a clear area of sky immediately downwind of the high ground. This gap in the cloud is known as the FOEHN GAP.

In moderate or strong winds this downdraught can be severe and the air in this region very turbulent.

LENTICULAR CLOUDS

A classic wave system is accompanied by classic clouds, called LENTICULAR CLOUDS. These clouds which, although they get their name from their more common "lens-shaped" cross-section, can come in a variety of shapes. They are normally long, thin clouds, orientated parallel to the ridge of high ground which is causing the wave system and therefore lie at right angles to the wind direction. They are distinct from cumulus by two features. Firstly they tend to have a very smooth profile

264

due to the laminar characteristics of the airflow causing them, and secondly, they are stationary in the sky despite the strong wind which may be blowing.

Their formation is totally due to the wave system. As the air rises up the front of the wave, it cools. As it cools it is no longer capable of retaining all of its water content as vapour. On reaching the dew point this water vapour will condense out as cloud, that is, a lenticular cloud will form. As the air descends again on the down side of the wave the air will be warmed and the water droplets of the cloud will be evaporated back to invisible water vapour. Therefore, in classic wave conditions, the clouds will be present only as a strip at the top of each wave as it reaches condensation level. The fact that the wave system is standing still relative to the high ground which is causing the wave means that the clouds also remain stationary, and rather conveniently, signpost the position of the rising air.

If conditions are favourable, then similar wave systems may exist above the lower one. These systems may also be marked by lenticular clouds at higher levels.

ROTOR AND ROTOR CLOUD

Beneath the crest of each wave, especially beneath the primary and those waves closer to the high ground, the airflow is often severely disrupted, causing severe turbulence. This area of air is called the ROTOR. Depending on the humidity of the air mass at this level, the rotor may be marked by a ragged cloud, the shape of which is constantly and rapidly changing. This cloud is known as the ROTOR CLOUD. Rotor, if present, will normally be found level with or just below the tops of the source hills or mountains and should be avoided at all costs.

Where rotor extends down to the ground, it can cause gusts, severe turbulence, wind shear and a complete reversal of the wind direction. Glider pilots, from sites where lee waves are common, are all too aware of the damage rotor can cause to trailers and club buildings and know when to suspend launching until there is a favourable change in wind direction.

CLOUDLESS WAVE DAYS

As with thermals, the presence of lee waves is not always indicated by the presence of cloud. If the air mass does not contain enough moisture then no condensation (and therefore no cloud) will occur even though a strong wave system may exist.

CHAPTER 31

WAVE SOARING

FINDING THE WAVE LIFT

The rising air associated with a wave system is the air which is moving up the front of the wave. Therefore the glider must be positioned in this area if it is to gain height.

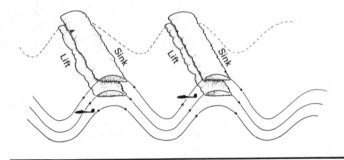

Fig 31.1   Position of wave lift. To climb, the glider must be positioned in the up-going part of the wave.

If the sky is cloudless, then finding this area of lift can be difficult, although local knowledge at such times is invaluable and well worth seeking before take-off.

Finding the wave lift becomes somewhat easier if there are lenticular clouds marking the crests of the wave. In this instance, you should fly the glider into a position upwind of the associated lenticular cloud. Typically, the lift will be found about a quarter, to one third, of the distance between one cloud and the next cloud upwind. This relationship will vary and as height is gained the lift will be closer to the cloud. In general, the better defined the lenticular cloud, the better the associated lift.

Whether or not lenticular clouds are present, entry into the wave lift will not only be marked by an indication of lift on the variometer, but also by the smoothness of the air in which the glider is flying. This air may be so smooth that often you will not need to make any control inputs for minutes on end. Indeed, the first time you experience good wave lift, you can easily be forgiven for distrusting the variometer and altimeter readings, both of which will be showing climb rates normally associated with large, turbulent thermals or strong hill lift.

METHODS OF ENTERING THE WAVE LIFT

The easiest method of entering wave lift, is to be aerotowed into it. This is common at many wave sites, and local tow-plane pilots usually know where the wave lift can be contacted in the prevailing wind conditions. This may mean towing the glider a considerable distance from the airfield and/or to a height greater than normal launch heights.

It is possible to contact wave lift directly from the top of a wire launch. However, contacting wave lift directly from a wire launch is much less likely than from an aerotow and will depend greatly on the wave system being low enough and in a position within reach with the height available.

Occasionally, a glider is able to gain enough height in hill lift to reach the wave lift. This may involve gliding out from the hill lift in the hope of contacting the wave lift. If such an attempt to reach the wave fails then the glider can be flown back to the safety of the hill lift to regain height. As any change in the wind conditions may result in a change in the position of the standing waves, the attempt to reach the wave lift should be repeated regularly.

At some hill soaring sites the up-going part of the wave may coincide with the hill lift. If this is the case, not only will the rate of climb the glider can achieve in the hill lift be increased, but also it will be possible for the glider to climb directly from hill lift into the wave system. It should be appreciated that any shift in the position of the wave system may result in the opposite effect, that is, the hill lift may be cancelled out completely by the down-going part of the wave. Therefore caution should be exercised on any occasion when the glider is scampering back to the hill hoping for hill lift to save it from an early landing.

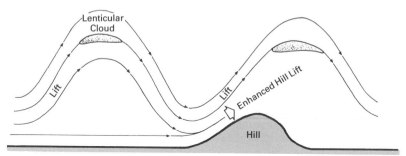

Fig 31.2   Wave affecting hill lift. When the up-going part of the wave coincides with the hill lift, a much increased rate of climb will be achieved in the hill lift.

On many days when thermal soaring is being carried out, mountain lee waves will interfere with the distribution and the strength of the thermals. This wave interference causes those thermals which coincide with the rising part of the wave, to give a higher rate of climb, whereas the rates of climb in those thermals in the descending part of the wave will be reduced. Some of these thermals may be very distorted, making climbing difficult. If a thermal giving an enhanced rate of climb can be used, it may be possible to climb into the wave system and enjoy some exceptional flying on what started out as a thermalling flight. On such days, the tops of any cumulus clouds may give a clue to the existence of a wave system by having a smoother shape than is normally expected of cumulus. It may even be possible to climb up the front of the cumulus by flying forwards out of the thermal into the wave lift as cloud base is reached.

267

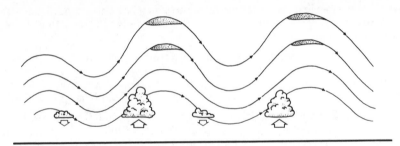

Fig 31.3   Wave interfering with thermals. Wave lift will often affect thermal distribution, enhancing some thermals and suppressing others.

Whichever method is used to enter the wave lift, if the glider encounters the wave system near its lower levels, the lift may be broken and difficult to use. If this is the case, flying the glider at the airspeed which gives the minimum sink might help gain enough height to place the glider into the better lift which may exist slightly higher up. Once established in better lift, you can afford to be more adventurous in trying to map how far the area of lift extends and the positions where the best rate of climb can be found.

WAVE SOARING TECHNIQUE

Once the area of best lift is found, the glider can be flown in this area until sufficient height has been gained or the top of the lift is reached. The area of lift will vary from a small area which may require a technique not unlike a modified thermalling technique, to large bands of lift, possibly miles long and many wingspans wide. These large "streets" of lift are the most common form of wave lift. They will lie parallel to the high ground which is causing the wave, and also parallel to their attendant lenticular clouds if these are present.

The lift can normally be used by "beating" backwards and forwards along the band of lift, in a similar way to the technique used when hill soaring. The lenticular cloud can almost be treated as the hill or ridge. As the glider gains altitude, the best lift may be further upwind of the cloud.

The wind will have an effect on the glider's track during its beats in the lift. In light winds, the effect may be small and can be countered by tracking the glider with its nose pointing slightly into wind. The amount by which this tracking will be necessary depends on the wind strength. As the wind strength will increase as altitude is gained, it is not uncommon to find that it is necessary to point the glider directly into wind, simply to remain in the lift and to avoid drifting back into the sink behind the lift. Even by flying the glider into wind in this way, there will still be occasions when the only way to remain in the lift will be to increase airspeed to counter what may be a very strong wind at flying levels.

Your position relative to the lift can always be judged relative to the lenticular cloud, and in the absence of this, by the glider's position above the ground. This latter reference will become more inaccurate as height is gained, but assuming the glider has not been turned onto a downwind heading for any length of time, the lift area will not be far away.

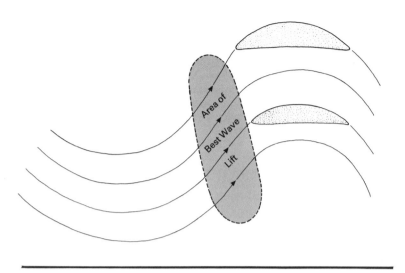

Fig 31.4   Wave lift position sloping with altitude. As altitude is gained the position of the best lift will often be further upwind.

Having established the glider in the lift, subsequent loss of the area of lift will probably be a result of one of four events. The first two of these involve the glider's speed through the air. The chances are that the glider has been allowed to drift back behind the lift area, or flown forwards to a position upwind of the lift area. Alternatively, through no fault of yours, the wave system may have changed and the lift has ceased or gone somewhere else. You may even have reached the top of the particular wave system.

It is quite common to drift back behind the lift area, so you should firstly fly the glider forwards into wind to see if the lift is re-encountered in this area. This can either be done by turning more into wind, or if the glider is already heading directly into wind, by increasing the airspeed. If the lift is rediscovered, the original track or airspeed can be reselected.

If you suspect that you have penetrated upwind of the lift area, turning across the direction of the wind may be enough to drift the glider back into the lift. Certainly, in strong winds this should be enough to displace the glider downwind sufficiently. On regaining the lift, turn back into wind, or track as necessary. On no account should you turn downwind if the wind is strong as this will increase your groundspeed so much that you may quickly fly through the lift and lose it altogether.

In both these situations, resuming a track or heading close to the original track may lead to the lift being lost in the same way again. Annoying as this may seem, at least you now know how to regain the lift, whereas adopting a different soaring track or airspeed may result in losing the lift in some other way, necessitating a completely new search.

If the wave system changes, the position of the lift, sink and lenticular clouds will change. In fact, the system may break down completely, making any search for the new position of the lift fruitless. All of this may occur almost instantly; all it needs is a change of wind direction or strength. If either of these events occur, the glider may find itself sitting in an area of sink, or even, as happened to the author on one occasion, inside a lenticular cloud, which was, until a few seconds before, well above and behind the glider. As if this was not annoying enough, the variometer needle quickly changed from indicating 4 knots up to 10 knots down!

The good news is that such changes in the wave system can provide better conditions as well as worse. There is nothing more pleasing than to be searching for the next bit of wave lift and to see a lenticular cloud forming beside your wing tip, as if by magic!

HAZARDS ASSOCIATED WITH WAVE FLYING

COMPLACENCY

Once established in lift, wave soaring can be remarkably easy. The air is smooth, the lift can often be strong and it is easy to become obsessed with the quest for altitude. All of this can lead to a false sense of security. The fact that the glider may be operating at altitudes and in wind strengths which are not normally associated with other forms of lift, means that safety during wave soaring flights depends on the pilot remaining vigilant.

STRONG OR VARIABLE WINDS

Many good wave soaring days are accompanied by strong winds, even at ground level. Extra care must be exercised during take-off and landing, as severe turbulence is a common feature of gliding sites near high ground. When landing, especially after a long flight, you may find that conditions have changed somewhat since your launch. This could mean that the wind strength or direction may have changed, possibly resulting in an increase in turbulence on approach. It is always a good policy to keep in radio contact with the base airfield in order that you can be informed if any deterioration in conditions has occurred. In turn, many gliding sites at which wave soaring takes place will broadcast warnings of such deteriorations, and may in bad cases advise an immediate landing or even a landing away from base if local rotor is the problem.

The strong winds will make it easy to lose track of one's position unless sight of the ground is maintained. Even when it is, one part of a mountain plateau can look like another from 20,000 feet when even a fraction of the ground is obscured by lenticular or orographic cloud. Maintain your orientation by keeping known ground features in view.

CLOUD COVER

Unlike other types of soaring, wave soaring can result in the glider climbing quickly above cloud, without the need to enter cloud. The danger lies in the fact that what may have been scattered clouds below the glider when altitude was first gained, can quickly become a thick layer of cloud, between the glider and the ground. As the gaps in cloud may have been caused by the presence of the wave system, any change in the conditions supporting the wave system may cause the system to collapse and the cloud gaps to fill in.

Even if your glider is equipped with cloud flying instruments, you will be in the unenvious position of having to descend through cloud which may extend below the height of the high ground below. Whether or not your glider is equipped with navigation aids, descending into mountain-filled clouds is an unhealthy pastime. The only safe answer to this problem is not to get into this predicament in the first place. With this in mind, never climb through small cloud gaps and always watch out for the areas of cloud below extending to join up and fill the cloud gaps. Start your descent early and do not underestimate how long it will take to get rid of your height. Losing 20,000 feet for instance, can take some minutes even when diving with full airbrake.

LACK OF OXYGEN

The higher you fly, the less oxygen there is in the atmosphere for you to breath. Above 10,000 feet, the amount of oxygen in the atmosphere will be reduced to a level where decision making and pilot performance will start to suffer, unless supplemented by an oxygen supply carried in the glider. By 18,000 feet the reduction in oxygen will result in a marked decrease in performance, and in time, irrational decision making and unconsciousness. The onset of HYPOXIA, as this lack of oxygen is known, can be quite innocuous. In fact, one of the main symptoms of its onset is a feeling of well-being which may well mask other symptoms, such as clumsiness, blue fingertips and narrowing field of vision.

By 20,000 feet useful consciousness will be about ten minutes unless supplementary oxygen is used. This period will reduce rapidly to about two minutes at 25,000 feet, and at 30,000 feet and above is measured in seconds rather than minutes.

These heights will vary depending on the fitness of the pilot. An unfit pilot can expect to show hypoxia symptoms at a lower altitude than one who is in good physical condition. The effect of cold at these altitudes will aggravate the situation.

Because of the inherent dangers of high altitude flight, an oxygen system capable of giving a satisfactory supply of oxygen should be carried if it is intended to fly above 10,000 feet. It should be used at all times above this altitude, and in the event of its suspected malfunction, the glider should be descended below 10,000 feet as quickly as possible.

ICING

Low temperatures and moisture go nicely together to give another potential problem, that is icing. Ice forming on the glider's wings and other outer surfaces will reduce its performance. Ice may also cause the controls to freeze if they are not moved regularly. The airbrakes are especially prone to this type of jamming. The canopy may also glaze over, reducing visibility. This icing of the canopy may also occur on the inside, due to moisture from the pilot's breath. Icing may take a long time to clear and in the event that an approach to land has to be made with restricted visibility through the canopy, the direct vision window should be opened fully to aid your landing.

ONSET OF DARKNESS

The sunset, when seen from altitude, occurs later than it does when observed from ground below. This means that it is possible to be soaring in daylight at altitude when it is already dark on the ground. Add to this the time it takes to descend from altitude and it becomes quite conceivable that, unless you are careful, you may find yourself searching for and attempting a landing at an unlit airfield in total darkness. To avoid such excitement, make a note of the local sunset times before take-off and make sure that you can get back to the airfield and land well before the onset of darkness.

THE EFFECT OF ALTITUDE ON LIMITING AIRSPEEDS

The airspeed limitations displayed in the cockpit of the glider will apply when the glider is being flown at lower altitudes. As altitude is increased, these limitations will reduce in value. The aerodynamic reasons for this need not be understood but it is important that the glider manufacturer's manual is consulted to establish what can be regarded as a safe airspeed at a particular altitude. These airspeed limits must not be exceeded.

SECTION 4

RULES OF THE AIR

CHAPTER 32

RULES OF THE AIR

There are many rules and regulations, as well as recommended practices, which you will be expected to obey when flying a glider. Some of these are essential in order to avoid conflict with other traffic. These you should learn and act upon as necessary. Others, such as airspace regulations and local regulations will be pointed out to you as your training and gliding career progress. As you reach various stages in your flying, you will be examined on these regulations.

In order to save you plodding through volumes of legally worded air law manuals which cover all aspects of aviation, most national gliding authorities produce a publication which gives the relevant regulations and recommended practices for glider pilots. You should regard it as your duty to obtain and read this publication as soon as is practical and certainly before you fly solo.

With safety in mind, and specifically to help you avoid the always present risk of a mid-air collision, a precis of some of the more immediate rules and conventions are listed below. For ease of reference, the rules for avoiding conflict with other gliders while hill soaring and thermalling are repeated below. The regulations which follow should be taken only as a guide and the exact wording and conditions of the appropriate rule cross-checked with the official publication.

GENERAL

- When two aircraft are approaching head-on at a similar altitude, each shall alter course by turning to the right.
- When two aircraft are on converging courses at a similar altitude, the aircraft which has the other on its right shall give way.

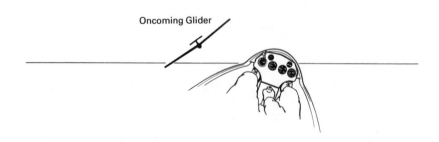

Fig 32.1   Approaching another aircraft head-on. When two aircraft are approaching each other head-on, each shall alter course to the right.

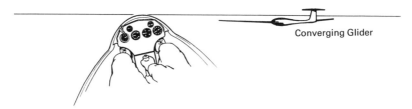

Converging Glider

Fig 32.2   Converging with another aircraft. When two aircraft are converging, the aircraft which has the other on its right shall give way.

- Overtaking aircraft should overtake by altering course to the right. (In the United Kingdom a glider overtaking another glider may do so on either side. The aircraft doing the overtaking is responsible for avoiding a collision.)

- Aeroplanes shall give way to gliders and aerotow combinations, and gliders shall give way to balloons.

- It is the responsibility of all pilots to avoid a collision.

- When landing, the lower glider has right of way but should not turn in front of a glider already on the final approach.

HILL SOARING

- When two aircraft are approaching head-on at a similar altitude while hill soaring, the glider with the hill on its left shall alter course to the right.

- In the United Kingdom and the U.S.A., when overtaking another glider while hill soaring you should overtake between the other glider and the hill. (Other countries overtake on the side away from the hill.)

THERMALLING

- When joining another glider in a thermal, you are required to circle in the same direction as the glider already in the thermal.

- The first glider established in a thermal dictates the direction of turn.

- When joining a thermal you should enter the thermal in such a way that your entering will not necessitate the need for other pilots already in the thermal to alter their turns to avoid you.

- Never fly for any length of time in another glider's blind spot.

- Should you lose sight of another glider known to be in the thermal, avoid sudden changes of track. If you suspect that this other glider is too close, you should consider leaving the thermal.

- On leaving a thermal, do so in such a way that reduces the risk of straightening up into another glider.

- Do not fly in the company of other gliders near the base of cloud, where the visibility, by definition, will be poor.

APPENDIX 1

HOW THE INSTRUMENTS WORK

Chapter 1 gave a brief description of the information which each of the basic instruments supplies to the pilot. Here it is intended to give a simple explanation of how these instruments measure the displayed information. Although many modern gliders are fitted with the latest electronic gadgets which may include computer displays and even utilise information from satellites to aid navigation, here we will only deal with the main instruments used in training and basic soaring.

The three basic instruments in which we are interested all use the pressure of the air to give an indication of airspeed, altitude or rate of climb or descent.

As altitude is increased, the atmospheric pressure decreases, that is, there is less air above pressing down upon us. This fact, although leading to some errors, especially with the airspeed indicator, allows us to measure altitude and rate of change of altitude.

THE AIRSPEED INDICATOR (ASI)

As the glider moves through the air, it has to push some of the air in front of it. This means that the air immediately in front of the glider will exert a pressure on the glider. This increase in pressure is sensed at the glider's PITOT TUBE and is compared with the local atmospheric pressure sensed at the STATIC VENTS.

The pressure from the pitot is fed into a flexible chamber inside the instrument. This chamber is surrounded by air taken from the static vents.

As the glider flies faster through the air, the pressure at the pitot tube will increase, which will expand the flexible chamber. A series of levers and linkages connected to this chamber, will move the needle on the face of the instrument, indicating the new airspeed. A reduction in airspeed will cause the chamber to reduce in size, moving the instrument's needle to indicate the new, lower airspeed.

MAIN CAUSES OF ERRONEOUS INDICATIONS

The position of the pitot tube and the static vents may well cause errors in the indicated airspeed. These are known, aptly enough, as POSITION ERRORS. Errors due to the situation of the static vents will be taken into account when the airspeeds placarded in the cockpit are set, and also where airspeeds are recommended for performance reasons.

Yawing often causes large errors, possibly even rendering the airspeed indicator useless for as long as the glider is flying sideways through the air. This is common on gliders fitted with a pitot tube which is fitted flush with the glider's nose (known as a POT PITOT) and is due to the sideways airflow causing turbulence over the front of the pitot due to the influence of the adjacent nose structure of the glider.

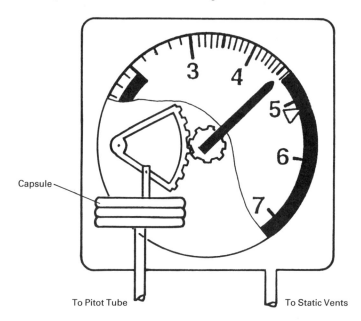

Fig A1.1   Simplified workings of the airspeed indicator.

LAG

As a new nose attitude is selected, the glider will take time to accelerate or decelerate. Therefore the airspeed will lag behind the glider's attitude. This will cause a delay in the indication of any airspeed changes. (Note: This particular delay is through no fault of the instrument.) Inevitably there will also be some mechanical friction to be overcome within the ASI itself. However, as long as the prime reference is the glider's attitude, and this is held constant for a few seconds before any reading is taken from the ASI, these errors should not cause any difficulties.

OTHER ERRORS

Variations in temperature and pressure of the atmosphere will cause the ASI to read incorrectly. These will only affect you if you are flying at high altitudes, and at this stage it is sufficient to realise that the ASI under-reads as the altitude increases (that is, the actual airspeed will be higher than that indicated).

THE ALTIMETER

The altimeter uses a sealed, flexible chamber called an aneroid capsule. In this instrument, this capsule is partially evacuated of air and has a spring to prevent it collapsing under external air pressure. (Fig A1.2)

Air from the static vents, or even directly from the cockpit, is allowed into the area around the capsule. The pressure of this air will depend on the glider's altitude. If the glider is at a high altitude, the pressure of the air around the capsule will be low and therefore the capsule will be in an extended state. At lower altitudes, the capsule will be more compressed by the pressure of the surrounding air. The state of expansion or compression of the capsule is relayed by mechanical linkage to the needles on the face of the instrument, thereby giving an indication of the glider's height.

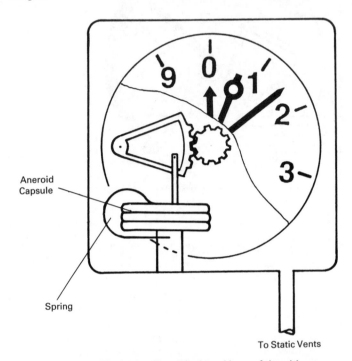

Fig A1.2   Simplified workings of the altimeter.

MAIN CAUSES OF ERRONEOUS INDICATIONS

LAG

Friction in the mechanical linkages and the time the capsule takes to change shape, cause the altimeter indications to lag behind the glider's true height when this height changes. This error can be very large on gliders.

TEMPERATURE AND PRESSURE ERRORS

From necessity, the calibration of the altimeter assumes that certain physical constants apply to the atmosphere. Unfortunately the atmosphere is rarely standard and its temperature and pressure vary irregularly with height. This leads to small errors in the altitude indicated.

WRONG INITIAL DATUM SETTING

A knob on the altimeter allows the pilot to adjust the altimeter sub-scale at any time. In a glider this setting is generally made before take-off. However if it is set incorrectly, the altimeter will read erroneously throughout the flight. Changes in atmospheric pressure due to a changing weather situation will also cause some error. However this will normally take many hours and is less significant to glider flight than power flying.

Surprising as it may seem, the altimeter is not that crucial an instrument in a glider and therefore these errors do not create any problems. The most obvious error, that of lag, can to some extent, be overcome by tapping gently on the instrument panel close to the altimeter. (Do not tap the instrument itself as, like all instruments, it can be easily damaged.) However, as the exact height of the glider is rarely required (except when flying near controlled airspace) even this action may only be necessary to check whether a marginal climb rate shown on the variometer is in fact being achieved.

THE VARIOMETER

Although the variometer is not an essential instrument as far as safety is concerned, it is invaluable when it comes to soaring. The variometer is a very sensitive flowmeter which reacts to the flow of any air which passes through it and uses this airflow to show the glider's rate of climb or descent.

In its simplest form, the variometer is connected to the glider's static vents by one tube and to an insulated flask holding a certain "capacity" of air by another tube. The air in this capacity is allowed to flow freely through the variometer and out through the glider's static vents. Likewise, the air is also allowed to flow into the capacity from the static vents.

Fig A1.3   Simplified variometer system.

As the glider ascends, the air pressure outside of the glider reduces. The air in the capacity will be at a higher pressure than the outside air and will flow out of the capacity, through the variometer and out through the static vents, in an attempt to equalise the pressure. In a mechanical variometer, this airflow is sensed by a vane which is linked to an indicator needle, which will show a corresponding rate of climb.

Conversely, in a descent, air will flow into the flask, due to the outside air being at a greater pressure than the air inside the flask, and a rate of descent will be shown by the needle. The incorporation of a spring in the linkage system prevents erroneous full deflections of the needle and causes the indication to be relative to the rate of change of height.

The capacity flask must be insulated to prevent expansion or contraction of the enclosed air due to changes in temperature, as this would result in airflow and false readings. For this reason a vacuum flask is normally used as a capacity.

Modern gliders are usually equipped with electronic variometers which use much more accurate sensors to measure the rate of change of height. These electronic variometers can easily be equipped with an audio system which gives a changing tone, depending on whether the glider is climbing or descending. (Such an audio device can be fitted to a mechanical variometer, but this is less common.) Audio variometers are a great contribution to flight safety as they reduce the need to look at the variometer dial when the glider is flying in crowded thermals, when lookout is much more important than instrument readings.

Another advantage of the electronic variometer is that its circuitry can be used to calculate and display many other pieces of information, including the best speed-to-fly and average rates of climb over a period of time. In fact, the later electronic variometers are comprehensive flight computers which even give navigational information.

However, the variometer's basic principle of operation has one big flaw. If the glider's nose is lowered to increase airspeed or raised to reduce airspeed, the variometer will sense the resulting rapid change of height. This will lead to indications which will make it difficult for the pilot to work out if the variometer indication is due to rising air or as a result of a pitch change by the pilot (jokingly called STICK LIFT).

To overcome this problem, all variometers should be fitted with a compensating device, resulting in what is known as TOTAL ENERGY indications.

A total energy system will compensate for changes in the airspeed resulting in the variometer giving more meaningful indications of the glider's rate of climb or descent.

The most common device used on gliders to give total energy compensation is a TOTAL ENERGY PROBE. One of these can be seen sticking out of the leading edge of the fin on most gliders. It comprises of a thin tube, some 20 inches (50 centimetres) long, with the forward 3 inches (8 centimetres) bent downwards through an angle of about 85° to 90°. The forward end is sealed but slightly above this end will be either two slits or holes on the rear of the tube.

The side of the variometer which is normally connected to the static vents is instead connected to this tube.

The situation of the small holes or slits will cause reduced air pressure on this side of the variometer. This suction effect will increase as the airspeed increases. This results in air flowing out of the capacity flask at the same rate as the air is trying to flow into it, due to the sudden rate of descent caused by the airspeed increase. The opposite effect occurs with a decrease in airspeed. What is left is an indication of the glider's rate of descent without the meaningless variometer indications which movements of the control column would otherwise cause.

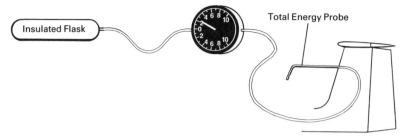

*Fig A1.4   Total energy system. Total energy tube showing its position in a
variometer system.*

APPENDIX 2

THE USE OF RADIO

These days, an increasing number of gliders are equipped with radio transmitters/receivers which allow the pilot to communicate with other gliders and ground stations. Some years ago, glider radios were fitted with only a few frequencies. The radio equipment used in most modern gliders is designed to transmit and receive on any one of the 720 frequencies allocated to aviation users. This means that a glider pilot, using one of these radios, is capable of transmitting on the same frequency as airliners as well as those used by the major air traffic control units controlling them in congested airspace around major airports. It is therefore essential that radios in gliders are used carefully and responsibly.

Given that all licensed airfields will need to be allocated at least one, and often several frequencies in order to operate, you can imagine the difficulty which sporting organisations have in obtaining permission to have certain frequencies allotted for their sole use. This means that a very large number of gliders may have to share just a few frequencies. In the United Kingdom, for instance, there are over 2000 gliders, and although not all are radio equipped, the majority of them are. Only 5 frequencies are allocated to gliding, and one of these is limited to ground-to-ground use and shared with other sporting users. This means that "air time" is limited, and the need for brevity of messages is essential, if you are not to annoy other users and interfere with their operation.

NOTE: As the frequency band used allows communication on a "line of sight" basis, the radio transmissions from a glider flying at 4000 feet may be capable of being heard by every other user of the frequency within 158 nautical miles. That is an area of over 78,500 square nautical miles! (This assumes that they are at a similar height and that the transmitter is reasonably powerful.) The higher they are, the further away they can be and still hear the transmissions.

There are official publications available which go into correct radiotelephony procedure for aviators. Courses leading to the acquisition of a radio licence are also run at some gliding clubs and many power flying clubs. Both of these methods of learning how to use an aeronautical radio are recommended.

In some countries, such as the United Kingdom (at the time of writing), glider pilots are permitted to use radios fitted in gliders and mobile sets without an operator's licence, PROVIDING THAT ONLY THE ALLOCATED GLIDING FREQUENCIES ARE USED. The owner must have a licence for the equipment itself, the grant of which will depend on it being of an approved type which will not interfere with other communication or navigation equipment.

In case you find yourself flying a glider which is radio-equipped before you have time to learn correct radio procedure, the following guidelines are included to make sure your use of the radio does not annoy other users or compromise safety. They are by no means comprehensive and should not be taken as a substitute for the official publication on the subject, or an approved course.

- Only use frequencies which you are permitted to use.

- Double check that the correct frequency is selected before transmitting.

- Listen on the frequency for a few seconds before you transmit, to make sure that you are not interrupting someone else's message.

- Always use the call-sign of the station you are calling and your own call-sign. These will normally be the registration or competition number of the glider or the name of the ground station.

- BE CONCISE BUT STATE YOUR MESSAGE CLEARLY. Think out what you want to say BEFORE you push the transmit button and then speak slowly and clearly. (Having to repeat messages wastes valuable "air-time".)

- A typical transmission would be:

  [call-sign of station being called] – [glider call-sign] : on receiving a reply – [state message]

- If it is a non-urgent message and there is no reply, DO NOT keep calling. Instead transmit "nothing heard" and leave any further attempt for a while.

- Always make sure that the transmit button is released after your transmission is finished. If the radio is silent for a suspiciously long period or adjusting the "squelch" control has no effect, suspect that your transmitter has "jammed" on and turn the power to the radio off. (The world does not need a karaoke session from you as you sing along with your audio variometer!)

- Avoid using busy frequencies, for example, frequencies being used for start or finish lines for competitions, unless you are participating.

- Using the radio has a very low priority where pilot workload is concerned. DO NOT MAKE UNNECESSARY CALLS DURING CRITICAL PHASES OF FLIGHT, SUCH AS WHEN LANDING.

- WHEN WORKLOAD IS HIGH, HAVE THE RADIO TURNED OFF UNLESS LEGALLY REQUIRED TO MONITOR IT.

Lastly, the words MAYDAY and PAN are internationally recognised expressions which imply distress and urgency, respectively. In the unlikely event of your hearing either of these expressions, you should:

- not interrupt the message or any subsequent conversation

- listen and take note of the call-sign, the position of the station and the nature of the problem

- if no reply is heard, you should, after a reasonable period of time, reply, stating that you will relay the message

- relay the message making it clear that you are not the station in distress and are only relaying

- continue monitoring the frequency on which the original message was heard unless instructed otherwise

- if the distressed station cancels the distress situation, inform the station to which you relayed the message of this fact.

On the VHF aeronautical band which is used by gliders, the frequency 121.5 MHz is the International Distress Frequency and is monitored constantly. In the event of an emergency, use of this frequency will put you in contact with highly-trained operators who will know how best to deal with the situation. Once contacted, their instructions must be followed.

APPENDIX 3

THE USE OF TAILCHUTES

The deployment of a tail parachute (or tailchute) from a glider will produce a large amount of drag. This may be used either to limit the glider's airspeed if control is lost while cloud flying or during aerobatic manoeuvres, or to increase the rate of descent on the approach.

The need to use a tailchute as an approach control device is normally rare due to the fact that most gliders are fitted with airbrakes. However, should you find yourself flying a glider which is fitted with a tailchute and decide to use it, then the following notes may add to the safety of your glider.

Experience has shown that a tailchute can be an unreliable device. Its successful deployment and opening will depend upon its having been stowed properly and whether or not it is dry. As a result the glider should not be flown into a situation where its safety depends solely on the tailchute working.

The essential ingredient for the safe use of a tailchute on the approach is to have some extra airspeed. Five to ten knots extra over the normal approach speed for the conditions prevailing should give a safe margin. The large increase in drag caused by the tailchute's opening may quickly rob the glider of some of this airspeed. The extra airspeed remaining will be required for the round out, which will be through a greater angle, as the attitude of the glider may be more nose down in order to maintain an adequate approach speed when the tailchute is deployed.

The increased rotation on round out and the fact that the elevator will be less responsive as a result of the tailchute (it increases the glider's longitudinal stability), will mean that the backward movement of the control column to round out will have to be more positive.

Since the drag produced by a tailchute contributes to the total profile drag, any increase in airspeed will result in a rapidly increasing amount of drag. This means that with a tailchute deployed, it is possible to "dive off" height by pointing the glider more nose down. The extra airspeed gained will soon be lost when the round out is started.

As a fully opened tailchute is very effective, there will always be a danger of undershooting the landing area. Therefore you should always be ready to jettison the tailchute immediately, should an undershoot look likely. Such an undershoot can develop very quickly.

A tailchute can also be used at any time after the round out to reduce the hold off and the length of the ground run after landing; although, without the faster airflow to help it open, there is an increased risk of its failing to deploy.

In general, tailchutes should be treated as ancillary approach control devices and used if necessary to supplement the airbrakes. If you regularly fly a glider fitted with a tailchute you should practise its use often enough to gain confidence for the occasion when you might need it. More important still, you should learn to control the approach accurately with the airbrakes and hopefully you will not get into a situation where you are dependent on the correct functioning of the tailchute.

APPENDIX 4

TOW-PLANE UPSETS

Allowing the glider to get badly out of position behind the tow-plane can be dangerous, especially when the glider gets too high. In this event you can end up with a situation where the glider "upsets" the tow-plane by pulling its tail up, resulting in the tow-plane diving into the ground. This type of accident will, more often than not, prove fatal for the tow-plane pilot.

At first sight, the tow-plane's dive appears to be simply the result of the glider pulling the tow-plane's tail up with a force greater that the downward force which can be exerted by the tow-plane's elevator. This event undoubtedly occurs and, if the tow combination is close to the ground at the time, will result in the tow-plane striking the ground.

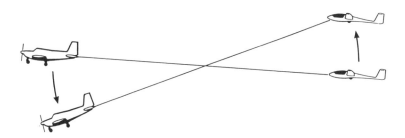

Fig A4.1   Tow-plane upsets. Getting too high on take-off can result in tipping up the tow-plane.

However, some of these tow-plane upsets have resulted in the tow-plane striking the ground in a vertical dive, which is inconsistent with the simple "pull up the tail" scenario. (For this to be the cause of the tow-plane entering a vertical dive, the glider would have to continue diverging upwards into a position directly above the tow-plane while still attached to it. In many instances, the tow-rope has broken well before the glider has reached this point.) (Fig A4.2)

There is therefore one other scenario which explains the vertical attitude achieved by the tow-plane, and which shows how powerful the glider's influence can be.

Let us assume for ease of calculation that a glider weighs 800 lbs and has a glide angle (lift/drag ratio) of 40:1. This means that on aerotow the glider's wing will be producing a lift force of 800 lbs to counter its weight. The glider's drag will equal 20 lbs, that is

$$\text{lift/drag} = 40/1 = 800/\text{DRAG} : \text{DRAG} = 20 \text{ lbs}$$

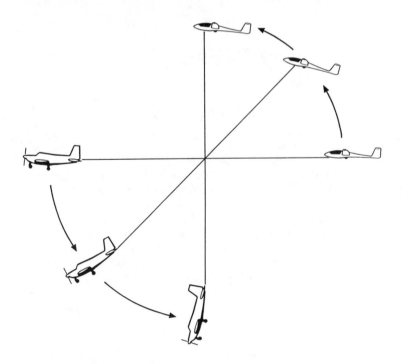

Fig A4.2   One theory of how a tow-plane upset occurs. The glider would, in theory, have to get into a position vertically above the tow-plane to result in the tow-plane being pulled into a vertical dive.

Therefore the extra drag on the tow-plane caused by the glider is only about 20 lbs force. In addition to this drag force, the tow-plane will have to support a small fraction of the glider's weight. This will add another 80 lbs or so to the total load on the tow-rope making the "drag" value around 100 lbs force.

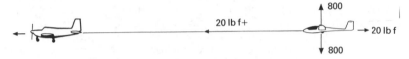

Fig A4.3   Normal load on an aerotow rope. Normally the load on the tow-rope is quite small.

Should the glider diverge upwards suddenly, the lift force will be tilted backwards and the load on the tow-rope will increase as a result. During such a manoeuvre the glider's wing-loading will increase and the load on the tow-rope may be increased from 100 lbs to a value exceeding 800 lbs within seconds. If the glider diverges suddenly, this force will cause a rapid deceleration, resulting in the tow-plane suddenly losing airspeed and stalling. The sharp stall and the nose drop which results, may offer little chance of recovery, even from a height of 1000 feet.

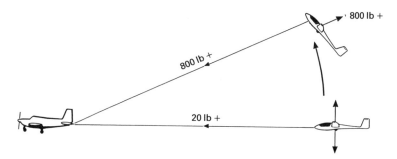

Fig A4.4   Load increase on aerotow rope if glider diverges. If the glider diverges rapidly the load on the tow-rope will increase causing the tow-plane to stall.

If you find it hard to believe that a force can cause such a deceleration, imagine that your car is attached to a very long chain at the end of which is a large stationary concrete weight. If you drive off and achieve a constant 60 mph before the chain starts pulling on the weight, imagine what the effect on the car's speed will be as the chain becomes taut and pulls on the weight. A speed loss will certainly occur. If this deceleration results in a speed loss of 20 mph or more, then this will be enough in an airborne situation to stall the tow-plane.

The analogy is a crude one but hopefully will illustrate the nature of the problem.

Such accidents are rare, but only by glider pilots being aware of the problem and exercising vigilance while aerotowing can these accidents be avoided.

Over the years, the use of various mechanical devices has been investigated as a way of reducing the risk of tow-plane upsets. Most of these have been devices which automatically release the tow-rope from the tow-plane if the angle of pull or the load on the tow-rope becomes excessive. As it is the combination of tow-rope angle and load which causes the problem, the successful functioning of such a release device is difficult to achieve.

The insertion of weak links in the tow-rope and the use of reasonably long tow-ropes will reduce the risk but ultimately it is you, the glider pilot, who has a major say in the tow-plane pilot's safety.

If the glider starts to diverge rapidly out of position, or if at any time you lose sight of the tow-plane, **RELEASE THE TOW-ROPE IMMEDIATELY**.

APPENDIX 5

GLIDING AWARDS AND RECORDS

As well as the pure enjoyment of flying a glider and the satisfaction of soaring, there are a number of qualifications which can be gained as your gliding progresses. Most of these qualifications are recognised by the award of a certificate and entitle the holder of a particular certificate to wear a badge signifying the achievement of this standard. For this reason most awards are known by their badge name.

The various qualifications are graded so as to offer a progressive challenge to the pilot and therefore each in turn is harder to achieve and will stretch the pilot's skills and demand greater judgement. Generally, the standards necessary for the gaining of these certificates are set by an international organisation, known as the FEDERATION AERONAUTIQUE INTERNATIONALE (FAI), although national gliding associations, such as the BRITISH GLIDING ASSOCIATION (BGA), often set their own initial and intermediate qualifications to provide more graded challenges and encourage pilot development. In the following list of awards and requirements, any British awards which are not recognised internationally are annotated by the letters "BGA", whereas those which are, are annotated "FAI".

The following list should be used only as a general guide and, as the requirements will occasionally change, the official rules and conditions for the grant of any particular award should be consulted before attempting any qualifying flight or claiming any record.

GLIDING AWARDS AND THEIR REQUIREMENTS

"A" BADGE (BGA)

- One solo circuit.
- Demonstrate a knowledge of the basic Rules of the Air.

"B" BADGE (BGA)

- A soaring flight of at least 5 minutes at or above the previous lowest height after launch.

BRONZE BADGE (BGA)

- 50 or more solo glider flights (or 20 solo flights in a glider and 10 hours pilot in command). Power flying experience will give some dispensation.

- Two soaring flights. Each of these flights must last for 30 minutes or more if launched by winch, car or bungee, or 60 minutes or more if launched by aerotow. The height of release of such an aerotow must not exceed 2000 feet.

- Two or more "check" flights with a fully rated instructor.

- Successful completion of a written test paper which will include Air Law, Principles of Flight, Navigation and Meteorology.

SILVER BADGE (FAI)

- One flight lasting not less than 5 hours.

- One flight covering a distance of at least 50 kilometres. This flight can be made either to a landing point 50 kilometres or more from the point of release, to a point 50 kilometres or more distant followed by a return to the base airfield, or as part of a triangular flight of which one of the legs is at least 50 kilometres in length. (For a straight line flight the difference between the altitude of release at launch and the altitude at the point of landing must not exceed 1% of the distance covered.)

- One flight during which a gain of height of at least 1,000 metres (3,281 feet) is achieved, measured from the lowest previous point after launch.

UK CROSS-COUNTRY DIPLOMA (BGA)

- Two flights, each covering a distance of 100 kilometres or more, around a pre-declared triangular course, one of which must be achieved at a minimum handicapped groundspeed of 60 kilometres/hour.

GOLD BADGE (FAI)

- One flight lasting not less than 5 hours.

- One flight covering a distance of at least 300 kilometres.

- One flight during which a gain of height of at least 3,000 metres (9,843 feet) is achieved, measured from the lowest previous point after launch.

DIAMOND BADGE (FAI)

- One pre-declared flight covering a distance of at least 300 kilometres which ends at the base airfield.

- One flight covering a distance of at least 500 kilometres.

- One flight during which a gain of height of at least 5,000 metres (16,404 feet) is achieved, measured from the lowest previous point after launch.

750 AND 1000 KILOMETRE DIPLOMAS

Diplomas are awarded for flights covering distances in excess of 750 kilometres (BGA) and 1000 kilometres (FAI).

GLIDING RECORDS

There are many records which any glider pilot can chase, both nationally and internationally. These records are for height achievements, cross-country speed and distance flown.

APPENDIX 6

LOG BOOKS AND PROGRESS CARDS

Once you decide to take up gliding, you should obtain a LOG BOOK. In it you can record details of your flights and your achievements as you progress from the first steps in your training to the soaring awards beyond.

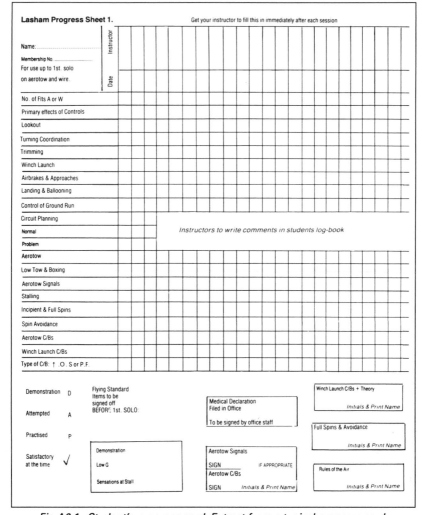

Fig A6.1 Student's progress card. Extract from a typical progress card.

Your instructors may also write comments on your progress in your log book, both as guidance and encouragement to you, and in order to let your next instructor know which exercises you should practise next. By doing so, they will avoid costly repetition of exercises and ensure that nothing is missed in your training.

In addition to this means of measuring your progress and assuring progressive instruction, most gliding clubs issue students with a PROGRESS CARD.

Progress cards give a list of exercises which must be completed satisfactorily and briefings which must have been received before the next stage of training is commenced or flying solo is permitted. As the weather will often determine whether or not some exercises can be covered satisfactorily on any one day, the order in which the exercises are covered may vary from that given on the club's progress card. This should not affect your training, as your instructor will know which exercises can be practised without upsetting the general pattern of your training.

Although most progress cards used at gliding clubs list exercises up to the point of the pilot flying solo for the first time, there is no reason why further progress cards should not be used to give an indication of further improvement exercises to be covered after solo. These can be practised during dual check flights or on days when conditions are unsuitable for relatively inexperienced pilots to fly solo.

An extract from a typical progress card of the type used by gliding clubs in the United Kingdom is shown as an example. (Fig A6.1)

APPENDIX 7

CONVERTING FROM POWER FLYING TO GLIDING

Many pilots of powered aircraft take up gliding. For a holder of a Private Pilot's Licence, the conversion from a single-engine aeroplane to a glider is a relatively simple transition. Most pilots possess an attitude towards being in the air (some call it "air-mindedness") which translates from one flying discipline to another, and is a tremendous help during such conversions.

Apart from the benefit of having an engine, there are other differences between flying a glider and flying a powered aircraft, which take some getting used to.

Firstly, the need for co-ordinated rudder when turning the glider may well be a new skill to many pilots of modern light aircraft. The leverage provided by the large wingspans of most gliders will mean that aileron drag is much more pronounced than on aeroplanes with shorter wingspans.

The relatively small amount of force required on a glider's controls may also come as a surprise as glider controls tend to be somewhat lighter than those of aeroplanes. In particular, the elevator will usually be more responsive. The range of control column movement available will be less, due to the restricted nature of the cockpit design.

Planning a circuit throughout which height is continuously changing and where the height available has to be weighed against the distance still to be flown, will require a new type of judgement. Exercises covering the action necessary if the glider ends up with insufficient height to complete a circuit will be an important part of any conversion training.

The use of the airbrakes should not present any problems. However, unlike a throttle, always remember that closing the airbrakes will not increase the glider's height.

Compared with the instrument array in an aeroplane, a glider's instruments are fewer and as instrument flying is less common, and maintaining a specified altitude unnecessary, they demand less of the pilot's attention. This will free more time for attitude monitoring and lookout.

Lookout, although an essential part of any flying activity, is paramount in gliding. Gliders sharing a thermal will often fly in such close proximity that might cause many power pilots, finding themselves with a similar separation, to file an air-miss report. Add to this the fact that in some thermals there may be as many as 40 or more competition gliders and you will appreciate the need for a good lookout.

Most aeroplane pilots will get used to all of these differences and progress to solo standard quite quickly. Gaining the circuit judgement will probably take longest to acquire. Although most two-seat motor gliders have slightly different handling characteristics to those of a glider, the use of a motor glider can be invaluable in speeding up the acquisition of such judgement. Providing your instructor prevents your hand touching the throttle, your judgement can be improved and tested in many situations by using a motor glider, which would otherwise take much longer to cover in a pure glider.

APPENDIX 8

CONVERTING TO NEW TYPES OF GLIDER

As your gliding experience increases, you will be allowed to fly different types of glider, with different handling characteristics and performance. Once beyond a certain standard, you may decide to buy your own glider. This will involve the test flying of several types before you commit yourself to spending money.

Leaving aside the problem of what to look for when choosing a glider, this appendix deals specifically with how to conduct your first flight(s) on a new type.

It may be that you will spend many happy hours during many flights getting to know this new type but the way in which you go about the initial conversion onto any glider will greatly affect the confidence with which you fly it.

Your aims during your first flight(s) on any glider should be to:

a)   Ensure that you can conduct the flight(s) safely.

b)   Find out as much as you can about the glider in the time available; in particular if it has any handling vices which will require care if problems are to be avoided.

c)   Explore the glider's climb and glide performance.

Before flying any glider, confirm that you meet the necessary insurance requirements.

Take a good look around the glider, noting details such as whether there is a separate release hook for aerotow or whether the release hook is well aft or even inside the wheel well. Observe how much wing tip clearance there is and whether there are any fittings such as tail dollies or tail handles which need to be removed before flight.

Ensure that your weight, including any parachute that you intend wearing, will be within the permitted range of cockpit loads. If you are close to or less than the lower limit, find and secure enough ballast to place you well above the minimum limit. If you are above the upper limit then I am afraid you will have to try another glider or go on a diet.

While sitting in the cockpit, you should receive a briefing from an instructor who is familiar with the handling characteristics of the glider. In the event that no such instructor is available, another suitably experienced pilot may be authorised to brief you. This briefing should include the cockpit layout, important airspeeds such as approach and limiting airspeeds, and warnings of any handling peculiarities, especially on take-off or landing. Listen carefully. Do not hesitate to ask any questions and do not be rushed into launching.

Establish if there are any restrictions on the type of manoeuvres which you will be permitted to attempt on your early flights. These may be imposed, depending on your experience and club rules.

Where possible, your first launch on a new type should be by aerotow, assuming of course that you are current on aerotow launching. Although eventually you will want to discover how the glider behaves on a wire launch, taking an aerotow on the first launch will avoid the workload of suddenly having to learn how effective the airbrakes and elevator are should the cable break at 50 feet! An aerotow will also give you more time to settle and explore the glider's handling.

Take a reasonably high aerotow in order to give you more time on this first flight. The tow-plane pilot should be briefed to stay well within gliding range of the airfield.

Throughout these first flights, always identify each control knob or lever visually before moving it, in order to avoid operating the wrong control.

After release from aerotow there are many aspects of the glider's handling which you should explore. These can be divided into two categories: those to be explored while higher up and those which can be looked at nearer circuit height. These characteristics are listed below.

CHARACTERISTICS WHICH SHOULD BE EXAMINED AT HEIGHT

Stalling and recovery characteristics

- in straight flight
- while turning
- at different flap settings (if applicable)

Spinning and recovery characteristics

Characteristics of the airbrakes at various approach speeds

- effectiveness
- operating forces
- effect on trim

Sideslip characteristics with and without airbrake.

CHARACTERISTICS WHICH CAN BE EXAMINED NEARER CIRCUIT HEIGHT

General handling and co-ordination of controls.

Rate of roll.

Effectiveness of trimmer.

If applicable, the effect of flaps on all aspects of handling, attitude and trim.

Should only wire launching be available, and unless soaring is possible, then several flights may have to be carried out in order to explore all aspects of the glider's handling.

Whatever exercises you try, remember to abandon your experiments by the time the glider reaches a height which gives you plenty of time to plan a circuit allowing for your lack of experience on this new type of glider.

Select a landing area well clear of other aircraft, even if this means landing some distance up the airfield.

The weather will be an important factor in whether a conversion flight can be conducted safely and successfully. Days with a low cloud base, strong winds, crosswinds or turbulence are unsuitable for first flights on a new type. A soarable day will offer the best chance to discover the attributes and shortcomings of a new glider, giving more time for the exercise and a chance to test the glider in the role for which it was designed – soaring.

APPENDIX 9

USEFUL CONVERSION FACTORS

To convert from a unit in the first column to one in the second column multiply by the conversion factor given in the third column.

DISTANCES AND HEIGHTS

Nautical Miles	Statute Miles	1.151
Statute Miles	Nautical Miles	0.869
Nautical Miles	Feet	6080
Kilometres	Nautical Miles	0.54
Nautical Miles	Kilometres	1.853
Metres	Feet	3.281
Feet	Metres	0.305

SPEEDS

Miles/hour	Knots	0.869
Knots	Miles/hour	1.151
Kilometres/hour	Knots	0.54
Knots	Kilometres/hour	1.853
Metres/second	Feet/minute	196.85
Feet/minute	Metres/second	0.00508
Knots	Feet/minute	101
Feet/minute	Knots	0.0099

WEIGHTS

Pounds	Kilograms	0.454
Kilograms	Pounds	2.205
Stones	Pounds	14
Pounds	Stones	0.0714

APPENDIX 10

USEFUL ADDRESSES

BRITISH GLIDING ASSOCIATION
Kimberley House
Vaughan Way
Leicester LE1 4SE
Telephone 0533 531051

0116 2

GLIDING FEDERATION OF AUSTRALIA
Building 130
Wirraway Road
Essendon Airport
Victoria 3041
Australia
Telephone 03 379 4629

K13 21

SOARING SOCIETY OF AMERICA
PO Box E
Hobbs
New Mexico 88241
Telephone (505) 392117

01757 702002

BARN SELBY

01757 270 296

Worlds   01 759 303 579
Coach

Trial→ 160.00 ← P.a.

Mon→Fri 225.00 Sep   2-3 weeks in July.

260 Jul Aug.

Pocklington York.

Jon Lake
14 Houingham
Leeds

INDEX

Addresses 301
Adverse yaw 44-46, 54, 205-207
Aerotow(ing) 12, 16-17, 76, 103-104,
126-138, 266-267, 287-289, 298
  boxing the tow 137
  emergency signals 171-174
  failures 168-171
  glider position 131-133, 173
  ground run 102-104, 107, 185-186
  lateral displacement 134
  releasing 132, 134-136
  signals 127-128
  stages of 129-136
  turning on 132
Aerotow emergency signals – air
  exercise 174
Aerotow launch failures – air exercise
  171
Aerotow launching – air exercise 138
Aileron(s) 3, 6, 33, 38-39, 41, 44-49, 67-
  68, 73, 85, 91, 105, 107, 118, 175,
  178-179, 184-186, 188, 205-207
  air exercise 41
  differential 205-206
  Frise 205-206
  response in wind gradient 112-113
  use at the stall 54, 59, 65
  use on the ground run 90, 118, 129
Aileron drag 44-46, 85, 184, 205-207
  air exercise 45-46
Air exercise – aerotow emergency
    signals 174
  aerotow launch failures 171
  aerotow launching 138
  aileron 41
  aileron drag 45-46
  airbrakes 83
  approach control using airbrakes 95
  circuit planning 158
  effect of controls 40-42
  elevator 40
  further spinning 72
  further stalling 60
  further turning 47-49
  incipient spin 60
  landing 90

  reduced "g' 62-63
  rudder 41-42
  sideslipping 180-181
  spinning 70
  spiral dive 72
  stalling 57-58
  trimming 77
  turning 46
  wire launch failures 167
  wire launching 125
Airbrake(s) 3, 6, 52, 70, 72, 78-83, 86,
  90, 91-95, 111-112, 144, 161-162,
  165, 167, 168, 172-175, 179-181, 185
  air exercise 83
  attitude change 80-81, 83
  check 35-36
  lever 6, 35-36, 144, 165
  operating forces 79-80
  trailing edge 81-82, 189-191
  use in the circuit 153
  use in wind gradient 111-112
Airfield 10, 136, 161-163, 166
Airflow 20-25, 27, 50-52, 54, 78, 80-82,
  112, 175-176, 178, 183, 187, 198-201,
  204, 207, 219-223, 225, 227-229
  noise 40, 52, 262
  turbulent 50, 54, 219-223
Airmanship 57
  checks "hassll" 57
  when hill soaring 241-242
  when thermalling 262
Airspeed 7-9, 17, 25, 40, 47, 48, 51-52,
  57, 64, 67-68, 70-77, 89, 94, 99,
  100-105, 129-130, 135, 161-163, 167,
  169, 175, 177-192, 208, 210, 213-215,
  218, 220, 229, 276-277, 280
  during winch launch 118-124, 159
  effect of airbrakes 78-83
  in the circuit 143-145, 147, 153
  in turbulent conditions 109
  in turns 43-44, 50
  in wind gradient 110-111
  on the approach 85-86, 89-91, 94-95,
  109
  "too fast" signal 124
  while hill soaring 238, 240

while thermalling 257, 261
while wave soaring 268-269, 272
Airspeed indicator 7-8, 47, 64, 85, 178-179, 191-192, 276-277
flap speeds 191-192
Alcohol 31
All-moving tailplane 208, 227
Altimeter 9, 139-140, 170, 277-279
Altitude flying 113, 270-272, 277
Anabatic lift/wind 237
Angle of attack 21-23, 25, 44, 50, 52-56, 64-69, 89, 177, 183, 186, 199-202, 211-212
in wind gradient 110-111
on winch launch 118-119, 159-160
Angle of bank 41, 44, 46-48, 50, 68-72, 112-113, 132, 145, 166, 178, 258-262
Anhedral 201
Anti-balance tab 74-75, 208, 227
Approach 84-86, 91-95, 105, 109-112, 139, 145-146, 149, 152-158, 160, 175-181, 187-191
angle 91-94, 101-102
speed 85-86, 89-91, 94-95, 111-112, 156, 170, 285
Approach control using airbrakes – air exercise 95
Aspect ratio 216, 225
Atmospheric pressure 276
Atmospheric stability 237, 245
Attitude 17, 40, 44, 46, 47, 52-53, 56-57, 68-71, 73-77, 85, 87, 90, 91, 94, 111, 159-161, 167, 178, 186-187, 261-262, 277, 285
change with airbrakes/spoilers 80-81, 83
on winch launch 118-119, 121, 159
while trimming 75-76
Audio variometer 262, 280
Autorotation 64-69
Awards 290-292

Back-release mechanism 36, 115, 123
Badges (see "awards")
Balance tab (see "geared tabs")
Ballast 34-35, 50, 64, 76, 203, 297
Ballooning – on landing 87, 89, 94
Bank(ing) 41, 134, 175-180
Bank angle 41, 50, 68-72, 132, 258-262
adjustment of 41
in wind gradient 112-113
Base leg 139-140, 145-146, 148-157, 166

Base leg turn 145, 148-149, 151-152, 155
Belly release hook 7, 36, 118, 121, 297
Bernoulli's theorem 20
Blue thermals 247, 249, 252
Boundary layer 219
"Boxing the tow" 137
Buffet 54, 80, 178
Bungee launch 12

Cable break(s) 114, 120, 121, 123-124, 159-167
recovery action 159, 167
Cable parachute 114-115
Cable release – check 36
knob 6-7, 118, 123, 129, 161, 173, 186
mechanism 6-7, 36, 115, 127
position 118, 121, 127, 297
Canard 202
"Cannot release" signal 173-174
Canopy 5, 32, 35, 241
Capacity flask 279-280
Car launch (see also "wire launch") 10-11, 16-18, 114, 124, 159
Catapult launch 12
Centre of gravity 19, 23, 37, 118, 198, 202-203, 230
Centre of pressure 23, 202, 212
movement at stall 55-56
Centripetal force 43
Certificate of airworthiness 32, 194
"Check airbrakes" signal 172-173
Chord 216
Chord line 21
Circuit flying – after a cable break 165
at hill sites 155-157
Circuit planning 139-158
air exercise 158
correcting the circuit 147-155
in older gliders 157-158
Clothing 30
Cloud – cover 270-271
cumulonimbus 246-247
cumulus 246-247, 249-252
lenticular 264-266, 268-270
rotor 265
shadows 253
streets 249-250
Clutching hand 234
Cockpit 5, 6-9, 191
loading 34-35, 50, 64, 76, 194, 202-203
Collision avoidance 147

Compass 9
Complacency – while wave soaring 270
Condensation level 246
Control(s) 6-7, 97
  air exercise 40-42
  axis 37-40
  check 33
  column 6, 33, 38-41, 44, 45, 73-77, 86-89, 117, 121-122, 177-178
  confusion 16-17, 185, 191, 298
  co-ordination 43-49, 60, 67-68, 72, 85, 91, 105, 130, 132, 145, 163, 166, 175, 179-180
  deflection 23, 38-39, 72, 90, 196, 226-227
  flutter 209-211
  force(s) 23, 38, 73-78, 137, 179, 197, 204-205, 207-209
  movement causing reduced "g" 60-63, 160-161
  position at stall 55
  primary 37-42
  response at stall 54
  response on aerotow 129, 130
  response on approach 85, 109, 144
  response on ground run 103-108, 117, 129
  use on approach/landing 85-90
Conversion factors 300
Crabbing approach 105-106
Crosswind 105-108, 162, 165
  affecting circuit 147-152
  leg (see "base leg") 147
  on landing 105-108
  on take-off 107-108, 118
Cruciform tail 223-226
Cumulonimbus cloud 246-247
Cumulus cloud 245-247, 249-252
Curl over 108, 234, 242

Daily inspections 31-33, 194
Dew point 245
Differential ailerons 205-206
Dihedral 198-201, 203-204
Directional control 85-86, 90, 91
Directional stability 197-198
Dive brakes (see also "airbrakes") 79, 81, 82
Dog-leg – after cable break 163
Dorsal strake 198
Downwind checks 143-144
Downwind landing 104-105, 241
  after launch failure 164-165, 169-171

Downwind leg 139-157, 166
Drag 24-25, 27-29, 78-82, 175-177, 182-190, 204, 206-209, 215-230, 287-288
  aileron 85, 205-207
  at stall 50-52, 56, 59
  definition 24, 27
  form 24
  induced 24, 25, 44-45, 203, 216-219
  interference 221-223, 225-226
  profile 24, 25, 182, 203, 215, 218, 220, 225, 285
  skin friction 24, 203, 219-220
Drift 97-100, 105, 107, 121-122, 130
  during a winch launch 121-122
  in the circuit 140, 147-153
  while hill soaring 234, 238-239, 242
Drugs 31
Dry thermals (see "blue thermals")
Dry adiabatic lapse rate 245

Effect of controls 38-42
  air exercise 40-42
Elevator 3, 6, 33, 38-40, 45-49, 54, 60, 65, 73-76, 80, 81, 85-90, 91, 94, 107, 118, 129, 178, 202, 207-208, 285
  air exercise 40
Elevator springs 74-75, 208
Emergencies on aerotow 171-174
Environmental lapse rate 244-245

Field landing 90, 139-140, 147, 162, 169, 171, 225, 240-241
Fin 3, 198, 225-226
Final turn 145, 149-150, 153, 155, 165
Fitness 18, 30-31
Flap(s) 5, 7, 182-192, 215
  aileron interlink 184, 186
  area changing 183, 215
  brakes 190-191
  check 35
  controls 184-185
  landing 184-185
  lever 7, 184-186
  limiting speeds 188-189
  optimum settings 186-187
  settings 184, 186-188
  use on the approach 184-185, 187-191
Foehn gap 264
Forces – balance of 19, 23, 25-29, 43-44, 110
  in a turn 6, 43-44

resolution of 25-27
Frise ailerons 205-206
Fuselage 3, 175, 198, 202, 221-223, 227-229
  design 227-229
  drag 183, 227-229

Geared tab 204-205
Glide angle 29, 78-79, 81-82, 101, 139, 157, 170-171, 175, 183, 186, 188, 214-215, 220, 229, 287
Glider – converting to new types 297-299
  description 2-9
  design 194-230
  performance 29, 78-79, 81-82, 143, 169, 213-230, 271
  sealing 221-223, 229
Gliding site 10-15
Gravity 19, 60-61
Ground handling 13-15
Ground loop (see "weathercocking") 90, 105-107, 118, 129
Ground reading 252-253
Ground run – aerotow launch 107, 129, 168, 185
  after landing 84, 90, 104-107, 188
  winch launch 107, 117-118
Groundspeed 7-8, 100-104, 110-111, 152
Gusts 108-109
  while thermalling 257-259, 261

Hail 246
Harness (see straps)
Hassll check 57
Heading 48, 97-99, 105
Height 57, 101-102, 108-113, 139-148, 152-167, 169-170, 175, 177, 179-181
  judgement 87-89
High key point 140-142
Hill lift 10, 12, 156-157, 234-243, 267
Hill sites 10, 12, 108, 155-157
Hill soaring 113, 135, 156, 238-243
  airmanship and rules 241-242
  curl over 108, 234, 242
  dangers 242-243
  orographic cloud 243
  shape and size of hill 235-236
  wind strength and direction 234-235
Hilltop airfields 10, 12, 108
Hold off 84, 89, 90, 94, 105-106
Horn balance 204-205

Humidity 245-246
"Hunting" on winch launch 121
Hypoxia 271

Icing 271
Incipient spin 58-60
  air exercise 60
  recovery 59
Induced drag 24, 25, 44-45, 203, 215-219, 225-226, 230
Instruments 7-9, 35, 276-281
Interference drag 221-223, 225-226
International Distress Frequency 284

Judgement 87-89, 146

Laminar airflow 219-223, 227, 235-236
  with lee waves 264-265
Laminar separation 220-221
Laminar separation bubble 220-221
Landing 84-90, 91, 94-95, 96, 104-107, 146, 178-181
  ahead after a cable break 161-162, 165-166
  air exercise 90
  area 84-89, 94-95, 101, 104, 111-112, 139-157, 162-167
  crosswind 105-107
  downwind 104-105, 240-241
  flap 184, 187-189
  in a field near a hill 240-241
Lapse rate – environmental 244-245
  dry adiabatic 245-246
  saturated adiabatic 246
Lateral displacement on aerotow 134
Lateral stability 198-201
Launch – cable 114-115, 159
  methods 10-12
  signals (aerotow) 127-129
  signals (wire) 115-117, 124
Launch failure –during wire launch 114, 120, 121, 123-124, 159-167
  while aerotowing 168-171
Launch point controller 115-116, 127
Lee waves 113, 263-272
  characteristics 263-265
  entering the lift 266-268
  favourable conditions for 264
  position of lift 266
  primary 263, 265
Lenticular clouds 264-270
Lift (force) 19-23, 27-29, 43, 47, 50-51, 56, 64-66, 78-79, 81, 86, 110-112,

130, 175-177, 182, 185-191, 199-204, 215-217, 222-223, 227, 229, 287-288
distribution 23, 216-217
Lift (rising air) 232-272
anabatic 237
effect on the circuit 144-145, 152-157
hill 234-243
thermal 244-262
wave 263-272
Lift/drag ratio 29, 78-79, 81-82, 214, 287
Lightening 246
Limitations placard 32, 34-35, 109, 119, 272, 276
Log books 293-294
Lookout 17, 46-47, 57, 135, 147, 241, 262, 280, 295
Low key point 144-145
Low tow position 136-137
Low turns – in wind gradient 112-113

Main wheel 5, 228-229
Manoeuvring 52
Mass balancing 209-211, 227
Maximum airspeed – on winch launch 119, 121, 124
Mayday call 283-284
Medical standards 18, 30-31
Minimum sink speed 214, 229
Mountain lee waves 113, 263-272

Navigation – while wave soaring 270-271
Negative flap 184-187, 189
Negative "g" (see "reduced g")
New types of glider – converting to 297-299
Normal tow position 131-132, 135, 136, 173
Nose drop at the stall 54-56
Nose wheel 228

Older gliders 157-158
Orientation – on aerotow 136
while wave soaring 270-271
Orographic cloud 243
Ottfur rings 115
Oxygen 271

Pan call 283-284
Parking the glider 15
Performance flaps 186-187
Pilot fitness 18, 30-31
Pilot induced oscillations 130

Pilot weight 34-35, 50, 64, 76, 202-203
Pitch(ing) 37-40, 47, 63, 159-161
at the stall 55-56
in the spin 64-66
on winch launch 118, 121
stability (see "stability-longitudinal")
Pitot tube 7, 178, 276-277
Polar curve 213-215, 229-230
Positive flap 183-188
Positive "g" 60-61, 71
Power pilots – conversion to gliding 295-296
Pre-take-off checks 33-36
Preparation for flight 30-36
Primary lee wave 263, 265
Profile drag 24, 25, 182, 203, 215, 218, 225, 285
Progress cards 293-294
Propeller wash 131, 136-138

Radio 270, 282-284
aerials 228-229
for launch signalling 116, 128-129
Radius of turn 259-261
Rate of climb 235, 245, 254, 257, 260, 262, 266-268, 279-280
Rate of descent 139, 144, 147, 153, 155, 173-175, 178-181, 184-185, 188-190, 213-215, 229, 232-233, 258-260, 279-280
at the stall 55, 56
in the spin 65
in wind gradient 110-112
on approach 86, 90, 91-94, 285
Reaction force 19
Records 292
Reduced "g" 60-63, 160-161
air exercise 62-63
Reference point 91-95, 145
Relative airflow 21, 23, 27, 50-52, 64-65, 100, 110-111, 118-119, 159, 175, 211
Release hook (see "cable release")
"Release immediately" signal 171-172
Releasing – from aerotow 132, 134-136
from wire launch 122-123
Resolution of forces 25-29, 175-176
Reverse pulley launch (see also "wire launch") 11, 114, 124-125, 159
Rising air (see "Lift")
Roll(ing) 38-39, 41, 47, 64-66
dampening 64-65, 201
Rotor 265, 270
Rotor cloud 265

Rough air speed 109
Round out 84, 86-90, 91, 94-95, 105-106, 111-112, 162, 285
Rudder 3, 6, 33, 39, 41, 45-49, 54, 59, 67-72, 73, 91, 105-107, 124, 175-181, 207
air exercise 41-42
during ground run 90, 118, 129
over-balance 179
pedals 6, 33, 39, 41
Ruddervator 226
Rules – of the air 274-275
when hill soaring 241-242, 275
when thermalling 262, 275
Runway 10, 102-103, 107, 122

"S" turn 157
after cable break 163-164
Safety – general 12-13, 194
on airfield 12-15
Saturated adiabatic lapse rate 246
Sensations 16-17, 47, 60-63, 257-259
Sideslip(ping) 175-181, 199
air exercise 180-181
Signals – aerotow emergencies 171-174
aerotow launching 127-129
wire launching 115-117
Sink(ing air) 233-234, 236, 242, 258-259
effect on the circuit 144, 152-157
street 249-250, 257
Skids 5
Skill 87
Skin friction 24, 203, 219-220
Sky reading 251-252
Slipping turn 180
Smoke – as a thermal indicator 254-255
Soaring – birds 254
gliders 254
in hill lift 113, 135, 157, 238-243
in thermals 251-262
in wave lift 113, 266-272
principle of 232-233
Span 2
Spin(ning) 54, 58-59, 64-72, 124, 166, 178, 211, 216
air exercise 70
further exercises 72
incipient 58-60
recovery 64, 69-70
Spiral dive 49, 70-72
air exercise 72
recovery 49, 71-72
Spoilers 3, 35-36, 80-81

Spring trimmer 74-75
Stabiliser 202
Stability 40, 196-204
atmospheric 237, 245
directional 197-198
lateral 198-201
longitudinal 40, 201-203
Stall(ing) 22, 50-70, 80, 85-86, 89, 105, 111, 118, 124, 135, 166-167, 178, 211
air exercise 57-58
after cable break 159, 161
angle 22, 50, 52, 53, 56, 110, 118, 159
further exercises 60
recovery 52, 56-58, 159-161
symptoms of 52-56, 80
Stalling speed 50, 52, 60, 85, 105, 183, 187-189, 220
in turns 50, 60
increase with airbrakes 60, 80-81, 161-162
on launch 102-103
on winch launch 119-120
Standing waves (see "lee waves")
Static vents 7, 178, 276, 278
Stick (see "control column")
Still air 97-99
"Stop" signal 116, 127
Straps 35
Streamlining 228-229
Sweepback 199-200
Sweepforward 199-201, 203

"T" tail 3, 224-226
Tail ballast 230
Tailchute/parachute 78, 285-286
Tailplane 3, 198, 202-203, 223-227, 230
all-moving 227
design 223-227
drag 224-227
Tail skid 107, 228
Tail wheel 107, 228-229
Take-off (see also "aerotow" and "wire launch") 76, 102-104, 107-108
Thermal(s) 76, 244-262, 267
blue 247, 249
centring 257-259
finding 251-257
formation 244-254
soaring 251-262
sources 247, 252-255
streets 249-250, 257
structure 248-249
triggers 248-249, 253

Thermalling – airmanship and rules 262
  faults 260-262
Thrust 25
Thunderstorms 109, 246
Tost rings 115
Total energy (probe) 280-281
Tow cable release 6-7, 36, 115
Tow car 7, 10-11
  failure 166-167
Tow-plane 103, 126-127, 168, 171-174
  climb angle 170
  upsets 130-132, 287-289
  slipstream 131, 136-138
Tow-rope 6, 126, 168, 173
  attaching to glider 127
  length 127, 136
Track(ing) 84-85, 98-100, 105-106, 139, 149-152
  in wave lift 268
  while hill soaring 238-239
  while sideslipping 176, 178
Trailing edge airbrakes 81-82, 189-191
Transition point 219-220
Trim – change with spoilers 81
  tab 5, 6, 73-74
Trimmer 35, 73-77, 207
  knob/lever 6, 74-77
  spring 74-75, 208
Trimming 73-77, 135, 137, 208
  air exercise 77
Tug aircraft (see "tow-plane")
Turbulators 220-221
Turbulence 108-109, 156-157, 171- 172, 234-236, 242, 264-265
  when aerotowing 132-133
Turbulent airflow 220-221, 228
Turn and slip indicator 9
Turning 41, 43-49, 50, 52, 67-68, 73, 75
  air exercise 46
  common faults 46-47
  forces 6
  further exercises 47-49
  in wind gradient 112-113
  on aerotow 132
  polar 260
  while hill soaring 239-240

"Unable to release tow-rope" signal 173-174
Undercarriage 5, 7, 123, 130, 135, 229
  lever 7
Undershooting on the approach 92-95, 111-112, 285

"V" tail 2, 69, 224-227
Variometer 9, 259, 262, 279-281
Venturi principle 20-22

Washout 211-212
Water ballast 229-230
"Wave off" signal 171-172
Wave soaring 113, 266-272
  associated hazards 270-272
  finding the lift 266-268
  technique 268-270
Weak link – aerotow launch 127, 289
  wire launch 115
Weathercocking 106-107, 118, 129, 176
Weight 19, 27-29, 43-44, 50-51, 55, 60, 229
  definition 19, 27
Wheel(s) 5, 107, 228-229
  brake 7, 79, 90
Winch failure 114, 166-167
Winch launch(ing) 11, 16, 17-18, 102-103, 114-125, 158-159, 186
  "hunting" on 121
  signals 115-118
  stages of 117-123
  release hook 7, 36, 118, 121, 297
Wind 7, 14-15, 96-113, 162, 164, 169-171
  anabatic 237
  assessment 96-97, 140
  effect on the circuit 146-152, 155-157
  effect on thermals 251-252
Wind gradient 109-113, 156, 171
  aileron response in 112-113
  airspeed in 110-111
  angle of attack in 110-111
  bank angle in 112-113
  effect on wire launch 123-124
  low turns in 112-113
  use of airbrakes in 111-112
Wind speed/strength 8, 94, 96-97, 99, 108-113, 135-136, 149-152, 157, 170-171, 234, 247, 249, 252, 264-265, 268-270
Wing 2, 19-23, 43
  area 215-216
  camber 182-187, 215
  chord 216
  design 198-201, 203, 215-221
  drop at stall 56, 58-60
  fences 217-218
  taper 216